POISONS

THEIR ISOLATION AND IDENTIFICATION

POISONS
THEIR ISOLATION AND IDENTIFICATION

BY

FRANK BAMFORD, B.Sc.

Late Director of the Medico-Legal Laboratory, Cairo

THIRD EDITION

Revised by

C. P. STEWART, D.Sc., Ph.D.

*Reader in Clinical Chemistry, University of Edinburgh.
Senior Biochemist, Royal Infirmary, Edinburgh*

With A Foreword by

SIR SYDNEY SMITH, *C.B.E.,*
M.D., F.R.C.P.

Regius Professor of Forensic Medicine, University of Edinburgh

23 ILLUSTRATIONS

THE BLAKISTON COMPANY

PHILADELPIHA

1951

First Edition   1940
Second Edition   1947
Third Edition   1951

Printed in Great Britain

FOREWORD

THE publication of a new book on toxicological analysis is a relatively rare event, due no doubt both to the highly specialized nature of the work and to the fact that cases of human poisoning are comparatively infrequent. Consequently practical experience in the isolation and identification of poisons is very restricted. It is therefore of great interest when a person who has had the unique opportunity of devoting a great part of his life to this subject undertakes the task of preparing a book giving the results of his experience. A good many years ago, Mr. Frank Bamford worked with me in Egypt as a chemist in the laboratory of the Medico-Legal Department of the Egyptian Government. At that time I impressed upon him the necessity of producing, on some future occasion, a thoroughly practical volume in which each test and procedure had been personally used in the examination of viscera for poisons, for such a book could be used with absolute trust by other workers. Mr. Bamford later became Director of the Chemical Laboratory and has had complete charge of all cases of poisoning throughout Egypt for several years. As readers possibly know, the number of such cases is sufficiently large to keep a staff of chemists permanently employed on this work alone.

A perusal of this book shows it to be the product of a practical, highly skilled specialist in toxicological analysis, and it can be recommended with complete confidence to all those whose work entails such analysis.

SYDNEY SMITH.

DEPT. OF FORENSIC MEDICINE,
UNIVERSITY OF EDINBURGH.

v

PREFACE TO THE FIRST EDITION

THIS book is intended as a laboratory manual for all chemists who have to deal with cases of poisoning. It is devised as a practical handbook, and for that reason the descriptive matter concerning the organic poisons (Chapters VII and VIII)[1] has been separated from the portion dealing with their identification in the laboratory (Chapters IX to XII). Emphasis has throughout been laid on practical details, but it is hoped that as much theoretical matter has been included as is necessary.

Chapter X, giving a systematic scheme for the identification of the alkaloids, was regarded by my father as the most important in the book, containing, as it does, the results of a large amount of original work. It is the chapter which he hoped would be of the most value.

The unfortunate death of my father, at the time when the first galley proofs of the book were being printed, robbed him of the opportunity to provide the final touches to his work, and to see it in its completed form. It has been left to me to carry on the work of correcting the proofs and preparing the book for the press. In this work I have been greatly helped by Dr. G. D. Elsdon, who has assisted me to check the proofs. His advice has considerably lightened the work of completing the volume.

In addition to Dr. Elsdon, other kind friends have helped, and I would like to thank all of them here. In particular, I must mention Mr. N. D. Howard, who supplied many of the drawings; Messrs. F. E. Becker & Co., of London, who were kind enough to provide the blocks for Figs. 5 and 13,[1] and who made the drawings for Figs. 11 and 14. Professor Sydney Smith has been good enough

[1] Chapter and Figure numbers refer, of course, to the First Edition.

to demonstrate his interest in, and good wishes for, the book by writing the Foreword. My father would also, I am sure, wish to make known his gratitude to H.E. Dr. Mahmoud Maher Bey, Chief Medico-Legal Expert in Cairo, for the sympathy and understanding that made much of the work possible, and to thank all his colleagues of the Medico-Legal Department for their kind co-operation.

H. F. BAMFORD.

SOUTHAMPTON.

PREFACE TO THE THIRD EDITION

IN preparing the third edition of this book I have tried to preserve its outstanding characteristic—that of describing methods known to the writer, by personal experience, to be reliable. In particular, I have left untouched the author's scheme for the identification of alkaloids, except for the addition of notes on the preparation of the reagents.

The general plan of the book has undergone some change with the object of producing a more logical order. Gaseous and volatile poisons are now considered together in a single chapter. The section on non-volatile organic poisons now opens with the chapter on methods of isolation. This is followed first by two chapters, descriptive and analytical respectively, on the non-basic poisons and then by two similar chapters on the commoner basic poisons.

The section on the barbiturates has been considerably altered in view of the increased variety and toxicological importance of these substances. Although it may be a little premature, a short section on the antihistaminic drugs has been included with hints rather than definitive methods, for their detection.

For valuable criticisms and advice in the preparation of this edition, I have to thank Dr. J. B. Firth, Director of the North Western Forensic Science Laboratory, Preston, and Dr. A. Stolman, Toxicologist to the State of Connecticut, U.S.A.

C. P. STEWART.

EDINBURGH.

CONTENTS

POISONS

INTRODUCTION

ORGANIZATION AND EQUIPMENT

The Sealing, Reception, and Storage of Packages

IN the organization of a laboratory, wholly or mainly concerned with matters which will come before the law courts, certain features require special emphasis. Foremost among these is that vitally important matter, the care of samples submitted for examination. Although the director of the laboratory is ultimately responsible for the safe custody of all articles submitted for examination, it is of first-rate importance that the sense of responsibility should be felt by every member of the staff, whether his duties be technical, clerical, or even menial.

All articles coming to the laboratory are potential court exhibits, and any loss or unnecessary damage is serious. Moreover, since there is frequent delay, sometimes considerable delay, before affairs are finally decided by the courts, and since it sometimes happens that re-examination of articles may be required, the question of storage is an important one.

One has also to bear in mind the possibility of wilful and malicious tampering. Even during post-mortem examinations attempts to interfere with specimens intended for chemical examination are not unknown; and whenever articles pass through several pairs of hands before reaching the laboratory, opportunities for such interference are multiplied.

The ideal arrangement, of course, would be for the person who is to examine the articles to collect them from their original source and to keep them in his personal care until the courts have come to a final decision. This is not always possible. The alternative is for the articles to be sent to the laboratory under seal, preferably by special messenger.

The sealing of packages is apparently a simple matter, but the number of people who fail to do it efficiently is astonishingly large. The essential point is that there must be no possibility of opening the package short of cutting it open or breaking the seals. It would be impossible to give detailed instructions as to how this should be done, since packages vary so greatly in form. A few examples of unsealed or badly sealed articles may, however, be mentioned; (1) parcels tied with string, sealed on the knot, which may be opened by slipping the string over the ends of the packages; (2) corked bottles with wax seals on the corks, permitting the removal and replacement of cork and seal together; (3) locked boxes with seals on the locks, which can be opened by removing screws from the hinges; and (4) (ridiculous though this may seem, examples have occurred) uncovered jam jars, empty tins, bowls covered only with gauze or cotton wool, cardboard boxes, etc.

It is the obvious duty of a person sending a sealed package to ensure that the sealing is effective: it is no less the duty of the receiver of the package to examine all seals and see that there has been no tampering or possibility of tampering. Any irregularity whatsoever should be reported immediately to the responsible authority. It is, in fact, doubtful whether any useful purpose can be served by the examination of the contents of a package when doubt exists on this point.

The sealing-wax should be of good quality, and the seals should be clearly cut so as to give easily legible impressions. Every package or collection of packages must be accompanied by a document giving a full description of all the articles enclosed and of the external characteristics of the packages. This document must also bear a facsimile of the seal or seals used. Facsimiles may be made in wax or in ink; the advantage of a wax impression is that it can be more easily compared with other wax impressions, but it is more liable to accidental damage.

Seals may be forged, and in Eastern countries where seal-cutting is a common craft, faked seals are not rare. If any suspicion arises, comparison should be made with the aid of a lens and, if necessary, by means of enlarged photographs. It may be necessary occasionally to examine the sealing-wax on a package and compare it with that used by the responsible person who despatched the package. The available methods of examination are described by Lucas: " Forensic Chemistry and Scientific Criminal Investigation ". Arnold. Third edition, p. 357. When articles have been accepted for examination a detailed description of them should be recorded in a special register kept for the purpose. It will usually be found advisable to give serial numbers to all affairs investigated. The register may be divided into columns in which are entered the date, the laboratory serial number, the place from which the articles are sent, the reference number of the authority submitting the articles, the number of packages and a brief description of them and the name of the person who sealed the packages. If the articles are received by anyone other than the chemist who is to examine them, the register should contain another column for the signature of the latter when he takes charge.

Storage of articles which have to be kept after examination, awaiting orders from the courts, is important, and in large departments may provide whole-time employment for one or more storekeepers. The storekeeper who takes the examined articles from the laboratory must see that they have been properly re-sealed by the chemist; he must give a receipt to the latter; he must keep the store and record the transactions in such a way that the articles will be readily accessible to the competent authority. He may also be called upon to serve on a committee which has the duty of destroying the articles when ordered to do so by the court. Needless to say, the store should be kept under seal. The sealing of doors is best done by means of a hasp such as is sold for use with a padlock, fitted so that no screw-heads are exposed when the hasp is in position. A piece of string is passed through the staple which normally would hold the padlock, and both ends of this string are passed through holes in a card. The string is then fastened in contact with the card with wax on which the seal is impressed.

The Opening of Packages and Preliminary Examination

Before breaking any of the seals of a package, a description with all necessary details of its external characteristics should be entered in the laboratory note-book. One or more of the wax seal impressions should be kept intact and preserved; sometimes disputes may arise in court as to the authenticity of the seals. The next step is to consider the order in which the articles should be taken for analysis. This may be important. If, for example, during the investigation of a poisoning case, a drinking vessel containing dregs of the last thing swallowed by the victim has been found, the identification of a poisonous substance in it will be a valuable indicator for the remainder of the work; although it may occasionally mislead.

Packages should be opened and their contents inspected in a good light, in a place free from draughts so as to avoid the possibility of loss of small articles and powders which might be blown away. No chemical test involving destruction of material should be made until all other possible observations, such as appearance with and without a lens, odour, and reaction to litmus, have been made and noted. This is, of course, specially important when the quantity of material is small.

Visual examination of excreta and the contents of the stomach and intestines is an indispensable preliminary to all toxicological analysis. The nature of the food in vomited matter, stomach-washings and the stomach itself, should be noted; even if no poisonous matter is seen the description of the ingredients of the last meal will be valuable; and again, if the stomach is empty, the fact may be important. A careful search must be made for foreign matter of any sort. Hard particles of mineral matter must be picked out, washed, and if possible identified. The identification of particles of white or yellow arsenic, for example, is a better piece of evidence than the proof of the presence of arsenic by other methods, since it indicates the form in which the poison was administered. Poisonous seeds, fragments of seeds, leaves or other parts of poisonous plants may be found. The examination of these should only be undertaken by a person having sound botanical knowledge and experience in microscopical pharmacognosy. If the chemist himself has not this experience he should call in the aid of an expert botanist. Sometimes it is possible to confirm the botanical findings by chemical analysis, but if the report is to depend on botanical examination alone there must be no doubt about it; it is not work for a half-trained observer.

Here let it be said that this applies to all the work of the forensic laboratory. Chemical tests must be carried out by chemists; if they have medical qualifications also, so much the better, but they must be fully trained and experienced as analysts. Many of the tests to be described later may appear simple enough to be left to a laboratory assistant; nevertheless, there may be pitfalls. It is not sufficient to know how to carry out an analytical process; one must be acutely conscious of the possible fallacies, and this implies knowledge and experience extending far beyond the immediate question of applying tests for a substance whose presence is suspected. There are few chemical tests which are absolutely and beyond question specific for the substances they are supposed to identify. It follows, therefore, that if a positive result can be obtained in one test only, the report must be very carefully expressed. Indeed, it may be the duty of the chemist, should he fail to confirm one result by a test of different character, to report that the result is negative. This point will be dealt with more fully in the chapter on alkaloidal poisons, but it may be laid down as a universal rule that no positive statement must be made as to the presence of poison on the evidence of a single test. Further, when the test depends on changes of colour a chemist should doubt the evidence of his own eyes; he should consult a colleague whenever possible.

In poisoning cases of which the complete history is known, i.e. in which the symptoms have been recorded by an experienced medical practitioner and in which observations at the autopsy have given indications of a poison of a definite kind, complete chemical analysis will seldom be required. The chemist, unless he is himself a medical man, may expect to receive guidance from his medical colleague; and when such effective co-operation exists the analyst's work may be restricted to the search for poisons of a particular group. The ideal conditions are attained when the medical officer's report at the autopsy confirms the opinion of the physician (if any) who has attended the patient and is itself confirmed by the findings of the analytical chemist.

It is usually recommended that not more than one-third of the available material should be used for the first analysis, the remaining two-thirds being reserved for repetition and for control by another analyst. This course is certainly advisable, and should be followed whenever possible. However, in the examination of viscera for alkaloids or similar drugs the quantity of poison is usually so small and the process of extraction is so far from perfect that it is sometimes necessary to use larger amounts of material.

Before beginning any analysis or other examination, the first thing is to read through the documents submitted, which should give the fullest possible details of the history of the case and the circumstances under which the articles were collected. It may be necessary to ask for fuller details, and if so, this should be done at once. It frequently happens that items of information are unintentionally withheld, the lack of which may result in waste of time and material, and may even render a successful analysis impossible.

Reagents and Glassware

One cardinal factor in all forensic chemistry is the absolute necessity of scrupulously clean apparatus, and of reagents of the purest quality obtainable. With regard to apparatus, it is the manifest duty of the chemist to supervise the cleaning, or to do it himself; in any case, he should do the final stages of the cleaning with his own hands. There can be no excuse for the chemist who uses dirty apparatus when the life and liberty of a fellow creature may depend on the trustworthiness of his analysis. Some authorities, indeed, have urged that none but new apparatus is trustworthy. Without going so far as that, we may say most emphatically that the highest standard of cleanliness is necessary.

Reagents nowadays seldom give any trouble provided that they are purchased from a firm of the highest repute and are guaranteed pure. Some manufacturers sell a special grade of reagents "for forensic purposes". But again, the responsibility for ensuring the *use* of pure reagents is on the analyst himself, and not on the manufacturer.

It is equally important that receptacles used for samples of viscera and excreta should conform to the same rigorous standard of cleanliness. Naturally, the responsibility for this is on the sender, but it may be necessary for the chemist to demonstrate to the sender how the word cleanliness is to be understood.

Equipment

The general equipment of a toxicological laboratory does not differ in essentials from that of an ordinary analytical laboratory. It may perhaps be worth while to mention the great convenience of glassware with standard ground joints, and the importance, for saving both time and material, of an efficient centrifuge. Every laboratory must, of course, be equipped with a fume chamber having a good through draught and well-fitting windows, and it is a further advantage to have one room set apart for the most unpleasant operations, a room in which the chemist need not spend much of his time.

Some additions are desirable. The chief of these is a photographic dark-room specially fitted for photomicrography and for spectroscopic work. The micro-camera need not be expensive. Quite efficient instruments which can be used with an ordinary microscope can be bought for about £10. Photomicrographs of crystals and of the botanical features of vegetable powders are invaluable as records, and can be produced in court if necessary. For serious spectroscopic work a precision instrument of first-rate quality is essential and a spectrograph is desirable. The instrument should at least be suitable for the visual observation and photography of arc-, spark- and absorption-spectra. If the work of the laboratory includes the examination of blood-stains a microspectroscope should be available.

The laboratory should have at least one electric refrigerator, several mincing machines of approved type and one or more powerful screw presses, for the mincing and squeezing of viscera. These must be such that all parts can be easily removed for thorough washing. A particularly good instrument for mixing and homogenizing material of the kind met in toxicological work is the Waring Blendor.

Other desiderata in the laboratory equipment are a supply of compressed air and a vacuum pump with a pipe-line. Compressed air is a valuable aid in the rapid evaporation of such liquids as do not lend themselves to vacuum-distillation, e.g. liquids which froth badly under reduced pressure.

Microscopes

In addition to ordinary microscopes, binocular magnifiers (Fig. 1), magnifying 5 to 150 diameters, will be found useful in the examination of dust, the particles of dirt found in finger-nail clippings and for the examination of seeds and fragments thereof. Needless to say, a good hand lens should be in more or less constant use.

FIG. 1.

Colorimeters

Methods based on the measurement of colour are invaluable because their sensitivity permits the accurate determination of very small amounts of an immense variety of substances which themselves yield coloured solutions or can be quantitatively converted to soluble coloured substances by suitable reagents. All such methods depend on the validity of *Beer's Law* which states that the colour intensity of a solution is directly proportional to the concentration of the coloured solute ; since the law is not strictly accurate it is necessary to define, in each case, the limits within which it is sufficiently nearly true for practical purposes.

Visual colorimeters of the Duboscq type must now be regarded as virtually obsolete, although in the absence of anything better they can still be extremely useful. They all depend upon the same principle. Two solutions, one containing a known concentration and one an unknown concentration of the same coloured substance are placed in small cylinders of which the bases are fine quality optical glass. These vessels are fitted with glass plungers and a system of racks and pinions allows movement of the vessels (or plungers) so that the depths of coloured liquid below the plungers can be varied independently. With a beam of light passing through the liquids and plungers, and then through a hexagonal prism (or a pair of rhombic prisms) the two colours can be viewed, side by side, in the eye piece of the instrument. By adjusting the depth of liquid in one vessel the colours can be made to match. It is obvious that the concentrations of coloured solute will then be inversely proportional to the depths of the solutions.

In all colorimeters it is the intensity of the *transmitted* light which is measured. Increased accuracy is attainable, interference by extraneous colours is more easily avoided, and the necessity of preparing a standard solution for every analysis is abolished if the instrument is adapted to measure the intensity of (nearly) mono-chromatic light *absorbed* by the solution. The Pulfrich photometer is specially constructed for this purpose but an ordinary visual colorimeter can readily be adapted by placing a suitable filter (e.g. one of the Ilford spectral filters) over the eye piece and substituting a neutral grey filter in contact with the plunger for one of the cups. The " unknown " solution is placed in the other cup and the coloured fields are equalized in the usual way. The correct filter, found by trial, is usually that which gives the greatest absorption. The grey filter provides the " standard " and by comparing it with a series of solutions of known concentration a permanent calibration curve can be constructed for each analytical method.

Most modern instruments use photo-electric cells instead of the human eye. In some the intensity of the light transmitted (or, more usually, absorbed) by the coloured solution contained in a cell of fixed size is measured directly in terms of the E.M.F. generated in a single photo-electric cell ; the instrument is calibrated for each analytical method by means of a series of standard solutions. In others, two cells are used in opposition, the light intensity being altered in one by change in thickness of the coloured layer or by an iris diaphragm until the " fields " are equalized and the galvanometer gives a zero reading.

Still more advanced are sphectrophotometers in which the photoelectric measurement of intensity is combined with a prism or diffraction grating method of varying the wave-length of the light.

This gives a much more sensitive method of choosing the optimum wave length for the particular solution being measured. Further, by using an instrument of quartz construction with a suitable " light " source the range of work possible can be enormously and usefully extended by using the ultra violet range. A similar extension to the infra red region of the spectrum is being developed but has not yet received much attention in toxocological analysis. Although these modern instruments are expensive, their convenience and versatility, together with the elimination of human fallibility in colour matching make them well worth while.

Spectrograph and Spectroscope

For certain purposes—e.g. the detection of carbon monoxide in blood—the Hartridge reversion spectroscope is exceedingly useful. This instrument provides two similar spectra, side by side, but reversed in direction. A micrometer mechanism allows them to be moved with respect to one another and for the movement to be measured accurately. With an oxyhaemoglobin solution between the light source and the slit, the spectra can be moved so that the two narrow bands coincide (Fig. 2 A). If a solution containing

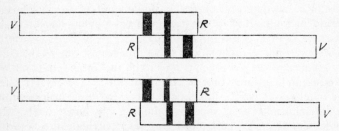

FIG. 2. Determination of carboxyhaemoglobin with the reversion spectroscope.

A. The spectra adjusted with a solution of oxyhaemoglobin in front of the slit.

B. The spectra when, without alteration of the adjustment, a solution of carboxyhaemoglobin is substituted for the oxyhaemoglobin.

carboxyhaemoglobin is substituted for the oxyhaemoglobin, the bands are found to have moved apart (Fig. 2 B). The amount of movement required to bring them into alignment can be measured and, after calibration with known mixtures of oxy- and carboxy-haemoglobin, used to determine quantitatively the relative amounts of these pigments in the solution.

For visual work with emission spectra for the detection, particularly, of traces of metals, a wavelength spectrometer of the constant deviation type is very convenient. The spectrograph, however, has many advantages. It is more sensitive; it gives a permanent photographic record which can be produced in court; it more readily allows quantitative analysis to be done; and, if a quartz spectrograph is used, it permits full use to be made of the much greater range and sensitivity provided by the ultra-violet region of the spectrum. With the sector photometer it makes possible the working out of absorption curves and it is to be remembered that absorption spectrometry, though as yet little developed for the analysis of complex mixtures of organic substances, is, nevertheless, steadily increasing in usefulness.

Refractometer

The refractometer, while not so much used by the toxicologist as by the food analyst, is occasionally needed for the examination of oils.

Micro-sublimation

Micro-sublimation is so important in the purification of organic substances that suitable apparatus is necessary, and since many substances decompose below the sublimation point under atmospheric pressure, it is often necessary to sublime under reduced pressure.

A simple micro-sublimation apparatus which can be made by any competent glass worker is illustrated in Fig. 3. It consists of an outer and an inner tube, each drawn out to a long blunt point. The outer vessel, which should be about 10 cm. long, has a side tube for attachment to a vacuum pump. The inner vessel is a condenser which is kept cool by water circulating through it. After the substance to be purified has been put into the lower extremity of the outer vessel, the apparatus is assembled and attached to the pump. When the air has been pumped out, the lower end of the outer vessel is immersed in a suitable bath of sulphuric acid, oil, or fusible alloy and the temperature is observed by means of a thermometer with the bulb immersed in the bath. The sublimate collects on the lower end of the condenser. This instrument can not only be used for the purification of substances, but, if a manometer is inserted between it and the vacuum pump, serves to determine the sublimation point under a given pressure; this may be useful as an aid to the identification of the substance.

An instrument on a larger scale is made by Messrs. Becker. In this the substance is heated in a boiling tube inserted in a hollow mass of metal which carries a thermometer. The upper part of the tube is surrounded by a water jacket like a Liebig condenser, and the sublimate is collected on an inner tube fitting loosely inside the boiling-tube (Fig. 4).

Sublimation can be also carried out on an electrically heated microscope stage which is intended primarily for melting point determinations. The heated stage is especially well designed for toxicological work, since it enables one to determine the melting point of a single crystal. The older models carry mercury thermometers, and although the makers claim that correct melting points are registered when the instruments are used in a room free from draughts, it appears to be the universal opinion that calibration is necessary, especially for temperatures above 150° C.

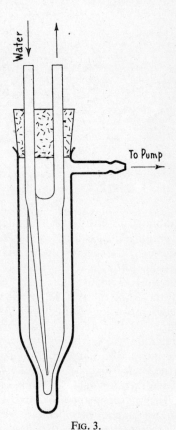

Fig. 3.

Apparatus for micro-sublimation under reduced pressure.

The method of using the heating stage for purification of specimens and observation of melting points is as follows: It is clamped to the microscope stage, and electrical connection to the current supply is made through a rheostat. A portion of an almost pure specimen is put into a depression in a microscope slide, covered with a large cover-slip and focussed under the microscope. Heating is begun by switching on the current and gently turning the knob which controls the rheostat. The rate of rise of temperature must depend on the sublimation point and melting point. It is usually convenient to raise the temperature by three or four degrees per minute until within about twenty degrees of the sublimation point, after which the rate should be slowed down to not more than one or two degrees per minute. At the first sign of the formation of sublimate the heating is stopped, and when two or three crystals have condensed, the cover-slip is transferred to a clean slide. Crystals so formed will usually be pure enough for the melting point to be determined. If not they can be further purified by repeating the sublimation process.

A more elaborate form of the electrically heated microscope stage is the Kofler apparatus (Fig. 5), in which the mercury thermometer is not used, temperatures being read on a millivolt-meter, usually

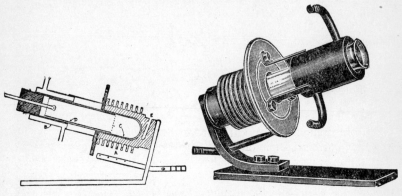

FIG. 4.   Messrs. Becker's sublimation apparatus.

calibrated to give direct readings in centigrade degrees; otherwise a graph must be used to convert the readings from millivolts to degrees. The microscope stage is heated by means of a current passing through a coil built into a cylindrical metal case. The current is regulated by means of a rheostat with an ammeter as part of the same unit. The temperature measured is the difference between two joints of a thermo-couple of which one pole is on the stage and the other is maintained at a constant low temperature, preferably 0° C., by immersing it in melting ice contained in a thermos flask; if the cold joint is not at 0° C. a small calculation is necessary in order to obtain correct readings. The two poles of the thermo-couple are connected with the millivolt-meter.

The makers supply a table showing the current required for various ranges of temperature: e.g. for melting points below 50° C. the required current is 0·6 amp., and for temperatures approaching 350° C., 2·7 amps. The rate at which the temperature is raised can be controlled with the rheostat, and this should be more or less rapid according to the danger of loss by volatilization. If the substance is so volatile that the whole of the sample is lost before the melting point is reached, a second sample is taken and the cover-slip is sealed on to the slide with such a cement as calcium caseinate, so as to enclose the crystals in an airtight space. For high temperatures a cement made of lead oxide and glycerine is recommended.

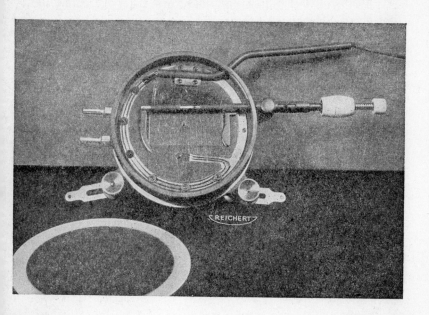

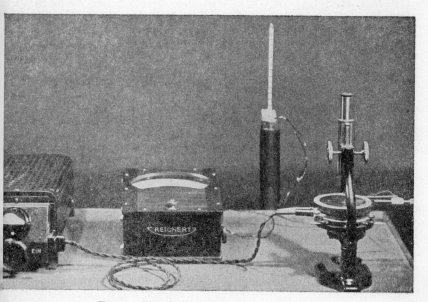

Fig. 5. Electrically heated microscope stage.

Like the simpler heating stage, the Kofler apparatus can be used for micro-sublimation, which process may, if necessary, be used as a means of purification or simply for noting the sublimation point. Special accessories also may be obtained for micro-sublimation *in vacuo* under the microscope.

The Kofler apparatus is particularly valuable in observing the melting point of polymorphous substances; in an ordinary melting-point apparatus the melting point of a metastable phase may be missed altogether.

Micro-Diffusion

Micro-diffusion affords a simple method widely applicable to the separation of a volatile substance by simple gaseous diffusion from one chamber where it exerts a measurable tension to another where at the surface of a suitable absorbing reagent its tension is zero.

FIG. 6.   Standard Micro-diffusion Apparatus

(Conway, E. J. and Byrne, A., *Biochemical Journal*, 1933, **27**, 420).

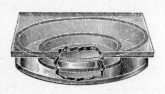

Vertical Section on Line A–B.

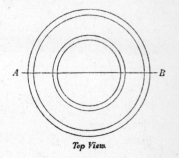

Top View.

The apparatus designed by Conway[1] makes the process reasonably rapid, and it is so simple and compact that multiple analyses are readily made. It consists (Fig. 6) of a thick-walled circular glass dish with an inner chamber formed by a circular glass wall rising from the floor to about half the height of the outer wall. The edges

[1] Conway, E. J. *Micro Diffusion Analysis and Volumetric Error*, London : Crosby Lockwood.

of the outer wall are ground flat so that the apparatus can be covered with a glass plate sealed with vaseline or similar material. Normally the absorbing reagent is placed in the inner chamber and the material containing the volatile substance in the outer annular space.

CHAPTER I

CLASSIFICATION OF POISONS AND GENERAL PROCEDURE

THE system of classification used by the pharmacologist, in which drugs are grouped according to their physiological effects, is not the most suitable for the analytical chemist who is concerned with the isolation of poisons and their identification. The pharmacological classification is nevertheless useful, since it may serve as a guide to the analyst when the symptoms of poisoning have been properly observed. When these symptoms are confirmed by the presence of characteristic lesions seen at the autopsy, this guidance is very valuable indeed. Unfortunately, symptoms and lesions are not always characteristic.

The pharmacological classification, according to Cushny, is as follows:—

(1) Substances characterized by their local actions. These include volatile oils, skin irritants, purgatives, anthelmintics, disinfectants and antiseptics.

(2) Substances characterized chiefly by their action after absorption, including narcotics, stimulants and other alkaloids, glycosides, prussic acid, toxalbumins, coal-tar products other than disinfectants, halogens, acids, alkalis, oxalates and alkaline-earth metals.

(3) Heavy metals and metalloids, including phosphorus among the metalloids.

A system differing slightly from that of Cushny is based definitely on the symptoms produced when poisonous doses have been ingested.

The *first group* includes the irritant poisons causing nausea, vomiting, purging, violent abdominal pains, blood in the vomit and the stools, albumen or blood in the urine, and sometimes convulsive attacks ending in coma and death. Among these are some volatile oils, especially those consisting mainly of terpenes, which are frequently used by the laity to bring about abortion. Abortion often does follow their use, but only when the dose is sufficiently large to endanger the life of the mother, since they do not act directly on the uterus. The group also includes some fatty oils like chaulmoogra oil, used in the treatment of leprosy, and the more violent vegetable purgatives like colocynth, jalap and scammony; anthelmintics like male fern produce some of the irritant symptoms as also do chenopodium and santonin. Carbolic acid and other phenols in doses too small to produce immediate unconsciousness cause nausea and vomiting. Metallic poisons such as arsenic and the soluble salts of mercury are, of course, powerful irritants. Potassium chlorate in large doses is also an irritant.

Alkaloids are not usually regarded as irritant poisons, but some of them cause marked nausea, vomiting, abdominal pain and diarrhoea. These include: colchicine, coniine, nicotine, cytisine, muscarine, aconitine (sometimes vomiting but rarely diarrhoea), apomorphine (vomiting only), narcissine, emetine, lobeline, pilocarpine, physostigmine, the alkaloids of ergot, gelsemine and veratrine.

The *second group* includes soporifics like chloral and narcotics like morphine, both of which in acute poisoning cases produce coma before death, and stimulants like strychnine, the most marked symptoms of which are convulsive spasms.

The *third group* consists of the mydriatic alkaloids which cause dilation of the pupil and also repression of secretions.

The *fourth group* includes alkaloids which contract the pupil and stimulate the secretions, causing excessive salivation and lachrymation. These are pilocarpine, muscarine and physostigmine.

The *fifth group* consists of the local anaesthetics derived from coca leaves and the synthetic cocaine substitutes.

The *sixth group* contains the cardiac stimulants, adrenaline, ephedrine and the digitalis glycosides.

The system of classification most useful to the analyst is based on the methods used for the isolation of the poisons from tissues and excreta, and this bears little relationship to the pharmacological grouping. In this manual seven groups of substances will be considered, viz.:—

(1) The volatile poisons which are isolated by distillation with or without a current of steam. These are: alcohols, aldehydes, some acids such as hydrocyanic and acetic acids, chloroform and similar halogen compounds, phenols and some other coal-tar derivatives, phosphorus and essential oils.

(2) Acids, alkalis, and irritant salts of alkali metals which can be extracted with water.

(3) " Common metallic poisons ", which are arbitrarily defined as those which are deposited on copper foil when heated with hydrochloric acid: arsenic, antimony, mercury and bismuth. This group may also include silver, although it is not a common poison.

(4) Other poisonous metals.

(5) Non-basic organic poisons, which are soluble in alcohol, usually slightly soluble in water or dilute alkalis, and can be extracted from acidified solutions by shaking with ether, chloroform or other immiscible solvent.

(6) Basic organic poisons, isolated in a similar manner to the substances in Group 5, but extracted with immiscible solvents from aqueous solution in presence of alkali.

(The usual process for the extraction of substances in Groups 5 and 6 is referred to as the Stas-Otto process.)

(7) Substances for which special methods of isolation, such as dialysis, are required, and substances for which no chemical methods of identification are known. These include toxalbumins like ricin, crotin and abrin, and many vegetable products of unknown constitution.

The groups are not mutually exclusive. For example, volatile substances may be found in all the groups, but when the volatility is relatively slight these may be missed in the first group and are more likely to be found later. Thus, some of the oils and volatile alkaloids are commonly found in Groups 5 and 6, and the concentrated extract so obtained may be submitted to steam distillation as a means of purification. Conversely, substances which are readily volatile in steam may have to be extracted from the distillate by shaking with an immiscible solvent.

Further, some compounds of arsenic and mercury are volatile; this fact may be utilized in extracting the metals, or if other methods are used, special precautions must be taken to avoid loss by volatilization.

In Groups 5 and 6 there are substances which can be extracted with organic solvents in either acidic or alkaline solution, although not with equal facility; the analyst must be aware of the possibility of extracting certain alkaloids along with the non-basic poisons.

General Procedure in Toxicological Analysis

No analytical work involving change in the material may be undertaken until the greatest possible amount of information has been gained by inspection and by study of the available data. In the great majority of cases the history will point to a particular poison or group of poisons and accordingly, provided enough material is retained for further search in the event of a negative result, the analysis may be appropriately directed, with omission of much tedious and unproductive work. Even in the absence of a suggestive history careful examination of such material as stomach or intestinal contents may give a useful lead (but should be made in all cases).

This examination will, in the first place, be visual, both by naked eye and with the aid of a suitable magnifier such as the low-power binocular dissecting microscope shown in Fig. 1. In this way recognizable fragments of seeds, leaves or other parts of poisonous plants may be picked out and, after botanical identification, indicate the lines along which chemical analysis should proceed; crystals of organic or inorganic substances may be so characteristic as to be identified and to suggest the confirmatory tests to be applied, or they may be picked out and subjected to micro-tests suggested by their shape and colour.

Careful note should be made of any odour which, even if not characteristic of any chemical individual, may be associated with some chemical group, for which search may then be instituted (aldehydes, phenols, essential oils are among those substances which have characteristic odours).

The reaction of gastric and intestinal contents, of urine, or of liquid in vessels suspected of having contained the poison should invariably be tested. For this a " Universal Indicator ", which gives a continuous change of colour over almost the entire pH range, is very useful. Failing it, the material should be tested with one indicator with a colour change near the neutral point (litmus, brom-cresol purple, phenol-red) and, according to the result either a second which changes colour at a rather low pH (Congo-red, methyl orange, thymol blue) or one with a colour change markedly on the alkaline side of neutrality (phenolphthalein, alizarin).

If this preliminary examination, either alone or in conjunction with such other data as the ante-mortem symptoms and the post-mortem findings, has given reasonably clear indications as to the poison or class of poison used, the way is clear for the appropriate chemical analysis. If no guidance has been obtained, a general search must be instituted. Since the amount of material available is strictly limited, the methods used must postpone final destruction until the maximum of information has been extracted.

Of the seven classes of poisons enumerated on pp. 17–18, the second and the seventh can be excluded from our present considera-tion. Acids, alkalis, and irritant salts of alkali metals all leave such traces that their presence will inevitably have been discovered either during the medical and pathological examinations or by the preliminary inspection and testing of the material. The substances grouped together in the seventh class require special methods for their detection, and these methods do not fit into any general scheme. We are therefore concerned with classes 1, 3, 4, 5, and 6.

Many analysts would begin by carrying out a Reinsch test (for arsenic, antimony, lead, mercury, and bismuth) on the grounds that this detects the most commonly used " metallic " poisons and that it requires only a small amount of material. On the whole it is a useful practice, although it is not very likely that such poisons would have escaped suspicion in the case-history and preliminary examination. For similar reasons a spectrographic examination might be undertaken at this stage.

Apart from this, the first step is to submit the material to distillation, first alone and then with a current of steam. This process effects the separation of any volatile poisons which may be present, but, if examination of the distillate should prove negative, the residue is available for the next stage.

This must be the search for organic poisons—Groups 5 and 6—since whichever method is employed for their separation, no reagent is added which will prevent the subsequent examination for inorganic poisons. The fact that the material has previously been submitted to distillation must be borne in mind if the examination for organic poisons proves negative for, though most such substances will withstand the treatment, a few are unstable and may be decomposed when heated to 100° C. for a considerable period. It may therefore be necessary to search for these in a fresh sample.

During the separation of organic poisons all residues must, of course, be kept. This applies not only to the matter left from the original extraction, but to the residues at all later stages, for some of these may contain inorganic poisons. Thus soluble inorganic salts might appear almost entirely in the aqueous-alcohol extract of the Stas-Otto process, or in a trichloracetic acid extract, and be left behind only at a later stage when the extracting solvent was one immiscible with water. For the final stage all these residues, whether solid or liquid, are combined, and now, all possible examination for volatile and organic poisons having been made, it is possible to proceed with the examination for toxic inorganic substances. This must be left to the last, since it involves the destruction, by oxidation, of all organic matter present.

The procedures involved in these various stages will be detailed later when the various classes of poisons are being considered separately. The object here has been merely to present, in broad outline, the order in which the analyses should be made for the purpose of conserving material. It may again be emphasized that only very rarely is such a general analysis required; in the vast majority of cases the toxicologist is, from the beginning, searching only for a definite chemical substance or, at worst, for one of a group of related substances. Then, naturally, he goes straight for his objective, taking care, however, to leave enough material for further search should that prove necessary.

POST-MORTEM SIGNS

Indications seen at the autopsy which are of definite value to the analyst are almost entirely confined to the lesions produced by corrosive and irritant poisons. The following summary, based largely on descriptions given in Sydney Smith's "Forensic Medicine", may be useful, though it is by no means complete.

Lesions of the Mouth

Blackening and severe corrosion · ·	Sulphuric acid.
Severe corrosion without blackening · ·	Hydrochloric acid.
Severe corrosion and yellow stains which are not removable by ammonia · · ·	Nitric acid.
Lips discoloured, tongue sodden and mucous membrane eroded · · · ·	Caustic alkalis.
Lips swollen, tongue raw, oesophagus white with red cracks: broncho-pneumonia if death is delayed · · · ·	Ammonia.
Mucous membrane whitened · · ·	Oxalic acid.
Scalded appearance of the mouth · ·	Acetic acid.
White stains on lips, becoming brown on exposure to air · · · · ·	Phenol.
Blue or black line on gums · · ·	Lead or bismuth.
Yellow stains about the lips, soluble in ammonia · · · · ·	Iodine.
Reddening of mucous membrane of mouth, eyes and glands · · · · ·	Formalin.
Inflammation sometimes accompanied by vesication · · · · ·	Cantharides.

Lesions of the Gastro-intestinal Tract

Corrosion · · · · · ·	Strong acids.
Soapiness · · · · · ·	Caustic alkalis.
Hardening of the mucosa with haemorrhage	Formalin.
Dark brown gelatinous mass in stomach ·	Oxalic acid.
Stomach greyish-white · · · ·	Acetic acid.
Stomach reddened either generally or in patches, sub-mucous haemorrhage, ulceration, sticky mucus on the stomach walls which may retain white or yellow particles · · · · ·	Arsenic.
Irritation more severe than above · ·	Mercury.
Irritation less severe than above · ·	Antimony.
Mild irritation with green stains · ·	Copper.
Acute irritation with green stains · ·	Chromates.
Acute irritation with chocolate-coloured blood	Chlorates.
Congestion, reddening of the mucous membrane · · · · · · ·	Barium salts.
Lesions similar to the above, but with odour resembling bitter almonds · · ·	Nitro-benzene.
Irritation with sub-mucous haemorrhage, odour of turpentine · · · ·	Turpentine.

Lesions of the Gastro-intestinal Tract

Mild irritation · · · · · Some essential oils, colchicine, taxine, aconitine.

Lesions of the Liver and Kidneys

Fatty degeneration · · · · · Phosphorus, *Amanita phalloides.*

Inflammation, kidneys suffused with blood · Cantharides.

Inflammation of the kidneys · · · Colchicine.

CHAPTER II

VOLATILE AND GASEOUS POISONS

DISTILLATION in a current of steam is the best general method for the separation of volatile poisons, though when specific substances are being sought simple distillation may be possible. The ideal apparatus is all glass, with well-fitting standard ground glass connections. It consists of a bolt-head flask, the stopper carrying a steam inlet tube reaching nearly to the bottom of the flask and a short outlet tube fitted with a trap and connected through a straight (Liebig) water-jacketed condenser to a receiving flask. The receiver should be immersed in an ice-bath and, when there is any possibility of a volatile acid being present, should contain dilute sodium hydroxide solution into which the delivery tube dips. If all-glass apparatus is not available, the two-hole stopper of the distilling-flask should be of cork coated with collodion, but not of rubber. The steam inlet tube should have some means—e.g. a screw clip—by which the rate of distillation can be controlled. Ordinarily a rapid stream of cold water must pass through the condenser jacket, but if the volatile substance should solidify inside the condenser tube, the water should be run out so that the steam may carry the deposit into the cooled receiver. (This rarely happens, but a few substances behave in this way—e.g. naphthalene.)

The material for distillation must be suitably prepared. Many bases which are steam-volatile form non-volatile salts with acids and conversely volatile acids may form non-volatile salts. Hence if the presence of a base is suspected the material should be made alkaline with sodium hydroxide; if an acid, it should be acidified with a non-volatile acid such as oxalic (if there is no possibility of that being already present), tartaric or succinic.

HYDROCYANIC ACID AND CYANIDES

The most common form of cyanide poisoning in the writer's experience is the ingestion of alkaline cyanides by the mouth. More rarely it is due to cyanogenetic glycosides; the use of a decoction of peach-leaves, probably mixed with crushed kernels, as a household remedy has been known to cause death in Egypt. Alkaline cyanides are frequently used for the malicious poisoning of cattle, being given to the animal mixed with food. In the East this is generally done by boring a hole longitudinally through the pith of a maize-cob and filling the hole with cyanide, although sometimes the poison is mixed with green fodder and occasionally with bread. Usually, if a sample of the food is submitted for analysis the odour of cyanide is at once noticed, but if the sample has been kept for some time exposed to the air the cyanide may have been wholly or partially hydrolyzed or oxidized. If no odour can be detected, the sample should be extracted with a small amount of distilled water and the extract tested with litmus. A neutral or acid reaction excludes the possibility of alkaline cyanides or decomposition products thereof. If the reaction is alkaline the Prussian blue test described below should be applied.

Owing to the smallness of the lethal dose of cyanides and the rapidity with which death follows ingestion, the question of the examination of the excreta seldom arises. Very often it is only necessary to examine the stomach, though sometimes the duodenum, blood, and organs rich in blood will repay analysis. If it is suspected that death is due to the inhaling of hydrocyanic acid gas the lungs should be examined. If the stomach has been opened at the autopsy the medical officer will in all probability have noticed the odour of cyanide, but the odour cannot be accepted as conclusive proof. It is the duty of the medical officer to place the stomach and any other organs of which the analysis is desired in jars with well-fitting stoppers and to forward them, properly sealed, to the laboratory without delay. If possible, the examination should be made at once, although the detection of cyanides both by the odour and by chemical tests when the viscera have been kept in stoppered jars for a week or more is not impossible. When the jar is opened the odour of cyanide may be noted at once (though some persons cannot detect it). After leaving the jar uncovered for a short time the odour may no longer be perceptible; but if the stopper is replaced for half an hour or so and again removed the accumulation of gas in the jar may be sufficient to make the odour once more apparent.

Two tests for hydrocyanic acid which, although not specific, are extraordinarily sensitive, are the guiacum and benzidine tests, which are very similar to one another. For the former test a strip of filter-paper which has been immersed in a 0·2 per cent. alcoholic solution of guiacum resin, and then, without drying, in a 0·1 per cent. solution of copper sulphate, is held in the mouth of the vessel which is supposed to contain a cyanide, i.e. in the air above the contents of the vessel. A fine blue colour is produced in presence of the most minute trace of cyanide. For the benzidine test the filter-paper is first treated with a solution of benzidine in acetic acid and then with a dilute solution of copper acetate;[1] hydrocyanic acid produces an immediate bluish-violet colour on the filter-paper.

[1] Cf. *Analyst*, 1938, **63**, 659.

Substances like ozone and certain peroxides produce similar colours, and the test-papers also become coloured when kept for some time in the air of the laboratory. It is therefore necessary to use a second test-paper as a control, noting the difference in time required for the production of the colour in the two papers.

For the definitive tests, the poison must be separated by distillation, or by micro-diffusion in a Conway apparatus. A portion of the stomach and its contents, or other viscera, is placed in the distillation flask, a slight excess of dilute acid is added and the stopper and connecting tubes are fitted. Distillation is begun by heating the steam-generator. The outlet of the condenser dips into a dilute solution of caustic alkali. The process is continued until, say, 100 ml. of the distillate have been collected, after which it is stopped by disconnecting the rubber tube between the steam-generator and the flask.

A portion of the distillate is then tested for cyanide by the Prussian-blue reaction, which is carried out as follows: the liquid is again tested with litmus paper; if it is not still alkaline it must be made so by the addition of caustic soda solution. A few centigrammes of ferrous sulphate or ferrous ammonium sulphate are then added and the liquid is heated to boiling ; excess of dilute sulphuric acid is added and also a few drops of a dilute solution of ferric chloride. A strong blue colour will be produced immediately if cyanide is present to the extent of about 1 part in 10,000. If the quantity is larger than this a blue precipitate will be produced either at once or on standing. If no colour appears, or if there is any doubt about the matter, another portion of the alkaline distillate should be evaporated on a water-bath to a small bulk which is then divided into two equal parts. With one of them the Prussian-blue test is repeated, and it is an advantage to carry out the reaction in a porcelain basin. If again no colour is perceptible the basin and its contents may be allowed to stand overnight, when a ring of Prussian-blue may sometimes be seen " creeping " up the sides of the basin from the circumference of the liquid surface.

The remainder of the distillate is evaporated to dryness on a water-bath after the addition of one or two drops of yellow ammonium sulphide solution. The yellow residue is moistened with dilute hydrochloric acid and a drop of ferric chloride solution is added. The formation of a blood-red colour which may take a little time to develop, but which is immediately discharged when mixed with mercuric chloride solution indicates that the distillate contains cyanide. This test is said to be much more delicate than the Prussian-blue test. Both tests should be applied.

Anderson[1] gives the limiting sensitivity of the Prussian-blue test as 1 in 100,000, and of the thiocyanate test as 1 in 1,000,000. The

[1] *J.C.S.I.*, 1917, **36**, 195–6. *Analyst*, 1917, **42**, 178.

thiocyanate test for cyanides can be made still more delicate by the following technique recommended by Lavialle and Varenne.[1]

The liquid to be tested is treated with slight excess of yellow ammonium sulphide solution, boiled gently for five minutes and then heated on the water-bath until the volume is reduced to about 1 ml. This residual liquid is diluted with 10 ml. of water, and sufficient concentrated hydrochloric acid is added to give a distinct blue with Congo-red paper. The liquid is then shaken with three successive portions of ether (20, 10 and 10 ml.). The united ethereal extracts are allowed to evaporate at the ordinary temperature of the room until all odour of ether has disappeared; 1 or 2 drops of very dilute ferric chloride solution are then added and the liquid is stirred. A blood-red colour is produced if the original liquid contains as little as $0·00005$ g. of hydrocyanic acid. We have obtained quite definite results by this method with quantities of cyanide which gave no perceptible trace of colour in the Prussian-blue test.

A further test which is also very delicate depends on the conversion of methaemoglobin into cyanmethaemoglobin. A piece of filter-paper is soaked in blood which has been treated with potassium chlorate to convert the haemoglobin into methaemoglobin, which is dark brown in colour. When this paper is dipped into a solution containing hydrocyanic acid the colour becomes bright red.

A useful method for the quantitative estimation of hydrocyanic acid has recently been published by Aldridge.[2] In the absence of thiocyanates (which react similarly) it can be made on urine without preliminary treatment or on blood plasma after deproteinization by trichloracetic acid. Since thiocyanic acid is not volatile, it is safest to separate hydrocyanic acid by distillation. To 1 ml. of solution (containing up to 3 μg. of hydrocyanic acid) acidified with acetic or trichloracetic acid, $0·5$ ml. of saturated bromine water is added. This, almost instantaneously, produces cyanogen bromide. Excess of bromine is removed by addition of $0·5$ ml. of $1·5$ per cent. sodium arsenite. To the solution are then added 5 ml. of pyridine reagent (25 ml. pure redistilled pyridine and 2 ml. concentrated hydrochloric acid diluted to 100 ml. with distilled water) and $0·2$ ml. of 2 per cent. benzidine solution. An orange colour appears at once and changes rapidly to red. After 10 minutes at room temperature it is compared with the colour of a standard solution similarly treated (or with the calibration curve previously prepared).

It should not be forgotten that other substances besides simple cyanides and glycosides liberate hydrocyanic acid under the conditions

---

[1] *J. Pharm. Chim.*, 1915, **12**, 74–81.   *Analyst*, 1915, **40**, 447.   Cf. also STUBBS and ELSDON.   *Analyst*, 1937, **62**, 540.

[2] *Analyst*, 1944, **69**, 262.

of distillation described above. Among these are the relatively non-toxic complex cyanides, such as ferro- and ferri-cyanides. From these, hydrocyanic acid is liberated very readily by heating even with tartaric acid. Simple cyanides are decomposed by carbon dioxide, and it is possible to distil off all the hydrocyanic acid by passing steam through a mixture of a simple cyanide and sodium bicarbonate in solution. Peterson, Haines and Webster recommend the general use of sodium bicarbonate instead of a mineral or organic acid, stating that if only a complex cyanide is present no hydrocyanic acid will be found in the distillate. This is not in exact accord with our experience. We have found traces of hydrocyanic acid liberated from potassium ferrocyanide by distilling with sodium bicarbonate solution in a current of steam, although, certainly, the ferrocyanide is decomposed much less readily than the cyanide; the distillate from the former may give a perfectly distinct Prussian-blue reaction. The best way of ensuring that the hydrocyanic acid in the distillate is not due to a complex cyanide is to test two portions of the original material with ferric chloride and ferrous sulphate for ferro- and ferri-cyanide respectively.

Cyanogenetic Glycosides

The most abundant of these are amygdalin, which occurs in the kernels of bitter almonds, peaches and apricots; prulaurasin from cherry laurel leaves; and prunasin from the Virginia prune. All of these are hydrolyzed by the action of emulsin, which is a mixture of enzymes, to benzaldehyde, hydrocyanic acid and glucose. The hydrolysis can be made to proceed in stages if the individual enzymes are used. Amygdalase eliminates one molecule of glucose, leaving mandelonitrile glucoside $C_6H_5CH(CN)OC_6H_{11}O_5$. Prunase completes the hydrolysis. Mineral acids also cause complete hydrolysis. Fabre and Josset assert that although only minute traces of hydrocyanic acid are liberated by acids in concentrations of about 1 per cent., and not more than 17 per cent. is liberated by 10 per cent. acids, the greater part of the hydrocyanic acid is set free if the matter to be distilled contains much protein. If the distillate obtained by passing steam through material acidified with mineral acid has the odour of bitter almonds, a portion of it should be tested for hydrocyanic acid. If this is present silver nitrate solution should be added to another portion of the distillate to precipitate silver cyanide and so remove the odour due to hydrocyanic acid. If the odour of bitter almonds persists after this it is due to benzaldehyde, and this is evidence of the presence of a cyanogenetic glycoside in the original material. Hydrocyanic acid, being much more volatile than benzaldehyde, will be found in the first portion of the distillate:

benzaldehyde can only be completely volatilized by prolonged distillation.

Traces of cyanogenetic glycosides occur in certain beans, notably Java or Mauritius beans and Burma or Rangoon beans (*Phaseolus lunatus*), and in linseed and other species of *Linum*. The names phaseolunatin and linamarin have been used for the glycosides from beans and linseed respectively, but the two glycosides appear to be identical. The seeds also contain appropriate enzymes to hydrolyze the glycosides, and since they are used as feeding-stuffs, especially for cattle, they are obviously a source of danger. In an investigation by Henry and Auld,[1] two samples of linseed cake were found to contain 0·032 and 0·048 per cent. respectively of hydrocyanic acid. The method of determination was to hydrolyze the glycosides with dilute mineral acids and distil off the hydrocyanic acid, after which the distillate was made faintly alkaline with sodium bicarbonate and the cyanide determined by titration with iodine until the permanent yellow colour indicated that all the cyanide had been converted into cyanogen iodide.

The method of testing for enzymes was to mix the freshly ground material with water at about 35° C., containing a little toluene or chloroform, and, after allowing to stand for some time to test for free hydrocyanic acid in the water. No enzyme was found in the samples of linseed cake, and the authors attributed the lack of toxicity of such cake to the destruction of enzymes during the hot-pressing process. They were of opinion, however, that it would be unsafe to assume that enzyme-free products containing cyanogenetic glycosides were free from danger, since they might be mixed with other fodder containing enzymes, or might even be hydrolyzed by enzymes occurring in the intestines. Grant, in Allen's " Commercial Organic Analysis ", states that there is conflicting evidence as to the toxicity of linseed cake; cases of poisoning have been recorded, yet it has been asserted that the glycosides may be excreted unchanged.

Auld and Henry agree with other observers that the dark-coloured Java or Mauritius beans are more likely to be toxic than the lighter-coloured Burma beans.

Hydrocyanic acid may be detected in such seeds by either the benzidine or the guiacum test.

Ten grammes of ground beans are mashed with 20 to 30 ml. of warm water in a small stoppered bottle, which is kept at 40° C. to 50° C. for half an hour. The test-paper, held in the neck of the bottle by means of the stopper, shows a blue colour within a few seconds if the beans contain a cyanogenetic glycoside and an appropriate enzyme.

[1] *J.C.S.I.*, 1908, **27**, 428–33. *Analyst*, 1908, **33**, 280. Cf. also *Analyst*, 1939, **64**, 187.

Cyanides of Heavy Metals

Cyanides of such heavy metals as mercury are not readily decomposed by steam distillation in the presence of acid as above described.   If the presence of such a cyanide is suspected, the original material should first be treated with sulphuretted hydrogen to precipitate the sulphide of the metal.

A case of poisoning has been reported[1] in which the victim swallowed 100 g. of a 1 per cent. solution of mercuric cyanide. The symptoms are described as typical of mercurial poisoning, and death was ascribed to uraemia.   The autopsy revealed lesions of subacute mercury poisoning.

ACETIC ACID

Of the volatile organic acids the only one which is commonly a cause of poisoning is acetic acid.   Almost invariably the poisoning is accidental and seldom fatal.   The acid is to be sought in the stomach washings or stomach contents.   The procedure of distillation and collecting the distillate in caustic alkali is precisely similar to that described for cyanides.   The alkaline liquid containing the distillate is evaporated to dryness on the water-bath, and the usual tests for acetates are applied.   The majority of these depend on the odour either of acetic acid itself or its derivatives.   The tests recommended are:—

(1) A portion of the residue is warmed with concentrated sulphuric acid.   The odour of acetic acid may be noticed at once, but occasionally it is masked by the presence of sulphur dioxide.   This can be removed in the following manner.   The test-tube containing the sulphuric acid and a portion of the residue is fitted with a cork carrying a tube bent at right angles; by heating the liquid, acetic acid, if present, can be distilled over into another test tube.   A current of air is then gently blown through the test tube containing the distillate to expel the sulphur dioxide.   The acetic acid odour is then, as a rule, easily perceptible.

(2) To a second portion of the residue a few drops of alcohol and a similar quantity of concentrated sulphuric acid are added and the mixture is heated in a boiling water-bath.   An odour of ethyl acetate is proof of the presence of acetic acid in the distillate.   Again the odour may be masked by sulphur dioxide, in which case the same treatment as described above may be employed to eliminate it and thus enable one to detect the odour of the ester.

(3) A portion of the residue is dissolved in a little water and to the solution are added equal volumes of 5 per cent. lanthanum nitrate solution and N/50 iodine solution.   Sufficient N ammonia

[1] *Deut. Zeit. f. Ges. Gericht. Med.*, 1937, Bd. 27, Hft. 6, s. 394.

is then added to remove the yellow colour of the iodine. With considerable quantities of acetate a blue colour appears in the cold. Minute traces produce a bluish violet colour on warming.

(4) Another portion of the residue is intimately mixed with a few milligrammes of arsenic trioxide and the mixture is heated in a dry test tube. The foul and powerful odour of cacodyl oxide is easily recognized. It is advisable, however, to carry out a control test with a mixture of sodium acetate and white arsenic. Cacodyl oxide is very poisonous, and it is necessary to use extreme caution in smelling it.

ALDEHYDES

Formaldehyde. Of the aliphatic aldehydes, formaldehyde is the one most commonly responsible for toxic symptoms. The ordinary 40 per cent. solution is strongly caustic and even a dilute solution containing 3 per cent. or 4 per cent. is a powerful irritant poison. It is said that death has also resulted from breathing air containing as little as 10 parts per 1,000,000 of gaseous formaldehyde.

In a fatal case of poisoning by formaldehyde the odour and the peculiar irritating effect on the eyes may be noted at the autopsy.

For chemical analysis the aldehyde is isolated from the stomach or its contents by steam distillation in the presence of mineral acid. The distillate should be tested from time to time with Schiff's reagent[1] (magenta solution decolourized by means of sulphur dioxide) and distillation should be continued until the distillate no longer restores the magenta colour. After the odour of the distillate has been noted the following tests should be applied to successive portions of it.

(1) A trace of morphine is dissolved in the first portion and concentrated sulphuric acid is cautiously poured into the test-tube so as to form a separate layer at the bottom. If formaldehyde is present a violet-coloured zone of contact quickly develops (cf. the Marquis test for morphine).

An alternative method of carrying out the morphine test can be applied if the quantity of formaldehyde in the distillate is not too small. A portion of the distillate is mixed with ammonia and then evaporated to dryness on the water-bath. The residue, which consists of hexamethylenetetramine (urotropine), is mixed with a particle of morphine and then with concentrated sulphuric acid. A blue to violet colour quickly appears. Urotropine forms characteristic crystals with some of the reagents used for precipitating alkaloids, e.g. Mayer's reagent, Wagner's reagent and mercuric chloride solution. These may be useful as confirmatory tests.

[1] According to Jones (*Analyst*, 1915, **40**, 218) Schiff's test is specific for formaldehyde in the presence of a definite amount of sulphuric acid (see p. 40).

(2) Hehner's test is very delicate, and, moreover, it can only be successfully carried out in very dilute solution. One drop of the distillate may be sufficient for the test, and if the odour of this is strong, it is advisable to add water until the odour is barely perceptible and to pour away all but one or two drops of the diluted liquid. To this a few ml. of milk are added, and concentrated sulphuric acid containing minute traces of iron is poured into the test-tube to form a separate layer. A blue-violet zone of contact, formed on standing, indicates the presence of formaldehyde.

(3) Schryver's test depends on the production of a pink colouring matter when a solution of formaldehyde is added to an acidified mixture of phenylhydrazine hydrochloride and potassium ferricyanide. Two ml. of a fresh, filtered, $0 \cdot 5$ per cent. solution of phenylhydrazine hydrochloride are mixed with 1 ml. of 5 per cent. ferricyanide solution, also freshly prepared. Five ml. of concentrated hydrochloric acid are now added, and finally the solution containing formaldehyde. A delicate rose-pink colour is produced. This test is said to be capable of detecting 1 part of formaldehyde in 1,000,000 parts of liquid.

(4) Dimedone (dimethyl dihydroresorcin) condenses with aldehydes in neutral solution containing sodium chloride to form almost insoluble crystalline products with well-defined melting points.[1] The reaction with formaldehyde is particularly characteristic (the product melts at 187° C.) and so sensitive as to be capable of detecting $0 \cdot 2$ mg. in 50 c.cm. of solution. To the neutral solution of the aldehyde, add sodium chloride to make the concentration about $0 \cdot 4$ per cent., and a few drops of a 10 per cent. alcoholic solution of the reagent. Stir. The condensation product settles out and becomes crystalline in about a quarter of an hour.

The tests for formaldehyde are also of importance in the detection of methylalcohol (q.v.).

Acetaldehyde is more readily distilled from aqueous solution than formaldehyde. It is possible to separate the two by careful fractional distillation in a special apparatus. The distillation flask is fitted with a spiral-form reflux condenser and the upper end of this is connected by means of a twice bent tube to a vertical descending condenser. The water circulating in the jacket of the reflux condenser is maintained at 40° to 50° C., while the descending condenser and the receiver are surrounded by a freezing mixture. By heating the distillation flask gently the acetaldehyde can be distilled over, leaving formaldehyde behind.

If acetaldehyde is present in animal tissues or fluids it can be isolated by the ordinary process of steam distillation. It can be recognized by the ordinary tests for aldehydes and by its peculiar

[1] WEINBERGER. *Ind. and Eng. Chem.* (Anal. Ed.), 1931, **3**, 365.

odour. It restores the magenta colour to Schiff's reagent in the absence of strong acid, and reduces Fehling's solution and ammoniacal silver solution. A special test depends on the formation of aldehyde-resin by treating a solution of aldehyde with concentrated caustic soda. If a sufficient quantity of aldehyde is present the reddish brown resin is precipitated and at the same time a gas with a disagreeable odour is liberated; with smaller quantities of aldehyde the liquid becomes brown in colour, and this colour has been used as a method of quantitative determination by Thresh.[1] One hundred ml. of a solution of aldehyde containing not more than 0·5 per cent., is treated with 5 ml. of saturated caustic soda solution and the mixture is boiled for a few seconds. When cold, 100 ml. of alcohol are added and the volume is made up to 250 ml. with distilled water. The solution should be clear and light yellow in colour. Colorimetric comparison is made with standards specially prepared by treating known quantities of aldehyde in the manner above described. Alternatively, permanent standards can be made from dichromate solutions which have been standardized by comparison with known quantities of aldehyde-resin.

In Rocque's method of determination, a definite volume of standard sodium sulphite solution in dilute alcohol is added to an acidified solution of aldehyde, so as to form the aldehyde-bisulphite compound. The excess of bisulphite is determined iodimetrically. Details are given in Allen's " Commercial Analysis " (loc. cit.). Poisoning with acetaldehyde as such is not common, but the use of the polymerized form, the so-called " solidified spirit " in small heating stoves is a source of danger. The substance known as " Meta " was the means used for attempted suicide in one of our cases. A sample of the substance was examined, with the following results:—

(1) It was completely soluble in hot chloroform.

(2) The crystals sublimed at 112°–115° C.

(3) By heating with dilute sulphuric acid a distillate was obtained which had the odour of acetaldehyde and which yielded positive reactions in the general tests for aldehydes.

There was no proof that any of the substance had been actually swallowed by the accused. The stomach washings, urine and faeces were separately subjected to the steam distillation process, but no aldehydic substance could be detected in any of the distillates. An experiment was therefore made by giving 1·5 g. of the substance, mixed with food, to a dog weighing 4 kg. Definite signs of poisoning were observed after one and a half hours, the symptoms being: continuous shivering, copious salivation and paralysis of the hind

---

[1] Pharm. J. 3, 1878–9, 9, 409. Allen's " Commercial Organic Analysis ", 5th ed., 1, 333.

legs. After three hours the dog was killed by shooting through the head. On the following day the viscera were removed and kept in stoppered jars in a refrigerator for a week. The stomach and intestines were then acidified with dilute sulphuric acid and distilled in a current of steam. The distillate gave positive results in general tests for aldehydes. It reduced Fehling's solution, ammoniacal silver nitrate, and potassium bichromate–sulphuric acid; and it restored the colour to Schiff's reagent.

Paraldehyde. This has caused death in cases where the patient has exceeded the therapeutic dose and it has also been used for attempted suicide. Chronic poisoning with this drug is fairly common. It is a liquid boiling between 121° and 125° C. It possesses the ordinary aldehydic reducing properties but does not react with sodium bisulphite.

The other important derivatives of acetaldehyde, viz. **chloral** and its homologue **butyl-chloral** will be dealt with among the volatile organic halogen compounds.

ALCOHOLS

Ethyl Alcohol. Chemical analysis of the body fluids for the presence of alcohol may be required for several reasons, e.g. to decide whether death has been caused by acute alcoholic poisoning or whether intoxication was a contributory factor in accidental death; or to decide whether a person was more or less intoxicated at the time when he was involved in a breach of the law. The commonest kind of investigation nowadays is the examination of persons concerned in motor accidents and contraventions of the law.

Both in the examination of the dead and the living the most suitable material for analysis is blood, or, failing blood, urine. Sometimes the analysis of stomach washings is asked for, but for obvious reasons this is of little value. One person who is perfectly sober but has just taken an alcoholic drink may have more alcohol in his stomach than another person who is helplessly drunk. It is equally obvious that only quantitative analyses are of value for diagnostic purposes.

It appears to be generally agreed that the alcoholic concentration reaches its maximum about forty to fifty minutes after drinking has ceased. The concentration in urine lags behind that in blood at first, but after about seventy minutes the two may be approximately equal. From that time onward the figure for urine is higher. Nevertheless, if curves are plotted to show the variations in concentration of alcohol in blood and urine with lapse of time, the descending portions of the two curves following the maxima are very nearly parallel.

Bowden and McCallum[1] have recently investigated the reliability of determinations of alcohol in blood *post-mortem*. Using the method of McNally and Coleman[2] which is similar to the first of the two processes described here, they found that blood taken from a peripheral vein up to two or three days after death gives reliable results, showing no significant changes when compared with blood taken just before death. Blood from the heart or from a large thoracic vein was valueless for quantitative work, since the alcohol concentration altered very considerably within a few hours of death.

Analysis of urine must always be made in the presence of alkali, the figure for acid urine being invariably too high, apparently owing to the presence of volatile matter, other than alcohol, which has the property of reducing dichromate. Moreover, urine from persons who have not taken alcohol contains volatile reducing matter which may be erroneously considered as alcohol. From alkaline urine this " reduction value ", not due to alcohol, is nearly always less than 0·009 per cent. From acid urine the figure may be as high as 0·075 per cent. The former is insignificant, but the latter would constitute a very serious error.

In the analysis of blood the only substance which is likely to cause the figures to be too high is acetone,[3] except in the rare cases in which volatile substances with reducing properties have been taken (e.g. other alcohols, paraldehyde, chloral, ether). The maximum possible error due to acetone, i.e. when the patient is in a state of diabetic coma, is (according to Widmark[4]) about 0·7 mg. per ml., and 0·3 mg. per ml. is a more usual figure for a patient in this condition ; and since 0·8 mg. per ml. is about the minimum quantity of alcohol corresponding to mild intoxication in the most susceptible subject, it is clear that errors due to acetone can seldom be of forensic significance. If the blood from a patient in a state of coma is found to contain a volatile reducing substance and the quantity corresponds to no more than 1 mg. per ml., acetone should be suspected.

Various methods of analysis are available both on the macro- and the micro-scale, all depending on the oxidation of alcohol by potassium dichromate in sulphuric acid.

A very simple process due to Nicloux which gives reasonably accurate results can be used when large quantities (20 ml. or more) of blood or urine are provided. The alcohol is isolated by

---

[1] *Med. J. Australia*, 1949, 16th July, p. 76.

[2] *J. Lab. Clin. Med.*, 1944, 29, 429.

[3] Acetonuria can, of course, give fictitiously high results in the estimation of " alcohol " in urine.

[4] " Die Theoretischen Grundlagen und die Praktischen Verwendbarkeit der Gerichtlich-medizinischen Alkoholbestimmung." Urban und Schwarzenberg. Berlin and Wien, 1932.

steam distillation from a capacious flask so as to minimize the danger of froth passing over into the receiver. Frothing in blood may be practically prevented by the addition of a little picric acid; but urine, as stated above, must be alkaline. Steam is passed through gently so that distillation may proceed at an even rate, and the condenser and receiver must be as cold as possible. The latter should be immersed in ice. For simplicity in the subsequent calculations it is convenient to collect in the receiver a volume exactly equal to the original volume of the body-fluid.

The determination is a colorimetric one and is carried out as follows. Seven test-tubes, preferably of Pyrex glass, are cleaned with sulphuric acid and dichromate, rinsed thoroughly with distilled water and dried in an oven. They are then numbered with a writing diamond or otherwise: 0·1, 0·09, 0·08, 0·07, 0·06, 0·05 and 0·04 per cent. A standard solution of alcohol is made by diluting 1 ml. of absolute alcohol to 1 litre with distilled water; both these quantities should be accurately measured, using a 1 ml. pipette and a measuring flask. The following quantities of this diluted alcohol are then measured out into the numbered test-tubes, 5, 4·5, 4, 3·5, 3, 2·5, and 2 ml. Each of these volumes is then made up to 5 ml. by adding distilled water from a burette. One ml. of 2 per cent. dichromate solution is added to each, and this is followed by 5 ml. of concentrated sulphuric acid. The contents of each tube are thoroughly mixed and sufficient heat is developed to complete the oxidation of the alcohol. The colours vary in gradation from the definite green of pure chromium sulphate in the first tube to a yellowish tinge in the last which is barely distinguishable from the colour of dichromate. The standards thus prepared may be kept for many months if the tubes are hermetically sealed by drawing out the upper ends in a blow-pipe flame. The determination of the alcoholic content of the distillate is made by comparison with the standard.

Five ml. of the distillate are mixed with 1 ml. of the dichromate solution and 5 ml. of concentrated sulphuric acid. If the dichromate is completely reduced the distillate must be diluted. One ml. is measured out and made up to 5 ml. with distilled water and the test is repeated.

If the colour now falls within the range of the standard the comparison can be made at once; but it may be necessary to make further trials, using 2 or 3 ml. of the distillate diluted to 5 ml. as before. Dilution of the distillate beyond 1 in 5 is very rarely necessary in the examination of blood, as a concentration of more than 5 parts per 1,000 is very seldom found; but higher concentration sometimes occurs in urine. In such cases it is convenient to measure out 10 ml. of the distillate, make up to 50 ml. with distilled water and repeat the tests with this diluted sample.

If the colour obtained from the undiluted distillate is less green than the sixth standard the sample may be regarded for forensic purposes as free from alcohol.

For the determination of alcohol in the blood of living people micro-methods only are suitable. Of these, two are in common use. (1) Distillation in a current of air which carries the alcohol vapour through a mixture of dichromate solution and sulphuric acid. (2) Widmark's method, in which the whole of the volatile portion of the blood is vaporized in a special container suspended inside a closed flask which contains the dichromate-sulphuric acid mixture. This process requires much special apparatus, but it has the advantage that a large number of determinations can be carried out at once; and as there is no distillation in the ordinary sense of the

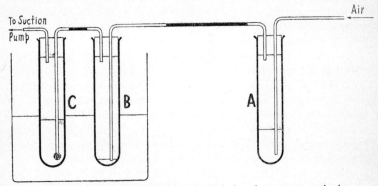

FIG. 7. Micro-determination of alcohol; air current method.
A. Tube containing sulphuric acid.
B. Tube containing sample of blood or urine.
C. Tube containing sulphuric acid and potassium dichromate.

word, the process, apart from the charging of the apparatus and the final titration, can go on without supervision.

In both methods the amount of alcohol oxidized by the dichromate is determined by iodimetric titration.

The details of the two processes are as follows:—

(1) The apparatus consists of three boiling-tubes fitted up as in Fig. 7. One contains concentrated sulphuric acid to wash the air before it passes into the distillation tube, the middle one, which contains the sample of blood or urine, and the third which contains a mixture of potassium dichromate and sulphuric acid. Air is drawn through the apparatus by means of a suction pump and is made to bubble through each of the liquids in turn. The lower end of the tube dipping into the dichromate terminates in a bulb with many small perforations so as to break up the bubbles as they enter the oxidizing mixture. The second and third tubes are immersed

in a water-bath maintained at 80° C. (In Liebesny's modified process an oil bath at 100° C. is used.) The quantity of blood or urine recommended for this process is 2 ml., and the oxidizing mixture consists of 10 ml. N/10 potassium dichromate solution and 10 ml. concentrated sulphuric acid. The air current is continued until the sample is completely evaporated, usually about an hour. The contents of the third tube are then cooled and transferred to a flask, washing out the tube well with distilled water and making up the total volume to about $\frac{1}{2}$ litre. Five ml. of a 5 per cent. solution of potassium iodide, free from elementary iodine, are then added, and the liberated iodine is titrated with N/10 thiosulphate solution. The calculation is made in the following way:—

If x ml. is the quantity of thiosulphate used $(10-x)$ is the quantity of dichromate reduced by the alcohol. 1 ml. of N/10 dichromate is equivalent to $1 \cdot 15$ mg. of alcohol, and since the volume of blood or urine is 2 ml., the quantity of alcohol per 100 ml. is $(10-x) \times 1 \cdot 15 \times 100/2$ mg.

(2) Widmark's process.

The apparatus recommended by Widmark consists of:—

(a) The distillation flask. This is a 50 ml. Erlenmeyer flask with a ground-in stopper to which glass rods are fused above and below. The upper rod is bent into a hook at the top, and the bottom of the lower rod carries a small bowl-like container for the blood sample; this container when the stopper is in position is about $\frac{1}{2}$–1 cm. above the surface of the dichromate-sulphuric acid at the bottom of the flask.

(b) A wooden stand from which the stoppers for a series of flasks can be suspended when not in use.

(c) Capillary tubes bent twice at acute angles in which the blood samples are collected and weighed. These should have a capacity of 100–150 c.mm.

(d) A torsion balance of the Hartmann and Braun type.

(e) Thin rubber tubing as used for bicycle valves.

(f) A micro-burette with a capacity of 10 ml. graduated in 20ths of a ml.

(g) A graduated glass syringe of a special type for measuring out 1 ml. of the dichromate-sulphuric acid mixture. This is similar to the glass portion of a hypodermic syringe except that the movement of the piston is controlled by means of a screw.

(h) A water-bath with a cover perforated with holes to hold two dozen flasks. A thermometer passes through a cork in another hole in the cover.

(i) Rubber caps to fit over the hooked rods and the necks of the flasks to hold the stoppers in position during distillation.

The apparatus is cleaned before use by means of sulphuric acid

and dichromate, after which the flasks are thoroughly washed with
distilled water and then steam is blown through them. Finally
they are dried by means of a suction pump.

The capillary tubes are obtained from the manufacturer in a
perfectly clean condition, and since each is only used once, no
further cleansing is needed.

The special measure for the dichromate-sulphuric acid mixture
is recommended because the ordinary pipette cannot be relied upon
to deliver always the same quantity of such a viscous liquid. For
samples of blood containing less than 0·2 per cent. alcohol, the
dichromate solution is made by dissolving 0·1 g. of pure crystallized
potassium dichromate in 1 ml. distilled water and making
up to 100 ml. with concentrated sulphuric acid. For alcoholic
concentrations between 0·2 and 0·5 per cent. the corresponding
quantity of dichromate should be 0·25 g.

The sample of blood is taken by pricking the finger-tip and
collecting directly in the capillary tube. Obviously no alcohol,
acetone, or ether may be used for cleansing the skin before puncture;
soap and water, or mercuric chloride, may be used. Traces of blood
are removed from the outside of the tube, which is then weighed on
the torsion balance, after which
the blood is blown out through
cycle-valve tubing attached to the
capillary tube into the container
below the stopper of the flask.
The stopper is then fitted and held
in position by means of the rubber
cap. The empty capillary tube is
re-weighed to find the quantity of
blood used in the determination.
The flask, which may be one of a
series examined together, is put into
the water-bath and kept at about
50°–60° C. for about two hours or
until the blood is quite dry.

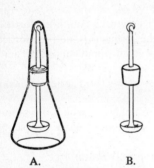

A.   B.

FIG. 8.
A.   Widmark flask with
rubber cap for use during
distillation.
B.   Stopper with capsule for
blood sample.

Great care is necessary in removing
the glass stoppers to avoid particles
of dried blood falling into the
oxidizing mixture. It may be necessary to re-immerse the flasks in
warm water after removing the rubber caps so as to loosen the stoppers.

The reaction mixture is diluted with 25 ml. of distilled water and
gently shaken. Half a ml. of 5 per cent. potassium iodide solution is
added, and after about half a minute to a minute the liquid is
titrated with sodium thiosulphate solution. If the larger amount of
dichromate has been used the thiosulphate should be N/100, but for

the smaller quantities of dichromate N/200 is recommended. A blank titration must be made, and the quantity of alcohol present is proportional to the difference between the amount of thiosulphate used for the sample and for the blank; 0·01 ml. N/100 thiosulphate corresponds to 1·13γ (=0·00113 mg.) of alcohol. The theoretical value, assuming that the alcohol is quantitatively oxidized to acetic acid, is 1·15.

Winnick (*J. Biol. Chem.*, 1941, **141**, 115 ; 1942, **142**, 451, 461) has adapted Widmark's method for use with the much simpler Conway micro-diffusion apparatus.

The method of Widmark has been critically examined[1] and compared with the micro-method of Liebesny, in which the alcohol vapour is carried into the dichromate-sulphuric acid mixture by a stream of air, the blood sample being kept at 100° C. by heating it in an oil-bath. It is claimed that in this process volatile substances which might reduce dichromate are drawn through the reaction mixture unchanged, whereas such substances do affect the dichromate in Widmark's process. The authors found that in the presence of ether, ethyl chloride, chloroform or acetone, Widmark's process produced a greater error than Liebesny's, and concluded that the former process had not the degree of accuracy necessary for forensic purposes. They gave as an instance a case in which the figure obtained by the Widmark method was 1·14 per 1,000 and by the Liebesny method 0·86 per 1,000, the difference being due to acetone. It may be noticed that this difference of 0·28 per 1,000 agrees with Widmark's own statement that in case of diabetic acidosis an error of 0·3 per 1,000 and in very rare cases even 0·7 per 1,000 may be expected. In a statistical table Widmark shows that these figures (0·86–1·14 per 1,000) represent border-line cases. The lower figure corresponds to a state of " being under the influence of alcohol " in 30 per cent. of the subjects examined, and the higher figure in 40 per cent. of them.

Widmark has further pointed out that in severe cases of diabetic acidosis the condition is made manifest by an examination of the urine and plasma for acetoacetic acid and acetone. The quantities of acetone in urine and blood are about equal, but the quantity of acetoacetic acid in urine may be as much as five times as great as in plasma.

Since alcohol, after absorption, is distributed fairly evenly over the blood and soft tissues (except adipose tissue), estimation of the blood alcohol permits the approximate calculation of the total amount of alcohol in the body at the time, and therefore of the minimum amount ingested.

---

[1] KRATZ and PLÄMBOCK. *Chem. Zeitg.*, 1938, **62**, 148–9. *Analyst*, 1938, **63**, 283. Cf. also JONES and EVANS. *Analyst*, 1929, **54**, 134.

Taking the weight of the soft tissues as two-thirds of the body weight in kilos (B.W.) and the blood alcohol as A mg./100 ml., the total amount of alcohol in the body is $\frac{2}{3} \times$ B.W. $\times 10$ A mg.

Methyl Alcohol. Although poisoning by pure methyl alcohol is a rare occurrence, methylated spirit drinking is not uncommon. Sydney Smith[1] quotes figures giving the annual convictions in England and Wales for drunkenness attributed to methylated spirit during the years 1928–1932. They varied from 409 to 596.

To distinguish chemically between methyl and ethyl alcohol in a concentrated form the simplest method is to drop into 1 or 2 ml. of the liquid a piece of red-hot copper foil which is, of course, coated with a film of oxide. With methyl alcohol formaldehyde is produced which is immediately recognized by its odour and its effect on the eyes. In dilute solutions also, the method is to oxidize the alcohol to aldehyde and to test for formaldehyde and acetaldehyde. The difficulty here arises that, with most of the ordinary methods of oxidation traces of formaldehyde are produced even from ethyl alcohol. Hinkel,[2] using an acidified solution of persulphate as oxidizing agent, found it impossible to detect with certainty less than 5 per cent. of methyl alcohol in ethyl alcohol; and as Jones[3] has pointed out, this method would fail to distinguish between pure ethyl alcohol and industrial spirit containing 5 per cent. of wood spirit. Jones criticized adversely all the methods previously described except that of Denigés.[4] In this process the oxidation is effected under such conditions that the amount of formaldehyde produced from the ethyl alcohol is too small to affect Schiff's reagent; and as the Schiff's test is made in presence of about 10 per cent. of concentrated sulphuric acid, the magenta colour is not restored by acetaldehyde. Simmond's modification of Denigés' method[5] is recommended by Jones. The alcohol is purified if necessary by distillation, and the alcoholic concentration of the distillate is adjusted to 10 per cent. either by redistillation or by the addition of distilled water as required. To 5 ml. of this liquid in a wide test-tube are added 2·5 ml. of a 2 per cent. solution of potassium permanganate and 0·2 ml. of concentrated sulphuric acid. After three minutes the oxidation is stopped by the addition of 0·5 ml. of oxalic acid solution (9·6 g. in 100 ml.). On shaking, the liquid becomes almost or quite colourless. One ml. of concentrated sulphuric acid is now added, and the whole is well mixed. This is an essential part of the process. Schiff's reagent (5 ml.) is now

[1] " Forensic Medicine ", 5th ed., 495.
[2] *Analyst*, 1908, **33**, 417–18.
[3] *Ibid.*, 1915, **40**, 218.
[4] *Compt. rend.*, 1910, **150**, 832.
[5] *Analyst*, 1912, **37**, 16.

added and, if the original alcohol contained more than a minute trace of methyl alcohol the magenta colour appears in a few minutes. Standards are made containing 0·001 g., 0·002 g. to 0·004 g. of methyl alcohol in 5 ml., and in every case the total alcoholic concentration is adjusted to 10 per cent.; these samples are oxidized in the same way, and it is found that the intensity of the colour produced with Schiff's reagent is proportional to the amount of methyl alcohol present. Jones points out that samples of Schiff's reagent are not always identical. His method of preparation is to dissolve 0·2 g. of magenta base in 10 ml. of a freshly prepared cold saturated solution of sulphur dioxide and after allowing the solution to stand for twenty-four hours, to dilute it to 200 ml. with water. Throughout the process strict adherence to standard conditions is necessary: the only latitude permissible is in the amount of oxalic acid, where 0·5 ml. of a cold saturated solution may be used.

The quantity of concentrated sulphuric acid should not be less than 1 ml.; even with 0·7 ml. the Schiff's reagent reacts with acetaldehyde. The quantity of Schiff's reagent must be constant, otherwise the acidic concentration will be altered. Jones found that by using this method he could detect as little as 0·2 per cent. of methyl alcohol in ethyl alcohol.

The results obtained by Jones indicate the possibility of detecting and determining the amount of methyl alcohol in blood after the ingestion of methylated spirit, provided that a sufficient quantity of blood is available for analysis, i.e. in fatal cases. Suppose, for example, we have 100 ml. of blood containing 0·1 per cent. of total alcohol. If this is distilled in a current of steam and 100 ml. of the distillate are collected, the distillate also will contain 0·1 per cent. of total alcohol. The alcoholic concentration of the distillate can be increased by repeated distillation until a final distillate measuring 10 ml. and containing 1 per cent. of total alcohol is obtained. If we add to this 1 ml. of absolute alcohol the alcoholic content is 1·1 in 11 ml. or 10 per cent. as recommended by Jones. If the spirit ingested contained 5 per cent. of methyl alcohol, the quantity of the latter in the 11 ml. of mixture would be 0·1/20 ml. or 0·005 ml. This is equivalent to 0·0023 in 5 ml. of the 10 per cent. solution which is within the range recommended for colorimetric determination.

VOLATILE ORGANIC CHLORINE DERIVATIVES

The commonest volatile compounds containing chlorine which may be encountered in forensic work are: chloroform, carbon tetrachloride, tetrachloracetylene (symmetrical tetrachlorethane), trichloroethylene, chloral hydrate, and butyl-chloral hydrate. With the exception of the last two they are volatile liquids, their boiling points being: chloroform 61° C., carbon tetrachloride 76° C., tetrachlorethane 146°–147° C., trichloroethylene 87° C. Chloral hydrate and butyl-chloral hydrate are solids melting at 57° C. and 78° C. respectively.

All these substances are easily volatile in steam, some of them distilling at a much lower temperature. All of them can be decomposed by passing the vapours through a red-hot tube, and chlorine can be detected in the decomposition products. This is the basis of Ragsky's process for the examination of blood and tissues supposed to contain chlorine derivatives (*vide infra*).

Special tests are available for the identification of some of the compounds, e.g. chloroform and chloral hydrate.

On warming a very dilute solution of chloroform with aqueous caustic potash and a drop of aniline, the foul and characteristic odour of phenylisonitrile is at once manifest.

$$CHCl_3 + 3KOH + C_6H_5NH_2 = C_6H_5NC + 3KCl + 3H_2O.$$

Chloral hydrate, treated in the same way, yields the same results, since hydrolysis of chloral with aqueous caustic potash produces chloroform. With butyl-chloral hydrate no isonitrile is formed, the products of hydrolysis being dichlorpropylene and formic acid. Both chloral hydrate and butyl-chloral hydrate, when treated with Nessler's reagent, yield brick-red precipitates which become brighter red and finally green. Chloroform does not behave in this way. These two tests, the isonitrile reaction and the Nessler's test, therefore serve to differentiate chloroform, chloral and butyl-chloral even in a dilute solution such as may be obtained by steam-distillation from tissues. Butyl-chloral is generally used in medicine in association with antipyrin (as butyl-hypnal) or pyramidone (as trigenin) which should be sought for in the viscera by means of the Stas-Otto process.

If a compound of this group, other than chloroform or the chlorals, is present there is little hope of the absolute identification of it in a distillate from blood or tissues. In some cases it may be possible to identify the poison as a chloro compound, and then, after hydrolysis by refluxing with sodium hydroxide solution to identify the alcohol produced. Thus methyl chloride (used as a refrigerating agent) yields methyl alcohol. Samples of the liquid ingested may be available for boiling-point determinations, or the history of the affair may furnish a clue. Carbon tetrachloride may have been administered as an anthelmintic. It is used in fire-extinguishers of the Pyrene type and may possibly be swallowed accidentally or with suicidal intent. In at least one instance tetrachloracetylene has been swallowed in a case of suicide. A portion of the liquid was found remaining in a tumbler; this served for the determination of the boiling point and for the detection of chlorine after hydrolysis. A volatile chlorine compound was also detected in the stomach contents by Ragsky's process. This appears to be the first known case of death from the deliberate ingestion of tetrachloracetylene, although many chronic and subacute poisoning cases have been recorded.

Tetrachloracetylene is said to be about four times as toxic as chloroform. Its use in aeroplane factories has caused severe symptoms, the outstanding feature in chronic cases being jaundice.[1][2][3][4][5] The most suitable material for analysis depends on the history of the affair. If death is the result of narcosis, due to breathing the vapours, the lungs and blood should be examined. Carbon tetrachloride taken by the mouth is most likely to be found in the caecum, which should be removed separately at the autopsy, tied tightly with string at both ends and sent to the laboratory in a separate jar. In other cases it may be necessary to examine the stomach, intestines, liver and other organs separately.

Detection and Estimation of Volatile Chlorine Compounds

Ragsky's Process. Essentially this is a distillation in a current of air. The apparatus is shown in Fig. 9. The air, before entering the distillation flask, is washed free from chlorine or nitrous fumes, which might be present in the laboratory atmosphere, by passing through two Dreschel wash-bottles containing caustic soda. The distillation flask which contains the material under examination is immersed in a hot water-bath; a bolt-head flask is the most suitable. The exit tube from this flask is connected to a hard-glass or silica tube of which the farther end passes through the stopper of a Liebig condenser. The lower end of the condenser is connected with absorption tubes containing a solution of silver nitrate acidified with nitric acid, and these in turn are connected to a suction pump or aspirator. A piece of starch-iodide paper is inserted into the lower portion of the inner tube of the condenser. The hard-glass or silica tube is heated to redness, the heated portion being as long as possible, and a very gentle current of air is drawn through the apparatus. The liberated chlorine decomposes the potassium iodide producing a blue colour in the starch paper; but if the quantity of chlorine is unusually great the excess of it discharges the colour. It is therefore necessary to watch the paper all the time, as

[1] LEHMANN. *Arch. f. Hygiene.*, 1911, **47**, 1.
[2] JUNGFER. *Zentralbl. f. Gewerbehyg.*, 1914, **2**, 222.
[3] WILCOX. *Lancet*, 1914, ii, 1489.
[4] WILCOX. *Ibid.*, 1915, i, 544.
[5] GRIMM. *Viertelj. schr. f. ger. Med.*, 1914, **48**, II. Supp., 161.

the blue colour may appear and disappear very rapidly. The hydrochloric acid also produced reacts with the silver nitrate in the absorption tubes and gives an immediate white precipitate of silver chloride. It is said to be possible to determine the amount of chloroform or other chlorine derivatives by weighing the quantity of silver chloride so precipitated, but experiments in our laboratory have failed to give consistent results owing to incomplete decomposition of the vapours in passing through the red-hot tube. It would appear that some of the chlorine always passes through the red-hot tube in organic combination.

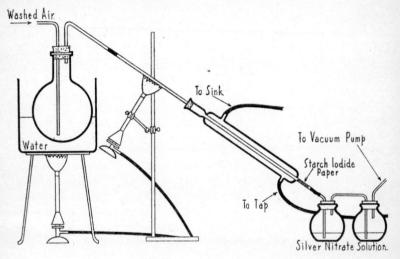

Fig. 9. Ragsky's apparatus for volatile organic chlorine compounds.

Methods for the quantitative determination of chloroform and chloral hydrate which are almost identical in principle and which have given satisfactory results in our hands are described by Wallis[1] and Nicloux.[2] The substances are hydrolyzed with alcoholic caustic alkali, and the sodium chloride produced is titrated in neutral solution with silver nitrate.

$$CHCl_3 + 4NaOH = 3NaCl + HCOONa + 2H_2O$$
$$CCl_3CH(OH)_2 + 5NaOH = 3NaCl + 2HCOONa + 3H_2O.$$

The distillate, which should not contain more than about 0·1 g. of the chlorine compound, is mixed with about an equal volume of alcohol and 10 ml. of a 10 per cent. alcoholic solution of pure caustic soda and heated to boiling for about three hours. Wallis suggests

[1] *Pharm. J.*, **76**, 162–3.
[2] *Comptes rendus*, **142**, 163–5.

heating in a bottle with a rubber stopper tied on with string, while Nicloux recommends a reflux condenser. When the liquid is cold it is made neutral to phenolphthalein by adding dilute sulphuric acid. It is then titrated with N/20 silver nitrate solution using potassium chromate as indicator. Each ml. of silver nitrate solution represents 2 mg. of chloroform or 2·8 mg. of chloral hydrate.

Examination of Blood. The blood must be mixed with alcohol containing 0·25 per cent. of tartaric acid. Each ml. of blood requires 5 ml. of the acidic alcohol. The mixture is then distilled, using a fractionating column and allowing the lower end of the condenser to dip into 10 ml. of 95 per cent. alcohol. One-third of the total volume is distilled off, the distillate is hydrolyzed as above described and the determination of chlorine is made in the same manner.

Examination of Urine in Chloral Hydrate Poisoning

Chloral hydrate is excreted in the urine as urochloralic acid which can be split up by boiling with sulphuric acid into trichlorethyl alcohol and glycuronic acid. The urine should first be examined for chloral hydrate itself by distilling in faintly acid solution, since alkali decomposes chloral hydrate. The latter substance volatilizes as chloral and water which re-combine in the distillate to form chloral hydrate. The Nessler test should be applied to the distillate.

The urine may be examined for the presence of urochloralic acid, which can be separated from an alcohol-ether extract either as a potassium salt[1] or as a lead salt.[2]

In the *lead-salt method* (due to Kulz) the alcohol-ether extract is treated with a solution of lead acetate and filtered. The precipitate, containing the lead salt of urochloralic acid, is taken up in water, decomposed with sulphuretted hydrogen and the lead sulphide is removed by filtration. The filtrate is warmed to expel the sulphuretted hydrogen and neutralized with baryta. It is then evaporated on the water-bath to small bulk and the barium precipitated by adding the exact amount of dilute sulphuric acid. Barium sulphate is removed by filtration and the filtrate is evaporated to dryness in a vacuum desiccator. The residue is repeatedly extracted with ether, and urochloralic acid separates as a crystalline mass from the ether extract.

Urochloralic acid forms colourless silky needles which melt at 142° C.; they are easily soluble in water and in alcohol. They reduce Fehling's solution and ammoniacal silver nitrate. The aqueous solution turns a feebly alkaline solution of indigo sulphate

[1] *Ber. d. Deutsch Chem. Ges.*, **8** (1875), 662.
[2] *Arch. f. d. Physiol.*, **28** (1883), 506; *ibid.*, **33** (1884), 227.

yellow. On heating, the acid turns yellow and emits a caramel-like odour. On gently warming with dilute mineral acid it is hydrolyzed into trichlorethyl alcohol (B.P. 151° C.) and glycuronic acid. The latter can be decomposed by heating strongly with hydrochloric or sulphuric acid, yielding furfural, carbon dioxide and water. Furfural may be detected by spotting the liquid on to a filter-paper moistened with aniline acetate solution, but it should be noted that traces of substances which yield furfural may be present in normal urine.

AVERTIN

Avertin, tribrom-ethyl alcohol, is now much used as an anaesthetic, being administered by the rectum. It is a solid substance melting at 80° C. It is moderately soluble in hot water, and very soluble in alcohol and ether. It has been regarded as a relatively safe drug but, on the other hand, yellow atrophy of the liver has been attributed to it. Moreover, in a report from America[1] there were records of seven deaths following its use. Alarming symptoms (writhing and rolling about on the bed) after avertin had been administered as a premedication before complete anaesthesia, have also been reported.[2]

When an aqueous solution of avertin is heated the substance decomposes with the formation of hydrobromic acid and dibromacetaldehyde. Therefore the product of steam-distillation should be tested with silver nitrate for the former, and with Schiff's reagent for the latter.

CARBON DISULPHIDE

CARBON disulphide is largely used in the vulcanization of india-rubber and in the manufacture of rayon. Rambousek,[3] quoting Lehmann, states that 1·5–3 mg. of the vapour in 1 litre of air causes congestion, giddiness and sickness. Chronic poisoning of workmen shows itself in nervous and psychical symptoms and in digestive derangements. In later stages there are insomnia, cramp, palpitation, numbness of the skin, trembling, muscular wasting and paralysis. The extremities may be cyanotic. On the other hand, he states[4] that in the manufacture of carbon disulphide there is little danger to health. Certainly, in the rayon industry the precautions taken to safeguard health leave little or nothing to be desired.

[1] BEECHER. *J. Amer. Med. Ass.*, 1938, **3**, 122.
[2] BARNSLEY. *B.M.J.*, 21.1.39.
[3] " Industrial Poisoning ": English translation. Arnold, 193.
[4] *Op. cit.*, 69.

Dr. Sydney Smith[1] gives the symptoms of acute poisoning as: difficulty in breathing, signs of asphyxia, blueness of the lips, dilated pupils, drowsiness, coma and death. Sometimes death is preceded by convulsions. These symptoms are non-specific.

In acute poisoning the vapour may be detected by the odour of the breath. If the liquid has been swallowed by mistake, a most unlikely contingency because of the foul odour, it may be isolated from the vomit or stomach-washings by distillation in steam; extraction of the distillate with ether is not recommended since the boiling point of carbon disulphide is only 46° C. If the odour is not detected in the distillate an aliquot part of the latter should be heated under a reflux condenser with caustic potash to hydrolyze the carbon disulphide, after which the potassium sulphide is tested for with sodium nitroprusside or lead acetate. A blank test should be made on another portion of the distillate to make sure that free hydrogen sulphide is not present in it.

Denigés[2] has described micro-tests for carbon disulphide depending on the formation of dithiotrimercuric salts and the examination of their crystalline forms. The mercury reagent may be:

(a) Mercuric sulphate prepared by heating 5 g. of mercuric oxide with 20 ml. of concentrated sulphuric acid and diluting the solution to 100 ml. with water.

(b) Mercuric chloride solution containing 0·3–0·4 g. per ml.

(c) Mercuric nitrate solution: a concentrated solution of the salt in strong nitric acid.

The solution to be tested is mixed with an equal volume of the reagent and heated on the water-bath. The reaction is complete in fifteen minutes with the sulphate or the nitrate, but the chloride mixture should be heated for an hour.

The crystals produced have the following forms:—

Sulphate: small prisms or lozenges.
Nitrate: hexagonal plates.
Chloride: fish-bone or fern-leaf crystals.

VOLATILE COAL-TAR PRODUCTS

The chief volatile products of coal-tar which are poisonous are the hydrocarbons, benzene and its homologues, and naphthalene; and some of their simpler derivatives, viz. phenol and the cresols and naphthols, nitro-benzene, dinitro-benzene, o-nitrophenol, aniline and the toluidines. Other substances, such as dihydric phenols, m- and p-nitrophenols, dinitrophenols, picric acid, and diaminophenols are not volatile and will be discussed later. Thymol,

[1] " Forensic Medicine ", 8th ed., 515.
[2] Bull. Soc. Chim., 1915, 17, 359–60. Analyst, 1916, 41, 12.

although not strictly a coal-tar product, is included among the phenols. Of the aminophenols, the *p*-compound is important as it is frequently found in the urine in aniline poisoning; it is slightly volatile in steam.

Benzene or Benzol. This, according to the experience of Sir Sydney Smith, when taken by the mouth, causes burning pain in the stomach, delirium, convulsions, and with large doses death from respiratory failure; 1 oz. has caused death. The method of isolation is simple steam distillation, followed by ether extraction of the distillate. If the quantity of fluid remaining after evaporation of the ether is sufficiently large the boiling point should be determined. Pure benzene boils at 80·5° C., but many commercial samples contain toluene and xylene which have higher boiling points. Chemically, benzene is identified by converting it into nitro-benzene. In order to obtain pure nitrobenzene the conditions of nitration must be carefully controlled. A mixture of nitric acid and sulphuric acid is used containing 8·1 ml. of nitric acid (sp. gr. 1·42) and 10 ml. of concentrated sulphuric acid. This quantity is sufficient for the nitration of 11 ml. of benzene. The mixed acid is added drop by drop with external cooling until the whole has been added and the reaction becomes less vigorous, after which the temperature is raised to 90° or 100° C. for a short time. When cold the mixture is poured into cold water from which the nitro-benzene is extracted with ether. The ethereal extract is washed by shaking with water, and after the separation of the aqueous washings it is dried over anhydrous sodium sulphate. The ether may be distilled off on the water-bath without serious loss of nitrobenzene, since the boiling point of the latter is 205° C. If larger quantities of mixed acid are used and the temperature is allowed to rise, a mixture of dinitrobenzenes, consisting mainly of the meta-compound, is produced. After re-crystallization from hot alcohol *m*-dinitrobenzene melts at 89·8° C.

Picric acid forms with benzene a compound which crystallizes in yellow needles and is decomposed by water.

Nitrobenzene, which is manufactured in enormous quantities in the coal-tar dye industry, is responsible for numerous cases of chronic poisoning, of which the chief symptoms are lassitude, headache and giddiness. In more acute cases there may be asphyxia, twitchings and even convulsions. The mucous membranes are sometimes dark-coloured.

Nitrobenzene may be recognized by its orange-yellow colour and its almond-like odour. When it is heated with concentrated sulphuric acid and resorcin, a violet-coloured liquid is formed. When cold, this may be diluted with water, neutralized with sodium carbonate solution and, if necessary, filtered. The solution shows a yellowish red fluorescence. Some other nitro- and nitroso-compounds, e.g. o-nitrotoluene and p-nitraniline and α-nitroso-β-naphthol behave in a similar way.[1]

Nitrobenzene may be reduced to aniline on a micro-scale by spotting on filter-paper. A drop of hydrochloric acid is put into the middle of the nitrobenzene spot, and on that is placed a minute quantity of very finely divided iron. After a short time aniline can be detected by adding a drop of hypochlorite solution, a violet colour changing to dirty red being produced. If, instead of hydrochloric acid and iron, acetic acid and magnesium powder are used, one of the reduction products is azoxybenzene, which is red in colour.

Dinitrobenzene. Of the dinitrobenzenes the commonest is the meta-compound. As it is a solid substance, its most dangerous form is fine dust which, when inhaled, causes symptoms similar to those produced by nitrobenzene.

Like nitrobenzene, it is volatile in steam and soluble in ether. When completely reduced with zinc or iron and a mineral acid, it forms m-phenylene diamine, and this, when treated with nitrous acid, forms the well-known azo-dyestuff, Bismarck brown. Care should be taken to avoid excess of nitrite, because in the formation of the dyestuff only one-third of the diamine should be tetrazotized. A sensitive reaction for dinitro compounds is described by Kulikow and Panowa.[2] A dilute solution of the substance in water is mixed with hydrochloric acid (1 : 1) and treated with zinc dust. After the reaction has ceased the liquid is decanted and treated with a few drops of a 1 per cent. alcoholic solution of acetyl-acetone. A violet colour, perceptible in a dilution of 1 in 200,000, is produced.

Naphthalene is said to have produced alarming symptoms of poisoning. Although several cases have been investigated in our laboratory in which broken moth-balls were found in the stomach washings, there were no fatal cases. Naphthalene is readily volatile in steam, but the substance is likely to solidify inside the condenser. If this happens the water-jacket should be emptied so as to allow the temperature to rise and the melted naphthalene to run into the receiver. The distillate is extracted with ether and the ether extract dried and allowed to evaporate in the usual way. Crystals which melt at 80° C. are deposited. When an ethereal or alcoholic solution of naphthalene is mixed with a similar solution of dry picric acid and the mixture is allowed to evaporate slowly, yellow crystals of naphthalene picrate, melting at 149° C., separate. In cases of naphthalene poisoning the urine should be tested for β-naphthol, which is sometimes produced by the oxidation of the

[1] ROSENTHALER. " Toxikologische Mikroanalyse ", 158.
[2] ibid., 156.

hydrocarbon in the organism.   Like other phenolic substances, it is likely to be present in the form of the sulphuric ether and/or the glycuronide which must be hydrolyzed before the isolation of the naphthol.   After this process of hydrolysis the urine may be extracted directly with ether, and the tests for β-naphthol, to be described below, applied to the extract.

PHENOLS

The phenolic poisons include phenol itself and the cresols, which are in common use in crude disinfecting fluid and in lysol, a suspension of mixed cresols in soap solution.   Phenol poisoning is usually accidental or suicidal, and the diagnosis is frequently made at the autopsy, the staining of the lips and the odour in the stomach being very characteristic.

The fatal dose of pure phenol is usually stated to be about 15 g. when taken by the mouth, but much smaller quantities have caused death when they have entered the blood stream in other ways, e.g. from wounds or by way of the vagina.   On the other hand, recovery has often followed the ingestion of much larger quantities when proper medical treatment has been given.

Sufficient evidence of fatal poisoning from phenol is sometimes obtained by the examination of the stomach alone, although in some cases larger quantities can be extracted from the blood, liver and other organs.

The method of isolation from viscera is the ordinary process of steam distillation in presence of acid.   The distillation should be continued until a sample of the distillate (about 5 ml.) no longer gives a red colour on boiling with 1 or 2 drops of Millon's reagent. From the distillate the phenol can, if necessary, be extracted by shaking with ether, and there is usually no difficulty in detecting the odour.

Of the qualitative tests for phenol, one has already been applied during the distillation as mentioned above.   To a very dilute solution of a phenolic substance 1 or 2 drops of Millon's reagent are added and the mixture is boiled.   The production of a red colour is a very sensitive, although not an absolutely specific, indication of the presence of a phenol.   A second reaction is the production of tribromphenol when excess of bromine water is added to a dilute solution of a phenol.   This appears as a pale yellow precipitate, solid in the case of phenol itself, oily in the case of cresols.   The individual phenols and cresols, when pure, give characteristic colours with ferric chloride solution, but these colour reactions are very seldom of value in examining distillates from viscera, since the commonest phenolic poison is the crude disinfecting fluid which contains a mixture of phenolic substances.

The quantitative determination of small quantities of phenolic substances in aqueous solution, such as may be obtained as a distillate from tissues, is carried out as follows[1]:—

The solution should contain approximately $0 \cdot 1$ g. of phenol or cresol in 60 ml. of water. To this, 5 ml. of concentrated hydrochloric acid are added and the mixture is washed into a bottle with a capacity of 500 ml., fitted with a glass stopper.

A burette is filled with N/10 bromide-bromate solution,[2] and from it sufficient of the reagent is run into the bottle to give the liquid a distinct yellow colour. The quantity of reagent added is observed and 10 per cent. more is then run in. The bottle is stoppered and shaken continuously for one minute, after which 5 ml. of 10 per cent. potassium iodide solution are added and the liberated iodine is titrated with N/10 thiosulphate solution. A blank experiment is carried out on the same quantity of bromide-bromate solution. The quantity of bromide-bromate solution used up in forming the tribromphenol is the measure of the phenol present.

One ml. of N/10 bromide-bromate solution represents $0 \cdot 0016$ g. of phenol or $0 \cdot 0018$ g. of cresol.

The quantity of phenols in urine can be determined by the method of Messinger and Vortman.[3]

Five hundred ml. of urine are made alkaline with caustic soda and evaporated on a water-bath to one-half this volume. Twenty ml. of concentrated sulphuric acid are added and the mixture is distilled, half the volume being collected. The residue in the flask is then diluted with water to its original volume, and again one-half is distilled off. The operation is repeated three times more and collected distillates are neutralized by the addition of calcium carbonate. The phenolic compounds are distilled from the neutralized liquid and the quantity in the distillate is determined by the bromide-bromate method above described.

Normal urine contains phenolic substances which are degradation products of proteins, the total quantity of mixed phenol and cresols excreted in twenty-four hours being from 15 to 30 mg.

In cases of phenol poisoning the urine is usually very dark in colour. A large part of the phenol ingested may be excreted in a combined form. When the urine is distilled with mineral acid the whole of the phenols present pass into the distillate. If it is desired to isolate only the uncombined phenols, the free acid in the urine should be neutralized and the liquid then acidified with acetic acid before distillation.

[1] EVERS and ELSDON. " Analysis of Drugs and Chemicals ", 163.
[2] N/10 bromide-bromate solution is prepared by dissolving $2 \cdot 784$ g. of potassium bromate and 15 g. of potassium bromide in distilled water and making the volume up to 1 litre.
[3] Ber. d. Deutsch. Chem. Ges., **22** (1889), 2312; ibid., **23** (1890), 2753.

α- **and** β-**Naphthols.** The two naphthols resemble one another in being soluble in caustic alkalis, but not in alkaline carbonates. The phenols derived from benzene, except the nitro-phenols, are similar in this respect. They differ slightly in odour and considerably in fusibility. The α-compound melts at 96° C., while β-naphthol melts at 122° C. β-naphthol is more soluble in hot water than α-naphthol. Both dissolve readily in alcohol and in ether.

With neutral ferric chloride solution, α-naphthol gives a violet coloration, β-naphthol, green. Both yield orange-coloured azo-dyestuffs when coupled with diazotized sulphanilic acid. This test is made in the usual way by adding the acidic solution of the diazo compound to the alkaline solution of the naphthol.

Both naphthols form dichroic crystals when they are dissolved in benzene, mixed with a benzene solution of benzoquinone and the solvent is allowed to evaporate. If α-naphthoquinone is substituted for benzoquinone only α-naphthol reacts, forming red prisms (Behrens). Both in the dyestuffs industry and in pharmacy β-naphthol is in more common use than the α-compound. Autenrieth,[1] quoting Lewin, reports several cases in which severe symptoms of poisoning, affecting especially the kidneys, followed the use of β-naphthol ointment in the treatment of scabies; one six-year-old patient died.

As mentioned above, β-naphthol may be found in the urine in combination with sulphuric acid or glycuronic acid when the poisoning is due to naphthalene itself.

Thymol. This substance is a constituent of many essential oils and constitutes 20 to 50 per cent. of oil of thyme. It is a white crystalline solid which melts at 50°–51° C. It exerts a considerable vapour pressure below 100° C., and is easily volatile in steam. It is seen in the distillate as oily drops which are almost insoluble in water; it is readily soluble in alcohol and in ether.

Chemically, it is a phenol of the terpene group, one of the hydroxy-derivatives of p-cymene.

It has been used in the treatment of hook-worm and in excessive doses it causes irritant symptoms, weakness of the heart and giddiness. Several deaths have been recorded. In the post-mortem examination fatty degeneration of the liver and congestion of the lungs have been observed in addition to the usual lesions of irritant poisons. Like other phenols, thymol is partially eliminated in the urine as glycuronic and sulphuric acid derivatives, which should be decomposed by boiling with hydrochloric acid before attempting to isolate the thymol by distillation in steam and extracting the distillate with ether. According to Blum,[2] an additional

---

[1] AUTENRIETH. " Lab. Manual for Detection of Poisons ", 6th ed., 58.
[2] *Zeitschr. f. Physiol. Chem.*, 1892, **16,** 514.

compound is found in thymol-containing urine; this compound, on boiling with concentrated hydrochloric acid, forms an indigo-blue colouring matter, which becomes purple on the addition of ammonia.

Material other than urine, i.e. samples of viscera, are examined for thymol as for other phenols by simple distillation in steam after acidification with tartaric acid.

Unlike other phenols, thymol does not give a red colour with Millon's reagent, and with bromine water there may be no precipitate but only a slight turbidity. When the alkaline solution is treated with iodine and warmed, a red colour is produced, and in concentrated solutions a red precipitate. With potassium nitrite and acetic acid an amorphous precipitate is formed which slowly changes into small needles; this crystallization can be accelerated by the addition of more acetic acid. A solution of thymol in concentrated caustic potash, when warmed and mixed with chloroform, yields a violet-red colour.

Nitrophenols. The only nitrophenol which is volatile in steam is the ortho-compound. It distils as a yellow oil which solidifies on cooling. The melting point is 45° C. It dissolves, like phenol itself, in caustic alkalis and, unlike phenol, in alkaline carbonate solution. The alkali salts are yellow to reddish yellow.

ANILINE

Poisoning with aniline is fairly common among workers in dyestuffs factories; breathing of the vapours may produce unpleasant symptoms. It is a blood poison and converts oxyhaemoglobin into methaemoglobin. In a case quoted by Autenrieth a healthy man died after swallowing less than 25 g. of the liquid.

Workers in the aniline industry were known to suffer from peculiar tumours in the bladder, almost certainly cancers, in the dye manufacturing districts of Germany and Switzerland before 1914. These tumours were first recorded in England in 1926, and since then about forty cases have been reported.[1] The number of recorded cases in all countries is at least 550. The cancer does not usually appear until the victim has been exposed to the risk for a very long time, and it may not be noticed until such exposure has ceased. Not only aniline but other amino compounds, such as benzidine and the naphthylamines, have been held responsible for this disease.

According to Engelhardt, aniline in the body is partially oxidized to aniline-black or some similar insoluble oxidation product, which can be seen by microscopic examination of the blood or urine.

[1] *B.M.J.*, 21.1.39, 119.

It is also eliminated in the urine as *p*-amino-phenol which, like other phenols, is found in the urine partly as an ethereal sulphuric acid and partly conjugated with glycuronic acid. Aniline has also been detected in the urine unchanged. As has been said already, aniline, being basic, distils most readily from an alkaline solution; although it is so feebly basic that its salts are partially hydrolyzed in hot water, and therefore the distillate from a neutral solution contains aniline. Aniline is somewhat soluble in water, but it can be extracted by repeatedly shaking the alkaline aqueous solution with ether. The ethereal extract, after drying over anhydrous sodium sulphate and filtering, is allowed to evaporate at a low temperature. The residue should respond to the following tests:—

(1) A drop of the oil is neutralized with a drop of hydrochloric acid and afterwards treated with platinic chloride solution; crystals of the platino-chloride are deposited as yellow plates.

(2) Heated with chloroform and alcoholic potash, aniline yields phenyl-iso-nitrile, the odour of which is readily recognized. (Other amines give compounds with a similar smell.)

(3) In aqueous solution aniline yields an intense purple colour on the addition of hypochlorite solution. This colour is not stable, but the addition of an ammoniacal solution of phenol produces a stable blue colour. This is known as the indo-phenol test; *p*-amino-phenol behaves in the same way.

(4) Aniline in dilute acid solution can be diazotized by the addition of sodium nitrite to the well-cooled solution and then coupled with β-naphthol dissolved in dilute alkali, to form an orange-coloured azo-dye. It is recommended that the sodium nitrite solution should be 0·5 per cent. and the naphthol solution 1·0 per cent. The volume of the naphthol solution should be a little less than that of the nitrite solution.

(5) A portion of the aniline-containing extract dissolved in concentrated sulphuric acid and treated with a drop of dichromate solution yields a blue colour, which is not discharged on the addition of water.

If *p*-aminophenol is present, it may not be found in the distillate as it is only slightly volatile in steam. It can be extracted with ether from neutral aqueous solution and identified by the following reactions:—

(1) On boiling with Millon's reagent a fine violet colour is produced, but it quickly fades to brown.

(2) A solution of sodium hypochlorite or ferric chloride produces a violet colour.

(3) Bromine water also produces a violet colour, which is discharged by excess of the reagent.

Acetanilide. This was formerly in common use as a remedy for headaches under the name of " Antifebrine ", but it has been largely replaced by safer remedies. It has toxic properties similar to those of aniline, although the symptoms are less severe. Between 1886 and 1907 American records showed 840 cases of acute poisoning with twenty-eight deaths.

Like aniline, it may be excreted in the urine as the oxidation product aceto-*p*-aminophenol, which is usually conjugated with sulphuric acid and/or glycuronic acid. This, if present in the urine, may be isolated by extraction with ether after boiling with hydrochloric acid, which converts it into *p*-aminophenol. The latter substance gives the indo-phenol reaction already described as a test for aniline.

Acetanilide may be extracted without hydrolysis from the aqueous acid solution in the Stas-Otto process (q.v.) by shaking with ether. It crystallizes from hot water in colourless leaflets melting at 113°–114° C. As the crystals sublime readily at 80° C., micro-sublimation, on the electrically heated microscope stage or otherwise, may be used as a method of purification.

When boiled with alcoholic potash, acetanilide is hydrolyzed to potassium acetate and aniline, and the solution then gives the iso-nitrile reaction for primary amines.

To detect the acetyl group in acetanilide (as also in **phenacetin, aspirin, heroin** and other acetylated compounds) the substance is heated in a test-tube with a few drops of concentrated sulphuric acid. The test-tube is fitted with a cork through which passes one end of a tube bent at right angles; the other end reaches nearly to the bottom of a second test-tube. One or two drops of liquid are distilled over into the second test-tube. It is sometimes possible to detect the odour of acetic acid, although this is sometimes masked by the odour of the sulphurous fumes. The fumes may be got rid of by blowing into the test-tube through a glass tube.

The tests for acetic acid already described are applied to the distillate. The lanthanum test is especially recommended.

TURPENTINE AND ESSENTIAL OILS

Turpentine. Oil of turpentine is a skin irritant and is in common use as a rubefacient. It is sometimes taken internally as an anthelmintic and as a diuretic, but it is contraindicated in cases of kidney disease. Symptoms of chronic poisoning, caused by inhaling the vapour, include nervous disturbances, bronchitis and inflammation of the kidneys.[1] Formerly it was recommended in the treatment of phosphorus poisoning, but this practice was based on error. In large quantities it is an irritant poison.

[1] After a large dose, the urine has an odour of violets.

It can be isolated from urine or viscera by steam distillation and recognized by its odour, and by its refractive index which is between 1·468 and 1·473 at 20° C. The oil reacts violently with iodine. When a crystal of iodine is put on to a drop of the oil on a filter paper, fumes are observed. A mixture of 5 or 6 drops of the oil with a few milligrams of iodine in a test-tube explodes. With concentrated sulphuric acid it gives a deep reddish brown colour.

The principal constituent of the oil is pinene, which reacts with nitrosyl chloride to form a crystalline derivative. The reaction takes place in chloroform solution, with external cooling. Another method of preparing the crystals is to mix equal parts of turpentine, amyl nitrite and acetic acid, and to add, drop by drop, hydrochloric acid. A blue colour is produced after the addition of each drop, and this is allowed to disappear before the next drop is added. A crystalline precipitate is formed, and this can be purified by dissolving in chloroform and re-precipitating with methyl alcohol. The crystals melt at 103° C.

Essential Oils. Some essential oils are commonly reputed to have abortifacient properties, and their use for this purpose frequently results in serious poisoning symptoms, sometimes with fatal results. The commonest of these are oil of savin, oil of rue, oil of pennyroyal, oil of tansy and oil of parsley (apiol). Most of them are powerful irritants, even vesicants, and there appears to be no direct action on the uterus; apiol is possibly an exception. They are isolated by steam distillation followed by ether extraction of the distillate, and can be identified by their characteristic odours and their refractive indices; some of them also yield characteristic colour reactions.

Oil of rue is either green or yellow in colour. It dissolves in an equal volume of 90 per cent. alcohol. Oil of good quality solidifies at 0·8° C. to form a crystalline solid. Its chief constituent is methyl-nonylketone (B.P. 230°–232° C.). Some samples of the oil contain traces of the methyl ester of methylanthranilic acid, which impart to it a blue fluorescence. The refractive index is 1·464 at 15° C. With concentrated sulphuric acid a yellowish brown colour is produced. When 1 drop of nitric acid (sp. gr. 1·42) is added to 1 drop of the oil there is a brisk effervescence, and when this ceases the liquid is pale yellow. Oil of rue does not explode with fuming nitric acid (cf. oil of savin).

When the oil is mixed with an alcoholic solution of p-dimethyl-aminobenzaldehyde acidified with sulphuric acid, a violet-coloured rim slowly appears in the cold; on warming, the rim becomes brownish red, and when the liquid is evaporated to dryness the residue is bright reddish purple.

Oil of savin, from the tops of the plant *Juniperus sabina*, is a colourless, or yellow, mobile liquid. One of its chief constituents is sabinol, which resembles thujone in odour and boils at 208° C. The refractive index is 1·472 to 1·477 at 20° C.

Oil of savin yields an intense blood-red colour with concentrated sulphuric acid and reacts explosively with fuming nitric acid, leaving a reddish orange liquid. With p-dimethylaminobenzaldehyde in acidified alcohol, a reddish violet rim forms in the cold, and the residue, after evaporating to dryness, is brown to reddish violet.

Oil of pennyroyal, from the leaves of *Mentha pulegium*, contains pulegone, limonene and menthol among other constituents. It has a strong peppermint-like odour. It dissolves in concentrated sulphuric acid to form an orange-coloured solution. With fuming nitric acid it does not explode, but forms a deep yellow solution. With the p-dimethylaminobenzaldehyde reagent a strongly coloured blue-violet rim appears in the cold. This turns bright red on warming, and the residue after evaporation is also red; if a little more of the reagent is added to this residue the colour changes again to very bright bluish violet. The refractive index is 1·482–1·487 at 20° C.

Oil of parsley is known in two varieties, green and yellow in colour respectively. The chief constituent is apiol, which may be obtained in crystalline form by cooling the oil. The crystals melt at 30° C. With nitric acid of sp. gr. 1·42, oil of parsley effervesces and the residual liquid is brick-red. With fuming nitric acid a bright carmine colour, changing to blood-red is produced. With the p-dimethylaminobenzaldehyde reagent there is no perceptible colour in the cold, but a red rim appears on warming and the final residue is dull violet. The refractive index is 1·538 at 20° C.

Oil of tansy is distilled from the leaves and tops of *Tanacetum vulgare*. It contains 70 per cent. of a ketone, tanacetone, which is said to be identical with thujone, and 26 per cent. of borneol. It is both an irritant and a narcotic which causes severe poisoning symptoms, such as colic, vomiting, epileptic convulsions, dilated pupils, respiratory disturbances and paralytic asphyxia; several deaths have been reported. The taste is at first bitter, then caustic, and causes a sensation of coldness on the tongue. The refractive index is 1·457 to 1·460 at 20° C.[1]

Oil of tansy shows the following colour reactions: With concentrated sulphuric acid the colour is brown. When a very minute quantity (the residue left after evaporating 1 or 2 drops of a dilute alcoholic solution of the oil) is treated with fuming nitric acid, a violet colour is produced. Mecke's reagent, added to a similar

---

[1] ALLEN. "Commercial Organic Analysis", **4**, 212, gives these figures for the American oil, but states that the English oil may have a refractive index up to 1·4750 at 20° C.

quantity of the oil in a basin, becomes brown, the rim being violet.

The oil reacts violently with iodine, yielding a greenish liquid and an almost black precipitate. With the alcoholic *p*-dimethylamino-benzaldehyde reagent no colour appears in the cold, but the residue left after evaporation is greyish green.

Oil of chenopodium is distilled from the seeds of *Chenopodium ambrosoides anthelminticum*, commonly known as American worm seed. It is a somewhat viscid yellow oil having a characteristic odour. Its chief constituent is ascaridol, and the oil is used in the treatment of round worms and hook worms. It is a gastro-intestinal irritant, and, according to Peterson, Haines and Webster, may produce such additional symptoms as cramp, hallucinations, drowsiness, coma, clonic convulsions and death from the arrest of respiration. Children have been known to die after treatment for a few days with three daily doses of 0·5 g. The oil is extracted from viscera by the usual method of distillation in steam and extraction of the distillate with ether.

The undiluted oil reacts explosively with iodine, like oil of turpentine. One drop of it gives a very intense reddish brown colour with a drop of concentrated sulphuric acid; but if 1 drop of the oil is diluted with 10 ml. of alcohol and 1 drop of this solution is evaporated, the colour with concentrated sulphuric acid is yellowish green. Warmed with alcoholic potash, the oil produces a brown colour. If a drop of it is boiled with concentrated hydrochloric acid a reddish turbid liquid is produced. One drop of the oil mixed with a few milligrams of vanillin and 1 drop of concentrated hydrochloric acid develops a pink colour in the cold; on warming it turns brown, becoming nearly black at the boiling point.

PARAFFIN OIL

Symptoms of poisoning sometimes follow the accidental swallowing of ordinary paraffin oil (kerosene), although death from paraffin poisoning has not come within our experience.

There is no distinctive chemical test for paraffin, the only means of recognizing it in small quantities being its odour and oily appearance; it can, however, be distinguished from fatty oils by the fact that it is unsaponifiable and from coal-tar hydrocarbons by the fact that it does not form nitro-derivatives. Very often it is impossible to recognize the odour in vomited matter or stomach washings owing to the strong smell of the stomach contents themselves. Sometimes it is possible to overcome this difficulty by adding a large excess of potassium permanganate, so that the characteristic colour of the latter persists, making strongly acid with sulphuric acid and distilling in a current of steam. The odour of paraffin may then be perceptible in the distillate, which should be collected in a tall cylinder and afterwards be allowed to stand overnight, the mouth of the cylinder being plugged with cotton wool. On the following day oily drops may be observed on the surface of the liquid. The liquid should then be extracted with ether and the ether extract, after drying over calcium chloride, evaporated at room temperature. If any residual oil is observed, the following test should be attempted:

(*a*) A portion of the residue should be transferred to a small porcelain basin and ignited; paraffin burns with a smoky flame.

(*b*) A second portion is boiled in a small flask with caustic potash solution under a reflux condenser for an hour. When cold the liquid is acidified with dilute sulphuric acid. If oily drops are still perceptible, this is evidence of the presence of an unsaponifiable oil.

(*c*) To exclude coal-tar hydrocarbons a portion of the oily residue should be treated with a mixture of sulphuric and nitric acids. (See Nitration Test for Benzene.)

PHOSPHORUS

Acute poisoning by yellow phosphorus is usually accidental, as when children swallow the pastes sold for killing beetles. Occasionally it has been used for suicide. Chronic phosphorus poisoning, the well-known " phossy-jaw ", is usually diagnosed clinically and seldom concerns the forensic chemist.

In fatal cases phosphorus may be suspected at the autopsy if there is severe fatty degeneration of the liver.

Most of the methods for the detection of yellow phosphorus depend on its volatility.

The ozone-like odour may be recognized on opening the stomach. The odour may be more marked after the stomach has been enclosed for some time in a stoppered jar. If any odour resembling ozone is noticed on opening the jar the stomach should be examined in a dark room when the characteristic luminescence of yellow phosphorus may be observed.

The first chemical test to be applied, preferably to the vomit or stomach-washings in non-fatal cases, or to the stomach itself in fatal cases, is Scherer's test. The material under examination is put into a flask with a capacity of about 400 ml. and covered with cold water. A few millilitres of a solution of cadmium sulphate are added and the liquid is acidified with dilute sulphuric acid. The flask is closed with a cork, in which two slits have been cut on opposite sides to support strips of test-paper measuring 5 mm. by 10 cm. These strips must hang freely without touching the walls of the flask or each other. One strip is soaked in a 5 per cent. silver nitrate solution, the other in a solution made by adding caustic soda to 5 per cent. lead acetate solution until the precipitate first formed is re-dissolved. The flask is then warmed in a subdued light. If the first strip darkens while the second remains unchanged, phosphorus may possibly be present. If the first strip does not darken, phosphorus is absent. If both strips darken, the test is inconclusive, since the blackening may possibly be due to sulphuretted hydrogen.

The Mitscherlich Test. Since phosphorus is not the only substance which may cause the blackening of the silver paper, a positive result

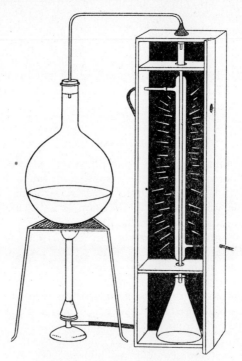

FIG. 10. Detection of phosphorus.
Mitscherlich apparatus with box screen.

must be confirmed by the luminescence test, for which the distillation method of Mitscherlich is used. Even the light from the " non-luminous " bunsen flame may be a disturbing factor, so the condenser must be as completely screened as possible. The apparatus shown in Fig 10 has been found useful. The wooden box, painted black, acts as a support for the condenser and screens it from the light; but even with this apparatus it is desirable to work in a dark room. The material to be examined is put into the distillation flask, mixed with water if necessary, and gently heated. If free yellow phosphorus is present, a more or less brilliant and persistent luminescence appears in the condenser; if this is unmistakably manifest there can be no doubt of the presence of yellow phosphorus. Certain organic liquids, if present, inhibit the phosphorescent effect, e.g. alcohol and turpentine. The former may have been added as a preservative; the latter may have been administered as an antidote.

If no phosphorescence is seen the distillation should be continued until the greater part of the liquid has passed over into the condenser. A few drops of nitric acid are added to the distillate, which is then boiled to oxidize any phosphorus which may be present, after which the liquid is concentrated to a small volume by heating in a basin on a water-bath, and tested for phosphate by boiling with ammonium molybdate solution.

Dr. J. B. Firth (personal communication) states that nearly all cases in his experience have shown the clinical history of phosphorus poisoning followed by apparent recovery and then a sudden fatal relapse ; in such circumstances he has been unable to detect phosphorus by the Mitscherlich test.

The Blondlot-Dusart Test. A further test for phosphorus which may be applied if the Mitscherlich test fails to give a decisive result

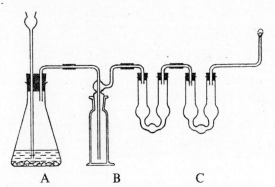

FIG. 11. Dusart apparatus for phosphorous detection.
A. Hydrogen generator containing silver phosphide precipitate.
B. Empty wash bottle.
C. Potash tubes.

depends on the production of phosphine by the action of nascent hydrogen, that is to say it is similar in principle to the Marsh test for arsenic. It is known as the Blondlot-Dusart test. The test should not be applied directly to tissues; attempts to do so result in unmanageable frothing. Therefore the process is carried out in two stages, the phosphine first produced being absorbed in silver nitrate solution, from which it is reliberated by means of nascent hydrogen, which is afterwards burnt at a platinum or silica nozzle, and if phosphorus is present the inner cone of the flame is coloured green. This last part of the process should be carried out in a dark room.

The technique recommended is to mince the tissues and macerate with recently boiled water to form a thin paste. This is put into a corked flask with inlet and outlet tubes passing through the cork and heated on a water-bath. Hydrogen, generated from pure zinc and acid, is passed through the paste and thence into the silver nitrate solution, the gas stream being continued for two hours. The precipitate formed is transferred to a Dusart apparatus, which consist of a hydrogen generator connected with an empty wash-bottle, which, in turn, is connected with two U-tubes containing caustic potash. To these is connected the leading tube ending in a jet. The reduction of the precipitate is somewhat slow at ordinary temperatures and is best carried out at about 550° C.

Selmi has shown that in cases of poisoning, phosphorus may be detected in the brain ; and, according to Halarz, the phosphorus in normal brains does not yield phosphine under the conditions described. Nevertheless, phosphorus may often be detected in the viscera when none is found in the brain.

GASEOUS POISONS

It is very rarely that a gaseous poison has to be identified without prior knowledge of its probable nature. The symptoms and the conditions under which the poison was inhaled almost invariably give such definite information that the problem is merely one of confirming the presence of a particular toxic gas and perhaps of determining the quantity present in the atmosphere. This is particularly the case since, except for carbon monoxide, cases of poisoning by toxic gases are usually industrial accidents.

For the detection of the commoner toxic gases at concentrations well below the danger limit, and for their rapid but approximate determinations, tests have been evolved under the aegis of the Department of Scientific and Industrial Research. Full details of the recommended apparatus, methods and prescribed conditions have been published by H.M. Stationery Office (*Methods for the Detection of Toxic Gases in Industry*, leaflets 1-12), and these should be consulted. They include standard colour-cards for use with methods involving test-papers.

Sampling

Two main methods are available for sampling gases.

1. By means of a hand exhaust pump of known capacity, the air is drawn slowly through the test solution contained in a test-tube

fitted with a bubbler (fine jet or sinter-glass). A suitable rate is usually about 10 c.c. per second. There should be a by-pass so that the air drawn into the pump can be ejected without repassing through the reagent. Pumping is continued until a colour of suitable depth is developed or until the test is obviously negative.

2. Air is drawn through the reagent by allowing water to run at a pre-determined rate from a filled aspirator. This method is particularly suitable when the air is to be drawn through slowly —e.g. 30-50 c.c. per minute—or when the reagent consists of an impregnated test-paper, as in the testing for arsine, carbon monoxide, etc. In such a case the test-paper should be so held that a definite area is exposed, and the gas is drawn through it.

Tests

Arsine. The gas is drawn through test-paper impregnated with silver nitrate or mercuric chloride and dried. The silver nitrate papers are the more sensitive, but they give a stain with arsine which is of varying colour and changes rapidly on exposure to light, and they must be freshly prepared. The mercuric chloride papers are stable if kept in a well-stoppered bottle, and give a definite yellow colour if approximately five litres of air containing ·013 mg. arsine per litre are drawn through a disc of paper $1\frac{1}{2}$ inches in diameter. The colour obtained is compared with standards or is measured by means of a calibrated comparator.

In fatal cases, of course, arsenic should be sought in the viscera by the usual methods.

Benzene and Toluene. The air is drawn through 10 ml. of reagent prepared by the addition of pure concentrated sulphuric acid to 0·5 ml. of formalin (40 per cent. formaldehyde). Benzene or toluene produces an orange-brown colour. Solvent naphthas, naphthalene, thiophene, etc., interfere but are not usually present in sufficient concentration.

Alternative methods depend upon absorbing the hydrocarbons in nitrating acid and determining, colorimetrically, the nitro-compounds produced.

Carbon bisulphide. The air, freed from any traces of hydrogen sulphide by being drawn through filter-paper impregnated with lead acetate, is bubbled through a standard volume of reagent. This is prepared by adding to 10 ml. of absolute alcohol, 2 ml. of a 2 per cent. (v/v) solution of diethylamine in benzene and 2 ml. of a 0·1 per cent. (w/v) of copper acetate in alcohol. In presence of carbon bisulphide, copper diethyldithiocarbonate is formed and, after fifteen minutes for full development, the colour is compared with that of a suitable standard. A concentration of 0·025 mg. CS$_2$ per litre is detectable.

Carbon monoxide. Probably the most accurate and sensitive method of determining carbon monoxide in air is to draw a sample of the air slowly through blood (preferably diluted with distilled water) using octyl alcohol to prevent frothing, and then determining the carbon monoxide content of the blood gasometrically by means of the Van Slyke and Neill manometer.[1] Alternatively, the carbon monoxide may be determined approximately by use of the Hartridge reversion spectroscope[2] or the tannic acid test.[3]

A simpler test, capable of detecting 0·01 per cent. of carbon monoxide in 2 litres of air, depends on the ability of carbon monoxide to reduce palladous chloride to metallic palladium. The air, at 15–25° C., is drawn first through activated charcoal and then through a test-paper impregnated, immediately before use, with a solution of palladium chloride (0·1 g. in 20 ml. distilled water and 20 ml. acetone). A suitable rate is 50 cc. per minute. The grey-brown stain produced by carbon monoxide is compared with standards.

In cases of suspected carbon monoxide poisoning, blood from the victims should be examined. Samples not being tested immediately should be kept under liquid paraffin. Carbon monoxide has been detected in post-mortem blood several days after death. The reversion spectroscope method is good and is capable of detecting carboxyhaemoglobin in the presence of seven or eight times as much oxyhaemoglobin. The tannic acid method is about equally sensitive. For this, 1 ml. of 10 per cent. potassium ferricyanide solution is added to each of two 5 ml. portions of the blood under test. One of the flasks (or large test-tubes) is stoppered and left undisturbed; the other is shaken for fifteen minutes, the stopper being occasionally removed to admit fresh air; the carbon monoxide is thus removed. To each sample, 10 ml. of 10 per cent. tannic acid solution is then added. The shaken flask gives a dirty olive-green precipitate; the unshaken flask gives one varying from the same to bright red according to the amount of carbon monoxide present. For roughly quantitative work the colour is compared after standing overnight with that of a series of standards prepared from mixtures of normal blood and blood saturated with carbon monoxide. Accurate measurement of the carbon monoxide content of blood is rarely needed for toxicological analysis ; it is perhaps best made by the manometric methods to which reference has been made above, but a simpler and sufficiently accurate procedure is founded on the reduction of palladium chloride to palladium. In the inner chamber

[1] HARINGTON and VAN SLYKE. *J. Biol. Chem.*, 1924, **61**, 523. ROUGHTON. *Ibid.*, 1941, **137**, 617.

[2] *Proc. Roy. Soc.*, 1928, A, **102**, 575.

[3] HENDERSON and HAGGARD. *J.A.M.A.*, 1922, **79**, 1143.

of a standard Conway micro-diffusion unit place $1 \cdot 0$ ml. of $\frac{N}{50}$ palladium chloride (1 ml. $\equiv 0 \cdot 224$ ml. of CO at N.T.P.), and in the outer chamber, $0 \cdot 25$ ml. of $4N.H_2SO_4$, followed, with minimal mixing, by $2 \cdot 0$ ml. of a 1 in 4 dilution of the blood in water. Quickly place the vaselined lid of the unit in position and mix the contents of the outer chamber by gentle rotation. After an hour either : (a) remove $0 \cdot 8$ ml. of the solution from the inner chamber and titrate the HCl released by the action of carbon monoxide ($PdCl_2$ $+ CO + H_2O = Pd + 2HCl + CO_2$) with $N/50$ or $\frac{N}{100}$ HaOH using bromphenol blue as indicator and the first purple tint as end-point, or (b) add $0 \cdot 15$ ml. of 10 per cent. aluminium sulphate to the inner chamber to flocculate the palladium, stir, transfer, and filter the fluid quantitatively (six separate washings of water) through No. 40. Whatman filter paper. To the filtrate add 1 ml. of gum ghatti with shaking, then 10 ml. of 15 per cent. (w/v) potassium iodide and make up to 50 ml. with distilled water. Measure the colour, and that of 1ml. of the $PdCl_2$ solution similarly diluted ; the difference represents the amount of $PdCl_2$ reduced and thence the amount of CO. Measuring extinctions in a photoelectric absorptiometer, with a filter transmitting at any wavelength below 550 mμ, and allowing for $PdCl_2$ absorbed on the filter paper, the amount of CO as ml. per 100 ml. blood is given by the formula $(0 \cdot 98 - A) \times 44 \cdot 8 \times 1 \cdot 02$, where A is the difference between the two extinctions.

Chlorine is detectable by smell at a concentration of one part per million ($\cdot 003$ mg. per litre) which is not dangerous. The most sensitive chemical test is that with o-tolidine, which is capable of detecting chlorine at this concentration in about 3 litres of air. The air is drawn, at about 10–15 cc. per second, through 10 ml. of the reagent. This is prepared by dissolving 1 g. pure o-tolidine in 100 ml. of concentrated hydrochloric acid and diluting to 1,000 ml. with distilled water. Chlorine gives a yellow colour. Nitrous fumes interfere, but only at a relatively high concentration.

Hydrogen cyanide (hydrocyanic acid) in relatively high concentrations can be detected by conversion to thiocyanate which gives red ferric thiocyanate, or by production of Prussian blue by allowing the gas to react with an alkaline solution of ferrous sulphate and ferric chloride and then acidifying. Much more sensitive, though less specific reactions are (1) oxidation of benzidine to a blue compound in presence of copper acetate, and (2) production of a blue colour with Congo-red in presence of silver nitrate. Benzidine and copper acetate react with other oxidizing gases like chlorine and the oxidation is inhibited by reducing agents like sulphur dioxide and hydrogen sulphide. The Congo-red test is invalid in the presence of acid or alkaline gases (e.g. HCl, NH_3, tobacco smoke).

Hydrogen sulphide. Air is drawn through test-paper impregnated with lead acetate, and the brown stain of lead sulphide is compared with suitable standards.

Nitrous fumes yield nitrous acid in solution, and this can be made to diazotize an aromatic amine. The diazo compound will then couple with an aromatic amine or phenol to form an azo dye. For the Bismarck-Brown test, air is drawn through a freshly prepared solution of m-phenylenediamine in acetic aid ; a positive result consists in the production of an orange colour. For the Griess-Illosvay test, the reagent consists of a freshly made mixture of equal volumes of (a) 0·5 g. sulphanilic acid in 150 ml. of 14 per cent. (v/v) acetic acid, (b) 0·1 g. of α-naphthylamine in 150 ml. of 14 per cent. (v/v) acetic acid. The colour developed in the presence of nitrous acid is a rose pink. Both tests can be used quantitatively. The Griess-Illosvay test is the more sensitive and will detect ·03 mg. of nitrous fumes in a litre of air.

Phosgene gives a transient yellow or orange stain with a test-paper impregnated with p-dimethylaminobenzaldehyde and diphenylamine. (Soak the paper in a solution containing 5 g. of each reagent in 100 ml. absolute alcohol ; dry in the dark in air free from phosgene or any acid gas). Chlorine and hydrochloric acid interfere but may be removed by passing the air over dry pumice impregnated with sodium iodide and sodium thiosulphate. A distinct colour is produced by ·004 mg. phosgene per litre, using 10 litres of air.

CHAPTER III

COMMON METALLIC POISONS

THE term " common metallic poisons " is somewhat arbitrarily applied to the poisonous compounds of arsenic, antimony, mercury, bismuth and silver. Arsenic is undoubtedly the commonest poison used for homicidal purposes in every country, and, although in Western countries the sale of it is very strictly controlled, in the East it is readily available, both in the form of white arsenic and the yellow artificial sulphide, as rat poison. In India and in Egypt arsenical poisoning of cattle, as well as human beings, is exceedingly common. Mercury, in the form of corrosive sublimate, is also fairly common as a means of homicide and suicide. Criminal poisoning with antimony compounds is more rare, but it is not unknown. In our experience fatal antimony poisoning has nearly always been accidental.

Bismuth compounds are not usually considered to be highly toxic, and many of them are regularly taken by the mouth in large doses with impunity. Nevertheless, the modern bismuth therapy, in which compounds of this metal are injected into the blood-stream, is by no means free from danger. Of the silver compounds, the nitrate is a powerful irritant, but very few cases of fatal poisoning with it have been recorded.

The reason for including bismuth and silver in this group is that their presence may be indicated by the preliminary test, the Reinsch test, which is always applied first, when metallic poisoning is suspected.

In investigating a case of poisoning by metallic compounds the analyst may hope to be guided by the medical officer's report, both on the clinical history of the victim and the post-mortem findings, as well as by the evidence provided by dregs in drinking vessels and remnants of food from the last meal and the presence or absence of symptoms in other persons.

When death has occurred a short time after the onset of symptoms, traces of poison may be found by visual examination of the stomach contents. This is an absolutely essential part of the routine; it must never be omitted and must be as thorough as possible. The stomach is opened out on a large dish such as the largest size of photographic developing dishes, and placed in a good light. After a note has been made of the nature of the stomach contents (i.e. whether it contains much or little food, whether the latter is fluid or not, and if possible, the nature of the food) a careful search is made among the food matter and in the folds of the stomach walls for foreign substances. Any hard particles must be picked out with forceps, washed, dried between pieces of blotting-paper and reserved for further examination. If any suspicious substance has been noted at the autopsy this must receive special attention. For example, in animal poisoning it frequently happens that the veterinary officer has noticed white particles among the food in the stomach. These may prove on examination to consist of starchy matter or something equally harmless, and if so the fact must be clearly stated in the report. Otherwise if arsenic should subsequently be found by chemical tests, the unwarranted conclusion may be drawn that the poison has necessarily been administered in the form of white arsenic. Particles of arsenic can be most readily identified by the sublimation test. A single particle which may be much smaller than a pin-head is dropped into a dry ignition tube about 8 cm. long and 4 mm. in internal diameter. A portion of the tube about 2 cm. from the closed end is gently warmed and thereafter the particle is heated in a small flame. This flame may be the by-pass flame of a by-pass bunsen burner, or alternatively, the lowest zone of the ordinary bunsen flame may be used. When cold, the tube is examined under the low power of the microscope, and if the particle consisted of either white or yellow arsenic a crystalline sublimate will be seen on the inner walls of the tube. Yellow arsenic, i.e. artificial arsenic sulphide, is partially converted to the oxide by thus heating in air and also yields crystals, but these are usually slightly coloured. If the preliminary warming of a portion of the tube has been omitted, the sublimate is liable to form too quickly and the crystals may be small and ill-formed, but if the test is carried out in the manner described the definite octahedral shape of the crystals of arsenic trioxide should be seen. The chemist should make himself familiar with the form of these crystals by preparing a number of samples from known specimens of both white and yellow arsenic and no test should be regarded as positive which fails to yield well-formed crystals. Furthermore, and this is a general principle which cannot be over-emphasized, a positive result must always be confirmed by a test of a different kind.

The Reinsch Test

After this visual examination the stomach and its contents should be weighed separately and samples taken for the Reinsch test. This test is of the utmost value to the toxicologist for two reasons. One is that it indicates quite small quantities of the commonest and most lethal of the metallic poisons, and the further advantage is that it can be applied with reasonable expectation of success to samples containing organic matter. The material to be tested is cut into small pieces, transferred to a large Erlenmeyer flask and covered with dilute hydrochloric acid. One or two pieces of copper-foil,[1] each about 1 sq. cm. in area are put in, and the mixture is boiled for some time. The acid and the copper must, of course, be absolutely pure. The concentration of the acid, when mixed with the fluids already present, may vary between 2 and 8 per cent. Acid weaker than 2 per cent. fails to yield positive results with certain arsenical compounds, notably the native sulphides, orpiment and realgar; and on the other hand, if the acid is stronger than 8 per cent. the arsenic chloride produced is liable to be lost by volatilization. The copper must be examined from time to time; this can be done without taking it out of the liquid, as the foil can be seen through the bottom of the flask if the latter is raised above the eye-level. If a thick black deposit is quickly formed on the copper the action should be stopped at once by pouring the liquid into another vessel and filling up the flask with water. If no darkening of the copper is seen the boiling must be continued for at least forty-five minutes, the volume being maintained by the addition of dilute hydrochloric acid as required. If the copper remains bright and absolutely unchanged in colour it may be concluded that arsenic, antimony and mercury as well as silver and bismuth are absent, or present only in very minute quantities.

The danger of prolonging the action after a thick deposit has already formed on the copper is that this deposit may fall from the foil in scales, leaving a bright surface exposed.

A black or dark purple deposit on the copper may be due to arsenic, antimony or bismuth. A silvery or grey deposit is probably due to either mercury or silver. In no case, however, can the appearance of the copper be accepted as a satisfactory proof of the presence of any of these metals. If a deposit, even a very thin film, is formed on the copper, the latter is removed from the liquid. This can be done by simply pouring the liquid into another vessel, filling up the flask with water and pouring the water into the sink. The copper almost invariably stays at the bottom of the flask and after repeated washings with water it may be thrown out on to filter-paper, transferred by means of forceps to dry filter-paper and dried without rubbing or undue pressure. When dry it is taken up in clean forceps and cut into strips, which should not be more than 2 mm. wide, by means of clean scissors. The strips are dropped into an ignition tube similar to that already described for use in the sublimation test. It is an advantage to keep these ignition tubes in alcohol

[1] It is useful for the purpose of examination to suspend the copper in the liquid by means of a fine platinum wire passing through a hole in the foil.

in a stoppered jar and to take them out and dry them by heating immediately before use. The metal is heated in the ignition tube in exactly the same manner as the heating of the particle in the sublimation test.

The deposit, if due to arsenic, is a compound of arsenic and copper. On heating in air the arsenic is oxidized to the trioxide which sublimes in crystals on the cooler part of the tube.

If well formed and typical crystals are seen under the microscope the presence of arsenic is almost certain. The writer has never seen crystals from antimony or bismuth, deposited on copper, which could be mistaken for arsenic by an experienced worker, but antimony does sometimes yield a crystalline sublimate, and the statement has been made that the crystals may be octahedral like those of arsenic.

A black deposit on copper which fails to yield crystals may be interpreted as follows:

(a) Arsenic may be present but the quantity is very minute; or

(b) Antimony or bismuth may be present.

Occasionally, when the test is applied to faecal matter, the copper may become dull and dark in colour, even in the absence of metals of this group; this is due to the presence of sulphur.

To decide between these possibilities further tests must be made, but for this purpose the organic matter must first be destroyed by one of the methods described below.

If a grey or silvery deposit be formed on the copper, leading to a suspicion of mercury, it is advisable, after putting the copper strips into the ignition tube, to draw out the middle portion of the latter to a capillary about 1 mm. in diameter.

When the tube is cold again the copper is heated in a small flame as in the case of arsenic, and the mercury, if any, is driven into the capillary portion of the tube. This portion of the tube is then examined under the microscope. Globules of mercury are characteristic in appearance, but it is nevertheless possible for an inexperienced observer to mistake drops of water for mercury. To guard against this error particular care should be taken to have the copper strips and the tube quite dry; and while looking through the microscope the observer should rotate the sub-stage mirror to and fro on its axis; in this way, by varying the light incident on the globule, variations in the light reflected from them make their appearance unmistakable. By this movement of the mirror water droplets are recognized by their transparency.

In general the Reinsch test is most useful for the examination of poisoned food, vomited matter, stomach-washings, and portions of the alimentary tract. In presence of relatively large quantities of the metals of this group the test may be applied successfully to samples of urine, faeces and even liver or kidney, but better results are usually obtained if the organic matter in such samples is first destroyed.

The Reinsch test is of little use for quantitative work except in the special process to be described later for the determination of antimony, but it may be made roughly quantitative by using copper strips of standard size and, after depositing the whole of the metal on the surface of the copper, comparing them with standard strips prepared in a similar manner from known quantities of the metals. We have found, for example, that on copper strips measuring $10 \times 1 \cdot 5$ cm., quantities of antimony corresponding to the following quantities of tartar emetic: $0 \cdot 1, 0 \cdot 2, 0 \cdot 3, 0 \cdot 4$ and $0 \cdot 5$ mg. showed definite gradations which could be easily recognized. Quantities greater than this formed a scaly deposit which did not adhere perfectly to the copper.

Destruction of Viscera

When tests for metals, other than the Reinsch test, are to be applied to viscera or excreta, the organic matter in the latter must be destroyed. For this purpose, simple calcination is unsuitable, since mercury and, in some of its forms, arsenic would be lost by volatilization.

The classical method is that of Babo and Fresenius, in which nascent chlorine is used as the agent of destructive oxidation. The weighed sample of viscera is cut into small pieces and mixed with dilute hydrochloric acid. As in the Reinsch test, the concentration of the acid should not exceed 8 per cent. A few grams of powdered potassium chlorate are stirred into the mixture, which is then heated on a boiling water-bath. Further quantities of potassium chlorate are added as required, i.e. as the amount of free chlorine present is diminished; and for these further additions compressed tablets are preferable, since the addition of finely divided chlorate to hot acid results in too copious an evolution of chlorine. After several hours' heating, the tissues, with the exception of some of the fat, are almost completely destroyed, although the liquid still contains some organic matter in solution. When this stage has been reached the liquid is allowed to cool and is filtered; the residue on the filter-paper is well washed with hot water and the washings are added to the filtrate. The only metallic compound which may remain in this insoluble residue is silver chloride, so that except in very rare cases it can be discarded.

The filtrate is mixed with sufficient sodium sulphite, bisulphite or metabisulphite to reduce the excess of chlorine present to hydrochloric acid. The liquid is then warmed and a current of air is bubbled through it to remove excess of sulphur dioxide ; it is then ready for the ordinary analytical tests.

The objections to this method are (1) it is long and tedious, and (2) it involves the use of a variety of reagents, some of which are difficult to obtain in a state of absolute purity. It is, however, still the best method for use in testing for mercury, and it is also recommended for the treatment of bones when they are to be tested for metallic poisons.

The next step in the Babo and Fresenius process is to pass a current of sulphuretted hydrogen through the liquid; and it is here that the most serious difficulty arises.

Nearly all the metallic sulphides used for the generation of sulphuretted hydrogen, even when sold " for analytical purposes " contain traces of arsenic, and when sulphuretted hydrogen is evolved by the addition of acid a portion of the arsenic is carried over with the gas. Various suggestions have been made for freeing the gas from arsenic, as, for example, passing it through a series of washbottles containing hydrochloric acid of different concentrations and passing it through a tube packed with asbestos fibres, on which iodine has been deposited in fine crystals. In our experience none of these expedients has been found satisfactory.

Autenrieth recommends the preparation of pure sodium sulphide solution in the laboratory by bubbling the gas from commercial iron sulphide through a solution of pure caustic soda, and the regeneration of the sulphuretted hydrogen from the alkaline sulphide by warming with acid.

The method we have found to be both suitable and convenient is to prepare a solution of magnesium hydrogen sulphide by passing the gas from commercial iron sulphide treated with hydrochloric acid in a Kipp apparatus into a suspension of magnesium oxide in water until the liquid is completely saturated with the gas. The solution, which may be decanted off from any unchanged magnesium oxide, has the advantage that it gives up pure sulphuretted hydrogen on warming without the addition of acid. The evolution of gas begins at about 60° C., and on raising to the boiling point the decomposition of the magnesium hydrogen sulphide is complete, with the regeneration of magnesium oxide, which may be used over again for the same purpose

The purified sulphuretted hydrogen is passed through the liquid obtained in the Babo and Fresenius process until the liquid is saturated with the gas. The precipitate is filtered off,[1] the filtrate is diluted with water and sulphuretted hydrogen is passed through again. Should any further precipitation occur the liquid must be poured again through the same filter.[1]

---

[1] The precipitate can readily be separated by centrifuging and the subsequent purification done without removal from the centrifuge tube. This simplifies the manipulation and minimizes the risk of loss.

The filtrate may contain salts of other metals, but in many cases it need not be examined.

The precipitate may contain mercury, lead, copper, arsenic, antimony or bismuth. Cadmium, tin and some of the rarer metals which might possibly be present are not usually met with in toxicological work. The precipitate is still contaminated with organic matter and must be further purified before being tested for metals. For example, it is not yet suitable for the Marsh-Berzelius test. The filter-paper with the precipitate is transferred to a flask, is covered with dilute hydrochloric acid, and a few drops of bromine are added. The flask is then heated on the water-bath until the precipitate is redissolved, the traces of organic matter are destroyed and the excess of bromine is driven off. During this process the filter-paper becomes disintegrated and can be removed by filtration. This paper pulp is well washed with acidified water and the washings are added to the filtrate. The liquid is then made up by the addition of water to a definite volume and aliquot parts of it are used for the special tests which are required.

When possible it is an advantage to use a process for the destruction of viscera, especially in testing for arsenic, in which the use of sulphuretted hydrogen is avoided altogether. The method adopted by the Home Office analyst[1] is somewhat similar to the Kjeldahl process for nitrogen determination. A small sample of the viscera (about 5 g.) is heated in a Kjeldahl flask with a mixture of sulphuric and nitric acids until the mass becomes fluid and colourless and the evolution of nitrous fumes has ceased. A reducing agent such as hydrazine sulphate is added and sufficient sodium chloride to convert any arsenic present into the volatile chloride. The flask is then connected by means of a ground-glass joint with a condenser, the end of which dips into water. When the flask is further heated the arsenic distils over in the form of arsenic chloride, and the distillate can be used directly for the Marsh test.

The method of destruction preferred in Cairo, where very large numbers of samples of viscera are tested for metallic poisons, especially arsenic, is that devised by Strzyzowski. This depends on the fact that arsenic and also antimony may be rendered non-volatile by conversion into magnesium pyro-arsenate, or the corresponding pyro-antimonate. A weighed sample of the material to be tested is cut into small pieces and mixed with a saturated solution of pure magnesium nitrate, using 35 ml. of solution for 100 g. of solid organs such as liver, and correspondingly less for wetter material. The mixture is made definitely alkaline by stirring in pure magnesium oxide, and is heated in a porcelain basin on a sand-bath with occasional stirring until the mass becomes dry and

---

[1] And which is preferred by the Editor of this edition.

begins to char. At this stage the oxidation is liable to become violent and there is a slight tendency for charred particles to fly out of the dish. This, however, can be easily controlled, either by turning out the flame for a time or by cautiously breaking up the mass with a glass rod. When the violence of the reaction has subsided, heating is continued on the sand-bath until the charred mass begins to glow, leaving a grey ash. The mass is then transferred to a silica basin and the incineration is completed over a gentle blow-pipe flame. The residual ash should be as nearly as possible pure white and free from nitrogen compounds; it consists of magnesium oxide, together with compounds of any foreign metal which may have been present in the original material. It is also liable to contain phosphates, a fact which must be borne in mind if metals other than those in the first two groups in the ordinary analytical tables are to be tested for. When the ash is cold it is mixed with distilled water so as to form a paste, and hydrochloric acid is added with constant stirring until the reaction is strongly acid to Congo red and the ash is completely dissolved. If any small particles of carbon remain they can be removed by filtration. The liquid is submitted to the ordinary analytical processes for the detection of metals; it is suitable for use in the Marsh test for arsenic after the addition of a little stannous chloride solution as a reducing agent.

The great advantages of this process are its simplicity and the fact that relatively large amounts of viscera can be readily destroyed with a minimum amount of unpleasantness.

The disadvantages are that it is unsuitable for the destruction of bones, and that mercury, if present originally, would be lost by volatilization.

ARSENIC

The Marsh-Berzelius Test

The underlying principle of this very delicate test for arsenic and antimony is well known. If compounds of either of these two metals are put into a vessel in which hydrogen is being generated, gaseous hydrides, arsine (AsH_3) and stibine (SbH_3) respectively, are produced and carried along with the hydrogen stream through the exit tube. The end of this tube is drawn out to a jet and the issuing gases ignited. In the original Marsh test, which was merely qualitative, a cold piece of porcelain was held in the hydrogen flame, and a deposit of arsenic or antimony was formed on the cold surface. The deposit of antimony is generally blacker than that of arsenic, but the most characteristic distinction between the two deposits is that arsenic is readily soluble in a solution of an alkaline hypochlorite while antimony is not. In the Berzelius modification of the test a portion of the exit tube is strongly heated (ideally, to 800° C.), while the space between the heated portion and the jet of burning hydrogen is kept cold by means of a pad of cotton, which is repeatedly dipped in iced water. The hydride is decomposed in the hot portion of the tube and the liberated element, arsenic or antimony,

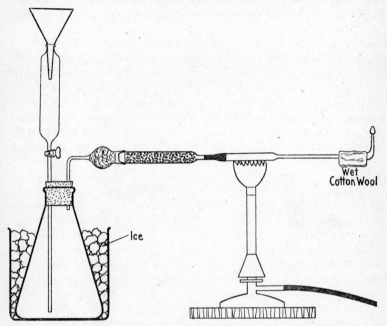

Ice

Wet Cotton Wool

FIG. 12. Marsh-Berzelius test for arsenic ; zinc and acid method.

is deposited as a dark brown or black mirror on the inner wall of the cold part. For arsenic the test is one of extraordinary delicacy, as little as $\frac{1}{1,000}$ mg. being readily detected in a tube with an internal diameter of about 1 mm. The test is much less delicate for antimony than for arsenic, and cannot be relied upon for quantitative determination of the former.

As in all methods involving the production of arsine, reducible heavy metals must not be present in considerable quantities (the traces ordinarily found in organic material do not interfere) ; iron, however, does not inhibit arsine formation unless it is present in unusually great amounts.

The hydrogen generator may be an electrolytic cell or an ordinary bottle containing zinc and hydrochloric or sulphuric acid. If zinc is used it must be absolutely pure. The quality sold by manufacturers of repute " for forensic purposes " has been found to be completely trustworthy. Zinc of this degree of purity does not react readily with acids, but hydrogen is freely evolved if a small quantity of another metal is present. Copper has been used for this purpose, but, according to Chapman, cadmium is better, and our own experience confirms this. The apparatus is shown in Fig. 12, and ideally, it is all glass with well-fitting ground joints. Alternatively, the generating bottle is fitted with an airtight stopper which may be of white india-rubber, or cork coated with collodion; red india-rubber should not be used since it usually contains antimony. The stopper has two holes, into one of which is fitted a dropping funnel and into the other an exit tube for the gas. The latter is connected with a drying tube containing calcium chloride, to the other end of which is fitted the " Marsh tube " which should be of hard glass, or, preferably, fused transparent silica. To prevent undue heating of the generating bottle and to check the violence of the reaction the bottle should stand in a vessel containing ice and water.

The procedure is to put the zinc into the bottle, cover it with water and add a few ml. of a solution of arsenic-free cadmium sulphate. Then, after making sure that all the joints are airtight, dilute hydrochloric or sulphuric acid is allowed to run into the bottle from the dropping funnel in sufficient quantity to produce a brisk but not too vigorous effervescence. The rate of evolution of hydrogen can be controlled by adding stronger acid or water as required. The reaction is allowed to continue until there is no doubt that all the air has been driven out of the apparatus, after which the issuing hydrogen can safely be ignited at the jet without risk of explosion. The gas should burn with a steady flame about 3 mm. high. The tube is then examined to make sure that it is free from water inside; if not, it is dried by running the Bunsen flame along it. A portion of the tube remote from the jet is then heated by means of a Bunsen burner fitted with a flame spreader. It is essential that at least 5 cm. of the tube should be maintained at a bright red heat, otherwise the decomposition of the hydride (arsine or stibine) will be incomplete. The portion of the tube nearest to the jet is kept cold by means of a pad of cotton soaked in iced water. The reaction is allowed to proceed for at least twenty minutes after which the cold part of the tube is examined against a white background, a porcelain spatula about 3 cm. wide being convenient for this purpose. If the tube is entirely free from any dark stain it may be concluded that the apparatus is clean and that the reagents are free from arsenic and antimony. If any stain, however minute, appears the apparatus cannot be used; the contents of the bottle must be thrown out and the whole apparatus thoroughly washed with pure nitric acid. If necessary, this process must be repeated until a satisfactory blank tube is obtained.

Electrolytic Hydrogen Generator. An alternative method of generating hydrogen for the Marsh test is by means of an electric current in the electrolytic cell of which several types are on the market. That devised by Monier-Williams[1] consists of a glass vessel divided into two parts by means of a porous pot which is just large enough to fit easily into the outer vessel and of which the walls are little more than 1 mm. in thickness. The anode, outside the porous pot, is a strip of lead-foil, and the cathode, inside the pot, is a leaden disc, 2·5 cm. in diameter. The anode chamber is as narrow as possible while still permitting the free escape of oxygen bubbles. The cover of the cathode compartment, the tap-funnel for the admission of liquids, and the exit tube leading to the Marsh tube are of one piece of glass (Fig. 13).

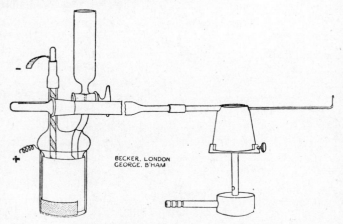

BECKER, LONDON
GEORGE. B'HAM

FIG. 13. Marsh-Berzelius test for arsenic ; electrolytic method.

The potential difference between the electrodes should be from 7 to 9 volts, and the current 5–6 amps. The portion of the Marsh tube which is heated is covered with metal gauze to ensure that the heating is even and localized. The capillary portion of the tube has an internal diameter of 2 mm. The acid used is 1 in 8 (v/v) sulphuric acid. In such an apparatus, using leaden electrodes, both arsenious and arsenic compounds can be reduced to arsine, although the time required for the latter is longer. According to Monier-Williams, certain types of food matter may be put directly into the apparatus without previous destruction of the organic constituents, but there is danger of frothing. This can be prevented by the addition of amyl alcohol.

Iron and phosphates which, when present in large quantities, have

[1] *Analyst,* 1923, **48**, 113.

an inhibiting effect on the production of arsine, are inactive if a fresh cathode is used for each operation.

Before the actual test a " blank " must be run as described above, to prove the absence of arsenic and antimony from the reagents.

Method. The solution under examination is added little by little through the dropping funnel until a sufficiently large dark mirror has been deposited in the tube. The reaction is allowed to continue for some time further until the mirror no longer increases in size, after which the tube is allowed to cool and is then detached from the apparatus. A solution of an alkaline hypochlorite is sucked up into the tube and allowed to run out. A mirror consisting of arsenic is completely dissolved by repeating this operation two or three times, but antimony mirrors are unaffected.

For the quantitative determination of antimony an entirely different process, to be described later, is used.

Arsenic is determined by comparison of the mirror with standard mirrors prepared from known quantities of arsenious oxide. In the preparation of these standards opinions differ as to the most suitable size, the range of possibilities being very wide indeed. Mirrors corresponding to quantities of arsenious oxide varying from $\frac{1}{200}$ to $\frac{1}{50}$ mg. are probably most commonly used; but it is equally possible to work with standards varying from $\frac{1}{50}$ to $\frac{1}{10}$ mg. or from $\frac{1}{10}$ to $\frac{1}{3}$ mg., using Marsh tubes of suitable sizes.

The relative errors involved in judging standards are approximately of the same order, whether large or small standards are used. Obviously, in testing samples of food and drugs for arsenic, where one's object is to determine whether the quantity of arsenic present exceeds or does not exceed a certain specified limit, small mirrors are most suitable; but in toxicological work, where quantities of arsenic less than 1 part in 5,000,000 should be ignored, there is much to be said for the production of larger mirrors. If the tubes are to be produced in court, a mirror representing $\frac{1}{4}$ mg. of arsenic is likely to be more convincing to a jury than one representing $\frac{1}{200}$ mg. To the analyst, who has seen the blank test, the small mirror may be just as convincing as the large one; but since the duty of the analyst is to convince the layman, the larger standards are probably more satisfactory.

We have found it convenient to prepare two sets of standard mirrors; the first set, in silica tubes having an internal diameter of about 4 mm., representing the deposits from $\frac{1}{3}$, $\frac{1}{4}$, $\frac{1}{5}$, $\frac{1}{6}$, $\frac{1}{8}$ and $\frac{1}{10}$ mg. respectively of white arsenic. The second set, made in tubes of internal diameter (tapering slightly) from 1·5 to 1 mm., represents $\frac{1}{10}$, $\frac{1}{12}$, $\frac{1}{15}$, $\frac{1}{20}$, $\frac{1}{25}$, $\frac{1}{30}$, $\frac{1}{40}$, $\frac{1}{50}$, and $\frac{1}{100}$ mg. The mirrors are produced from a standard solution which can be prepared as follows:

A sample of arsenious oxide is carefully re-sublimed and 100 mg.

of it are weighed out. This is dissolved in pure dilute sodium carbonate solution, diluted to 500 c.cm. and acidified with pure hydrochloric acid. The volume is then made up to 1,000 c.cm. Of this solution 10 c.cm. contain 1 mg. of arsenious oxide, and by diluting 10 c.cm. to 1 litre, a solution is obtained of which 10 c.cm. contain $\frac{1}{100}$ mg.

Obviously, either of these solutions may be used, the more dilute being preferable for the smaller mirrors.

When the operator is satisfied that his apparatus is clean, the joints are airtight, the gas is issuing freely, the Marsh tube is dry and the " blank " is negligible, the preparation of the standard tubes can be begun. It is necessary to emphasize that the heated portion must be as hot as possible. The measured quantity of the standard is then introduced into the tap-funnel from which it is allowed gradually to run into the hydrogen generator, the whole being added in about twenty minutes, after which the tap-funnel is washed down with pure dilute acid. The growth of the mirror is watched until no further increase can be seen, usually about twenty minutes more. The tubes may then be sealed up at both ends with a blow-pipe flame and can be kept without appreciable change for several weeks.

In the actual operation of determining arsenic, the Reinsch test will have given an indication as to whether a large or small standard tube should be used. A convenient aliquot portion of the solution is measured out, mixed with a little stannous chloride solution and again made up to a definite volume. This solution is then introduced little by little into the apparatus, the Marsh tube being examined continually, until a mirror comparable with one of the standards has been obtained. The quantity of solution remaining is noted and by subtraction the quantity used up is found. The tap-funnel is then washed down with a little dilute acid and a further fifteen or twenty minutes is allowed to elapse before making the final comparison with the standard tube, both being held in front of a white background. The determination of the total quantity of arsenic in the whole of the sample destroyed is then a matter of simple calculation, and from that to the quantity in the whole of the organ.

Materials for analysis and Special Preparative Procedures

Exhumed bodies require somewhat special treatment. Samples should be taken (a) from the remains of the abdominal viscera, (b) from the bones, (c) from the hair, (d) from the nails, (e) from the shroud. In the East, where coffins are not used, samples of the earth from under the body and of the earth from a remote place in the same cemetery should be taken. In the Cairo laboratory weighed samples of remains of viscera, hair, nails and shroud are prepared for the Marsh test by the method of incineration with magnesium nitrate; bones are treated by the method of Babo and Fresenius.

Samples of earth are soaked in distilled water, made alkaline with caustic soda, for twenty-four hours. They are then filtered through glass wool and the filtrate is evaporated to dryness on the water-bath. The residue is taken up in diluted hydrochloric acid, a little bromine is added and the liquid is heated on the water-bath until the organic matter is destroyed and the excess of bromine is removed. The solutions thus obtained, after the addition of stannous chloride solution in the usual way, are ready for the Marsh test. The solutions from the equal quantities of earth, one from under the body and the other from a remote place, are examined side by side and the quantities of arsenic, if any, are compared and estimated.

The examination of exhibits other than viscera and excreta is usually required in cases of suspected poisoning whether accidental, homicidal or suicidal. These usually include: remains of the last meal eaten by the victim, dregs of tea or coffee, suspected powders or liquids seized by the police on the scene of the crime or in the houses of accused persons, pockets of accused persons and clippings from their finger-nails. It is worth while to devote some time and thought to the order in which such materials are taken for analysis, the decision being influenced by such factors as the history of the affair and the nature and quantities of the materials to be examined.

White or yellow powders or particles found in food, in imperfectly cleaned vessels or in the pocket-contents should be examined first under the binocular magnifier, or a good hand-lens. White and yellow arsenic as usually sold are vitreous rather than crystalline, and this vitreous form can often be seen in magnified particles. Such particles are picked up with clean forceps and examined by the sublimation test already described.

Liquids such as beverages, soups, stomach-washings and fluid faeces are examined for particles by pouring into conical urine glasses, taking care to transfer to the latter all the contents of the original vessels. Arsenical particles sink to the bottom of the urine glasses and the supernatant liquid is poured off into other vessels. Any particles remaining are washed by decantation, after which they can be thrown out on to clock-glasses, picked up with forceps, dried between pieces of filter-paper, and tested. Liquids containing vegetable matter, such as stews, vomits and some samples of faeces can be treated in a similar way if sufficient time is allowed for particles to settle. With such samples it is advisable to decant about three-quarters of the fluid and to preserve this for further examination; the urine glass is then filled up with water and the upper portion is again poured off before sedimentation is complete.

By repeating this process the lighter organic matter is gradually removed, leaving the heavier inorganic sediment behind.

The method recommended for the examination of dust in pockets is to cut the pocket from the garment and to turn it inside out over a large sheet of glossy paper. The paper should be spread out in a place free from draughts and in a good light. The loose dust is scraped off by means of a knife, after which the stitches are carefully cut by means of a knife or small scissors and the dust which accumulates between the stitches is scraped off. All the dust is then gathered into a small area and examined with the binocular magnifier. Suspicious particles are picked out with forceps for the sublimation test. If no such particles are found the dust is transferred to a small conical flask and covered with water. The reaction to litmus of the soaked dust should be noted and the odour, if any. If the reaction is alkaline an aliquot portion should be tested for cyanides by the Prussian-blue test. Otherwise the soak should be kept for further examination if any poisonous matter is detected in the viscera or other exhibit. In cases of arsenic poisoning the liquid is acidified with dilute hydrochloric acid and allowed to stand for twenty-four hours in a flask plugged with cotton, after which it is filtered into a measuring cylinder and an aliquot part of it, or the whole if necessary, is examined by the Marsh test.

When symptoms of arsenical poisoning (*a fortiori*, death) are due to the presence of arsenic in food or beverages, the Reinsch test applied to a small portion usually reveals it. For quantitative determination a weighed or measured fraction of the whole amount available is treated with an oxidizing agent to destroy the organic matter before submitting it to the Marsh test. For fluids containing little or no solid organic matter a convenient method is to add a quantity of strong hydrochloric acid equal to one-quarter of the volume of the fluid and a few drops of bromine; this mixture is warmed on the water-bath until the last traces of excess of bromine have been driven off. A clear liquid should remain; otherwise the bromine treatment is repeated. The liquid, after the addition of a few crystals of stannous chloride to reduce the arsenic to the trivalent form, is ready for the Marsh test. Food containing much solid matter is treated with magnesium nitrate in the manner above described for the destruction of tissues.

It is frequently necessary to examine finger-nail clippings of accused persons for the presence of poison. In our laboratory we have not yet succeeded in detecting poisons other than arsenic in finger-nail clippings. The clippings are placed with the concave sides up under the binocular magnifier and carefully examined one by one for suspicious particles. Occasionally such particles have been picked out and identified as arsenic by the sublimation test. If no particles can be detected the clippings are soaked for twenty-four hours in dilute hydrochloric acid (1 in 5) and the liquid after filtration is examined by the Marsh test. The result of this examination should be interpreted with extreme caution. Some years ago we examined a large number of samples of finger-nail clippings of Egyptian peasants from various parts of the country at a time when arsenical preparations were being freely used on the land to kill locusts. Traces of arsenic were found in a large proportion of the clippings. We therefore ignore quantities of arsenic less than $\frac{1}{50}$ mg. and even up to $\frac{1}{10}$ mg. unless the evidence against the accused person is otherwise very strong.

Other Tests for Arsenic

The Reinsch and Marsh tests when properly carried out can be relied on to provide all the evidence necessary for proving the presence of arsenic and determining the quantity of it in poisoning cases. This proper carrying out of the tests means the production of characteristic octahedral crystals of arsenic trioxide in the former test and the formation of a definite dark-brown to black mirror, freely soluble in hypochlorite solution, in the latter.

They have been treated in detail because they are still regarded by many toxicologists as the standard procedures. In some quarters the Marsh-Berzelius test has been largely superseded by the Gutzeit method, and it seems that this, in turn, will give way to the competition of more recent titrimetric or colorimetric procedures.

The Gutzeit test depends on the fact that arsine decomposes silver nitrate with the formation of metallic silver. The reaction can be represented in two stages by the following two equations:—

$$(a) \quad 6AgNO_3 + AsH_3 = 3HNO_3 + AsAg_3.3AgNO_3 \text{ (yellow)}$$
$$(b) \quad AsAg_3.3AgNO_3 + 3H_2O = H_3AsO_3 + 3HNO_3 + 6Ag \text{ (black)}.$$

The arsine is produced as in the Marsh test and is brought into contact with filter-paper which has been moistened with a 1 in 1 solution of silver nitrate and subsequently dried. For qualitative purposes a convenient apparatus is a bottle fitted with a stopper, through which passes a glass tube having at the top an arrangement for holding the test-paper firmly over the mouth of the tube. This may consist of two discs with holes in the centre slightly less in diameter than the glass tube. The lower disc is rigidly attached to the tube, and the two discs with the test-paper between them are held in contact with one another by means of metal clips.

As in the Marsh test, hydrogen is evolved for some time before the addition of the solution to be tested to ensure that the reagents are arsenic-free; the test solution is added and the stopper is replaced. If the evolution of hydrogen is gentle, the area above the tube which has been treated with silver nitrate becomes yellow if arsenic is present. Frequently the edges darken, and when the evolution of hydrogen is violent the whole area rapidly blackens. The addition of a drop of water causes the spot to become black immediately.

By a suitable modification of the apparatus the Gutzeit test may be made quantitative. As shown in Fig. 14 the hydrogen generator is fitted with a ground-glass stopper carrying a thistle funnel, which extends nearly to the bottom of the bottle, and an exit tube which widens into a drying-tube, which is divided into two parts connected by means of a ground-glass joint. The upper portion of the drying-tube is fused into a tube of 4 mm. internal diameter bent at right angles. The lower part of the drying-tube contains a disc of filter-paper which has been moistened with lead acetate solution

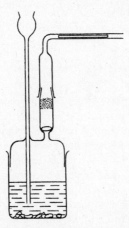

FIG. 14. The Gutzeit apparatus for the determination of arsenic.

and dried, and above this a plug of absorbent cotton dried over sulphuric acid. The test-paper consists of a strip of filter-paper which has been moistened throughout its length with 1 in 1 silver nitrate solution and subsequently dried; it should be about 10 cm. long and just wide enough to fit inside the horizontal portion of the exit tube. The procedure is in general similar to that of the Marsh test. The reaction is usually complete in about thirty minutes after the last portion of the arsenical solution has been added. The determination is made by comparison with standard strips of similar size which have been treated as above, using known quantities of arsenic.

The test is extremely sensitive, the lower limit of absolute sensitivity being stated to be $0 \cdot 00008$ mg. of arsenious oxide. According to A. A. King, much smaller quantities than this can be detected by examining the strips in ultra-violet light. For practical purposes the limit of sensitivity may be taken to be about 0·001 mg. In toxicological work it is very rare that such minute traces of arsenic are significant, and therefore the Gutzeit test is not to be preferred to the Marsh test merely because of its greater sensitivity.

Flückiger has modified the Gutzeit test by substituting mercuric chloride for silver nitrate, and Beck and Merres recommend mercuric bromide. The mercury salts yield yellow to brown stains.

Both phosphine and stibine give stains similar to arsine in the Gutzeit test, and therefore it can only be used for arsenic if phosphorus and antimony have been proved absent.

Bettendorf's test for arsenic has the advantage that it can be applied even in the presence of antimony, and, indeed, its chief use is in examining antimony compounds, such as tartar emetic, for the presence of arsenic. It depends on the reduction of arsenic trioxide to elementary arsenic by stannous chloride in presence of concentrated hydrochloric acid.

$$As_2O_3 + 6HCl = 2AsCl_3 + 3H_2O.$$
$$2AsCl_3 + 3SnCl_2 = 2As + 3SnCl_4.$$

The reaction takes place slowly in the cold, but more rapidly on heating, the elementary arsenic separating as a black precipitate.

Bettendorf's reagent can be made in a variety of ways, of which the following is probably the best: Five parts of crystallized hydrated stannous chloride are made into a paste with one part of 25 per cent. hydrochloric acid, and this paste is saturated with dry hydrochloric acid gas. The liquid is filtered by suction through asbestos and the filtrate is preserved in a stoppered bottle.

Iodometric Determination of Arsenic. Several methods have been evolved in recent years for the titrimetric determination of arsenic. They depend on the separation of arsenic as arsine, the absorption of this in silver nitrate solution, and titration of the arsenite so formed with iodine. The technique described by Levvy[1] permits the determination, in biological material, of 5-50 μg. (·005 to ·05 mg.) arsenic, with, in a single determination of 20 μg. a standard deviation of 3·7 per cent. This is better than is claimed by many authors for stain-matching methods and titrimetry is much more objective. The sensitivity is of the same order as that of Marsh and Gutzeit methods.

For a detailed discussion of the method, the original paper by Levvy should be consulted. The procedure he describes as follows:

" *Digestion—small scale.* Up to 5 ml. blood, 10 ml. urine or 2 g. tissue are measured into a 100 ml. Kjeldahl flask, and conc. HNO_3 (5 ml.), $HClO_4$ (3 ml., 60 per cent. w/v), conc. H_2SO_4 (10 ml.)

[1] LEVVY, G. A. (1943). *Biochem. J.*, **37**, 598.

and two or three clean glass beads are added. The flask is warmed, with shaking, over a naked flame till brown fumes are given off, and heating is continued on a digestion stand over a very small flame (to avoid bumping) till they are no longer evolved. The contents are then gently boiled till H_2SO_4 fumes appear, and the clear liquid becomes colourless. Heating is continued for 10 minutes. If the mixture chars at any time, the flask is cooled slightly and a few drops of fuming HNO_3 added.

" When digestion is complete, the flask is allowed to cool and saturated $(NH_4)_2C_2O_4$ solution (5 ml.) is added. The liquid is brought to the boil and heating continued till white fumes appear. Distilled water (5 ml.) is added to the cooled liquid, which is again brought to the boil, and heating continued till 5 min. after the first appearance of white fumes.

" Control experiments, with reagents alone, are carried out in exactly the same manner. It is important that heating of the digest at each stage should be continued for at least the period specified.

" *Digestion—large scale. Tissue.* Up to 20 g. of minced, moist tissue are wrapped in very thin paper and placed in a 300 ml. Kjeldahl flask (with ground joint). After the addition of conc. HNO_3 (30 ml.) and two or three clean glass beads, the flask is set aside overnight.

" *Blood.* Up to 30 ml. blood are treated as described above.

" *Urine.* To not more than 150 ml. urine one-fifth its volume of fuming HNO_3 and two or three glass beads are added, the liquid evaporated to about 10 ml., and the digestion then carried out.

" $HClO_4$ (15 ml., 60 per cent. w/v) and conc. H_2SO_4 (20 ml.) are added to the flask, which is warmed cautiously with shaking over a naked flame till reaction sets in, and is then placed on a digestion stand. After the first violent reaction subsides, the burner is lit and the contents brought to the boil. When digestion is complete, 20 ml. of saturated $(NH_4)_2C_2O_4$ solution and of water are added. It may be necessary to make several additions of fuming HNO_3 before digestion is complete.

" *AsCl_3 distillation.* This is necessary only after large-scale digestion. A delivery tube is connected, with conc. H_2SO_4 as lubricant for the ground-glass joint, to a 150 ml. Fresenius flask containing distilled water (40 ml.) immersed in ice-water.

" Distilled water (50 ml.) is added to the Kjeldahl flask and the contents are cooled thoroughly. Through a wide-bore funnel, $FeSO_4$, $7H_2O$ (8 g.), KBr (2 g.) and NaCl (25 g.) are added and the flask immediately connected to the previously lubricated joint of the delivery tube. A 200 ml. volumetric flask is placed over the exit of the Fresenius flask. The liquid in the Kjeldahl flask is boiled vigorously for exactly 10 min., the ice around the receiver being renewed as necessary. With the liquid still boiling, the delivery tube is disconnected from the Kjeldahl flask. The contents of the Fresenius flask are then transferred to the 200 ml. volumetric flask, and, when cool, diluted to the mark.

"*Separation of As as AsH₃*. Two absorption tubes (Fig. 15), the second of which acts as a guard tube, are charged with N/50 AgNO₃ (1·5 ml.). The tubes are stoppered and connected to a small wash-tube containing 10N NaOH (renewed after 12 estimations), glycerine being used as a lubricant for rubber tubing. A

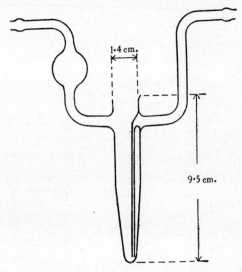

FIG. 15. The absorption tube (*Levvy: Biochem. Jl.*).

right-angle tube, bearing a stopper to fit the AsH₃ generation flask, is attached to the wash-tube.

" After a small-scale digestion, the contents of the Kjeldahl flask are transferred to a 150 ml. conical flask, with 40 ml. distilled water as washing fluid. Alternatively, a measured fraction of the diluted digest is made up to 50 ml. with 20 per cent. H₂SO₄. 40 per cent. SnCl₂ (10 drops) and 5 per cent. CuSO₄ (3 drops) are added. The liquid is warmed if necessary, Zn shot (15 g. freed from dust and of fairly uniform size) quickly introduced, and the flask at once connected to the previously prepared absorption apparatus.

" After a large-scale digestion, if the portion taken is less than 100 ml., it is made up to this volume in a 150 ml. conical flask with

20 per cent. H_2SO_4. When the total distillate is used, it is transferred to a 250 ml. conical flask. 40 per cent. $SnCl_2$ (10 drops/100 ml. total vol.) and 5 per cent. $CuSO_4$ (3 drops/100 ml. total vol.) are added and the liquid is warmed. Zn (25 g.) is introduced and the flask immediately connected to the absorption apparatus.

"*Titration of arsenite.* When H_2 has been passed through the absorption apparatus for 30 min. the tubes are disconnected. The rubber stopper of the absorption tube is washed down with a few drops of distilled water, and the gas inlet is connected to the compressed air. KI is added till the precipitated AgI redissolves.

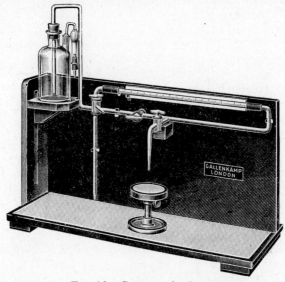

Fig. 16.   Conway microburette.

After the addition of a spatula-point of $NaHCO_3$ and a drop of starch solution the tube is slipped over the jet of the Conway burette[1] (Fig. 16). It is held in place by sliding the titration platform under it, and with air passing through the liquid at a gentle rate I_2 is run in till a red-brown colour appears and persists for 30 sec. Before the end of the titration, the gas exit is washed down by increasing the flow of air till a little of the liquid is blown into it. A daylight lamp is of advantage in observing the end-point. If the liquid in the guard tube darkens, it is titrated in the same way.

"At the beginning of each day, the glass tubing in the burette is thoroughly washed out with fresh I_2 from the reservoir. To

[1] CONWAY, E. J. (1939). " Micro Diffusion Analysis and Volumetric Error." London: Crosby Lockwood.

standardize the I_2, two different quantities of arsenite solution are measured into absorption tubes, the volume made up to about 2 ml. with N/50 $AgNO_3$, and the titrations carried out as described above. The amount of As (μg.) is plotted against ml. I_2, and the analytical results are read off from the straight line joining the two points. This line cuts the I_2 axis at the volume required to cause a colour change in 2 ml. N/50 $AgNO_3$ treated as above, in absence of arsenite."

The " Molybdenum Blue " Method.   The following description of a method based on the ability of As^v to form with ammonium molybdate a complex which is readily and quantitatively reducible to a blue substance, is adapted from that of Sandell.[1]

Transfer 25 ml. of the sample containing not more than 15 μg. of arsenic (prepared, e.g. by digestion with sulphuric-nitric acid as described on p. 71) to a 50 ml. Erlenmeyer flask provided with a well-fitting stopper through which passes a single delivery tube.   This tube suitably bent, has the end drawn out to a fine ($0\cdot5$ mm. bore) tip which dips into a tapered absorption tube (e.g. a centrifuge tube) such that $1\cdot35$ ml. occupies a depth of about 6 cm.   A loose collar over the delivery tube near the tip is helpful in aiding absorption.   The delivery tube should contain one or two loose plugs of glass wool impregnated with lead acetate.   Add concentrated hydrochloric acid to the Erlenmeyer flask to make the total present equal to 5 ml., 2 ml. of 15 per cent. potassium iodide solution, and $0\cdot5$ ml. of stannous chloride solution (40 g. $SnCl_2.H_2O$ in 100 ml. concentrated hydrochloric acid).   Allow about twenty minutes at room temperature for reduction of As^v to As^{iii}.   Meanwhile measure into the absorption tube $1\cdot0$ ml. of $1\cdot5$ per cent. (w/v) mercuric chloride, $0\cdot2$ ml. of 6N sulphuric acid and $0\cdot15$ ml. of $0\cdot03$N potassium permanganate solution.

Quickly add 2 g. of pure zinc to the Erlenmeyer flask, replace the stopper, and lower the delivery tube so that its tip almost touches the bottom of the absorption tube (it should not previously have been in the tube, since if the solution is drawn into the delivery tube mercury arsenide may be formed).   Allow the gas to bubble through for about thirty minutes, without heating, when the absorption solution, though possibly turbid, should still contain permanganate. (If it does not, repeat, using a smaller volume of sample, diluted to 25 ml.).   Disconnect the delivery tube from the Erlenmeyer flask, leaving it in the absorber, and add to this vessel 5 ml. of molybdate-hydrazine reagent (prepared fresh by mixing equal volumes of (*a*) $1\cdot0$ g. ammonium molybdate dissolved in 10 ml. water and made to 100 ml. with 6N Sulphuric acid and (*b*) $0\cdot15$ g. hydrazine sulphate

[1] *Colorimetric Determination of Traces of Metals.* By E. B. Sandell. Interscience Publishers Inc., 1944, p. 136.

dissolved in 100 ml. water.)   Heat for fifteen minutes in a water bath at 95-100° C., cool and make up to 25 ml. with water.   Filter through a fine plug of glass wool, discarding the first 5 ml. of filtrate. Measure the transmittancy using a red filter (max. transmission ca. 700 mμ) and, in the reference cell, a solution prepared as follows. Heat for five minutes in the water bath a mixture of 1 ml. mercuric chloride solution, $0 \cdot 2$ ml. of $6N.H_2SO_4$ and $0 \cdot 10$ ml. of $0 \cdot 03N$ potassium permanganate, add $5 \cdot 0$ ml. of the molybdate-hydrazine. reagent, heat at 95-100° C. for fifteen minutes, cool and make up to 25 ml.

A standard curve is constructed by carrying out the complete procedure with standard arsenic solutions or, since Beer's Law holds, by the procedure given for the reference solution with addition of known amounts of arsenic (e.g. 5μg. and 20 μg.).

A " blank " test of reagents should be made.

Choice of material for analysis

It may not always be the work of the analytical chemist, collaborating with a medico-legal expert, to decide which organs should be examined for metallic poisons, or to give the final interpretation of the results of analysis; nevertheless, the analyst should be aware of the general principles on which the conclusions of the medical jurist are based.

The organs most suitable for analysis are :   the stomach, the intestines, the liver and the kidneys.   The spleen is of much less importance; usually it contains a much smaller proportion of the metallic poison than the other organs.   The difference between the amount of poison in the liver and in the spleen is particularly great, and it is of the utmost importance that these two organs should not be mixed.   The medical man conducting the autopsy should send to the analyst a sample of each organ in a separate jar.   It is better to omit the spleen altogether than to put it in the same jar as the liver, since it is difficult for the analyst to separate them, especially if putrefaction is far advanced before the beginning of the analysis; and if spleen and liver are examined together the quantitative result will be completely misleading.

In the tables on pp. 90 and 91, taken mainly from Taylor's " Medical Jurisprudence ", 9th ed., Vol. 2, pp. 505–8, the quantities of arsenic detected in the different organs of the victims in some of the more famous cases of fatal poisoning are given.   In some of the cases the time which elapsed between the onset of the symptoms and the death of the victim is known, and in one or two instances the quantity of arsenic ingested is also known.   From these figures it is possible to form an idea of the changes in the relative amounts of arsenic in the various organs with lapse of time.

ARSENIC DETECTED IN VARIOUS ORGANS

Case.	Period of time between onset and death.	Quantity of arsenic taken.	Quantity detected. A mg. per 100 gm.	Quantity detected. B In mgs. in whole organ.	Notes.
Gascard's case (1) Stomach Small Intestine Liver Kidneys	22 hours	1 g.	74 28 2·7 4·7	224 223 44 } 505 14	Column A estimated from published figures.
Gascard's case (2) Stomach Small intestine Liver Kidneys	9 days	0·4 g.	0·7 0·75 0·5 2·3	2 6 8 } 23 7	Column A estimated.
Maybrick case Stomach Intestine Liver			*Nil* ? 2·3	*Nil* 6 21 } 27	Quantity in liver estimated.
Margaret Bingham Stomach Liver Kidneys	3 or 4 days		0·08 4·4 0·16	0·25 70 } 70.75 0·5	Column A estimated.
James Bingham Stomach Liver Kidneys Spleen	3½ days		1·9 0·2 0·06	Minute traces 30 0·7 } 30·8 0·1	Column A estimated.
W. H. Bingham Stomach Small intestine Liver Kidneys Spleen	36 hours		0·16 0·2 3·8 0·8 0·07	5 1·5 60 } 68·875 0·25 0·125	Column A estimated.
Armstrong Stomach Stomach content Caecum, etc. Liver Kidneys			0·8 ? ? 8·6 4·3	2·5 2·0 37·6 } 193·1 138 13	Column A estimated. Hair 0·5 mg. in 100 g.
Greenwood Stomach Small intestine Large intestine Liver Kidneys Spleen	15 hours ?		0·2 0·5 ? 0·5 0·4	0·6 4·3 0·55 } 15·55 8·5 1·2 0·4	Column A estimated. Greenwood was acquitted. Note.—These quantities were considered small and the analyst was submitted to close cross-examination.

IN A NUMBER OF WELL-KNOWN CASES

Case.	Period of time between onset and death.	Quantity of arsenic taken.	Quantity detected.		Notes.
			A mg. per 100 gm.	B In mgs. in whole organ.	
Seddon	4½ hours ?				Column A estimated. Wilcox estimated for whole body 300 mg., but admitted under cross-examination that he calculated in the dry weight of exhumed body. Doubt was expressed as to whether symptoms were acute or simply diarrhoea.
Stomach			2·4	7·3 ⎫	
Intestine			?	41 ⎟	
Liver			7·0	11·1 ⎬ 61·7	
Kidneys			0·6	1·9 ⎟	
Spleen			0·23	0·4 ⎭	
McNally (1)	4½ hours ?				Estimated as elementary arsenic. Factor 1·32.
Stomach			25·0		
Large intestine			26·0		
Liver			14		
Small intestine			13		
Kidneys			17		
Stomach contents			890		
McNally (2)	Two doses : death 3 weeks after 1st dose, 20 days after 2nd dose.				Factor 1·32. (See above.)
Stomach walls			0·5		
Kidneys			1·6		
Liver			1·3		
Blood			0·5		
Stomach contents			0·5		
Chattenden					Quantity calculated for whole body, 187 mg. Body found in water; suspected drowning.
Stomach and oesophagus				10	
Liver				14	
Lungs and spleen				9·2	
Brain					

" Normal " Arsenic

Conflicting opinons have been expressed as to whether arsenic is or is not a normal constituent of the body. Our experience in Egypt leads to the belief that in that country at least, minute traces of arsenic are almost invariably found in the human body. Arsenic is always present in the soil in Egypt, and, presumably, in the ordinary vegetables. We regard one part of arsenic in five million parts of human tissue as normal, i.e. if the Marsh test shows not more than $\frac{1}{50}$ mg. of arsenic in 100 g. of tissue, the chemist reports that the result of the Marsh test is negative. When the quantity is greater than this the medico-legal expert decides whether the result of the analysis, together with the history of the case and the observations at the autopsy, justify the opinion that death was due to arsenical poisoning.

It is interesting to note that whereas in the Greenwood trial much doubt was expressed as to whether the quantity of arsenic detected in the viscera, amounting to 15·5 mg. in the stomach, intestines, liver, kidneys and spleen was sufficient to account for death, an American court[1] has held that the death of a boy who lived for twelve days after the onset of symptoms was due to arsenical poisoning, although no arsenic could be detected in the viscera. The verdict of murder, which was confirmed on appeal, was based on the ante-mortem symptoms and the findings at the autopsy; the stomach was found to be red, irritated and covered internally with sticky mucus.

Organic Arsenical Compounds

Their Detection and Determination. The use of organic arsenical compounds in the treatment of syphilis and other diseases has introduced a new type of problem for the toxicologist. Severe poisoning symptoms and sometimes death may follow the use of these drugs; death is not always due to the accumulation of arsenic in the body, and, indeed, some of the drugs are eliminated through the kidneys remarkably quickly. Special methods for the investigation of such cases are therefore sometimes necessary.

Atoxyl. This is the sodium salt of p-arsanilic acid $(NH_2C_6H_4AsO(OH)_2)$, and is, as its name implies, relatively non-toxic. It is given by subcutaneous injection in the treatment of sleeping sickness and certain skin diseases. According to Croner and Seligmann,[2] it is eliminated almost completely and almost unchanged within twenty-four hours after injection; sometimes the elimination is complete within nine hours.

[1] *J.A.M.A.*, 3.10.36. *Medico-legal Review*, 1937, **5**. 99.
[2] *Deutsche. Med. Wochenschrift.*, **33**, 995.

The method of detecting it in the urine is based on the fact that the atoxyl molecule contains a free arylamino group, which can be diazotized, and the resulting compound coupled with β-naphthol (dissolved in caustic soda) or with α- or β-naphthylamine dissolved in dilute acid. The urine is acidified with hydrochloric acid and cooled by the addition of ice. Sodium nitrite solution is added from a burette until a test with starch-iodide paper shows the presence of excess. The diazotized urine is then added to the naphthol or naphthylamine solution. A red colour is produced which should be compared with the azo colour made from atoxyl itself by similar treatment. The production of an azo colour is not, of course, a proof of the presence of atoxyl; other arylamino compounds may be present in urine and produce similar if not identical colours. The presence of arsenic must be confirmed by reducing another sample to ash, using one of the methods described, and applying the Reinsch and the Marsh tests to portions of the ash dissolved in hydrochloric acid.

Other reactions of atoxyl have been described by Covelli.[1] Thus solutions of atoxyl give:—

(1) A yellow precipitate or colour with calcium hypochlorite solution.

(2) A blue colour with calcium hypochlorite in presence of ammonia (this is a sensitive test, revealing 1 part of atoxyl in 100,000 of liquid).

(3) A yellow precipitate in the cold with reducing agents.

(4) A yellow colour when heated with an aliphatic aldehyde in presence of a mineral acid.

(5) The fifth test is applied to a diazotized solution of atoxyl. The addition of a drop of acetaldehyde and a few drops of caustic potash solution produces a carmine-red colour which fades to yellow unless the alkali is in considerable excess.

Salvarsan ("606"; Arsphenamine; Kharsivan). Salvarsan is a derivative of the arsenic analogue of azo-benzene, namely arseno-benzene. Each benzene nucleus contains an amino group in the meta position and a hydroxyl group in the para position with respect to the arsenic atoms. In virtue of the amino groups it is soluble in mineral acids, and in virtue of the hydroxyl groups it forms soluble alkali metal compounds. The alkali compounds are unstable, but the drug is most suitable for administration in this form. Salvarsan as sold is the hydrochloride of 3-3'diamino-4-4'dihydroxy-arseno-benzene, and this must be carefully treated with the requisite amount of standard sodium hydroxide solution immediately before use. Salvarsan and its later modifications have been used in the treatment of syphilis and some other diseases since about 1910.

[1] *Chem. Zeit.*, 1908, **32,** p. 1006. *Analyst*, 1908, **33,** 477.

Its use in the early days was often followed by untoward symptoms and there were many fatalities, and even more recently fatal results have occurred. Such accidents have been ascribed to partial decomposition of the drug, giving rise to more toxic decomposition products. Theoretically salvarsan should contain 33·6 per cent. of arsenic, but the proportion found by analysis is usually below 30 per cent.

The technique of the preparation for injection has been found tedious by practitioners, and a derivative which is less troublesome has to a very large extent supseded it.   This is the sodium salt of the ω-sulphonic acid of N-methylsalvarsan, prepared by the treatment of the parent substance with formaldehyde-sulphoxylic acid.   It is sold as **neo-salvarsan, neo-arsphenamine or neo-kharsivan**. This derivative is reasonably stable if preserved in sealed ampoules in which the air has been replaced by an inert gas, but the contents of the ampoules must be used within twenty minutes of exposure to the air.   It is essential that ampoules of salvarsan and neo-salvarsan should not be confused; a mistake may well be fatal.

Unlike atoxyl, salvarsan and its derivatives are excreted slowly by the kidneys.   Being arylamino compounds, they can be converted into azo dyes by treatment with nitrous acid and coupling with a phenol (preferably resorcinol).   Since the salvarsan content of urine rapidly diminishes after excretion, the determination should be made on freshly voided samples.   In the examination of the cadaver when salvarsan treatment is followed by death, the ordinary methods for the destruction of organic material may be used and the arsenic determined by the Marsh process.

Other organic arsenicals which are used therapeutically include silver arsphenamine (a complex or compound of arsphenamine and silver oxide) and silver neo-arsphenamine; sulpharsphenamine (formaldehyde sulphoxylate derivative of arsphenamine) and the related trisodarsen and bismarsen (sulpharsphenamine-bismuth); acetarsone (stovarsol) which, like tryparsamide, contains pentavalent arsenic and is a derivative of atoxyl; and mapharsen (arsenoxide, m-amino-p-hydroxy phenyl arsine oxide).   Except for the sulpharsphenamine group and the two atoxyl derivatives, these are primary aryl amines and so yield azo dyes.   All can, of course, be identified as arsenic derivatives by detection of the arsenic.   Their individual identification in urine or other biological material is, however, a matter of very considerable difficulty as, *inter alia*, their instability militates against their isolation.

ANTIMONY

Qualitative evidence of poisoning by antimony is provided by the Reinsch and Marsh tests already described.   If the copper foil in the Reinsch test is blackened, but does not yield characteristic crystals on heating in the ignition tube the presence of antimony may be suspected. For the subsequent tests and for the quantitative determination to be described later, it is usually advisable to destroy the organic material present by the magnesium nitrate process, and, after dissolving the ash in hydrochloric acid, to use aliquot portions of the solution for each test; it is possible, however, to apply the method of determination devised by Beam and Freak, to be described later, to samples of excreta without preliminary oxidation.

A portion of the solution of the ash is submitted to the Marsh test; a black stain insoluble in hypochlorite solution is confirmatory evidence of the presence of antimony. It should be emphasized, however, that the Marsh test is not recommended for the quantitative determination of antimony.

Another useful confirmatory test which can be applied to the solution of the ash left by destruction of the organic matter is that of Feigl.[1] A drop of the solution, on a microscope slide, is stirred with a crystal of pyrogallol until this dissolves. A crystalline precipitate appears in a short time if antimony is present. Under the conditions—acid solution—the test is claimed to be specific for antimony.

The final proof of the presence of antimony is its conversion into the orange-coloured sulphide, the colour of which is quite characteristic. A portion of the solution of the ash is diluted with distilled water and treated with hydrogen sulphide. A bright orange-coloured precipitate is produced if antimony is present, although the colour may, in some cases, be indefinite owing to the presence of other metals, which form dark-coloured insoluble sulphides. Even in the absence of these, if the quantity of antimony is too small to form an immediate precipitate, the colour may be somewhat modified owing to the presence of ferric chloride in solution. It is therefore advisable, after passing the hydrogen sulphide through the liquid, to warm the latter so as to help the precipitate to coagulate, and, after allowing it to stand for some time, to pour on to a filter and wash with water containing hydrogen sulphide. The iron passes into the filtrate, leaving the antimony sulphide, if any, on the filter-paper. This residue is re-dissolved by warming it, with the paper, in hydrochloric acid (about 1 in 5), together with a few drops of bromine. When the last trace of bromine has been expelled by heat, the liquid is filtered and the residue is washed with very dilute acid. The combined filtrate and washings are diluted with distilled water and hydrogen sulphide is again passed through.[2] In the

---

[1] *Mikrochem.*, 1923, **1,** 74.

[2] Alternatively the separation and washing of the antimony sulphide may be accomplished by centrifuging—a method likely to minimize loss.

absence of other metals forming insoluble sulphides the bright orange colour of the antimony sulphide will then be manifest. The colour of the sulphide thus obtained may be compared with that produced by passing hydrogen sulphide through an acidified solution of pure tartar emetic. If the two colours are identical the quantity of antimony in the material may be determined directly by colorimetric comparison, using the following technique.

A standard solution of acidified tartar emetic containing 40 mg. of metallic antimony per litre is made by dissolving 0·01106 g. of pure tartar emetic in water, adding 20 ml. of 10 per cent. gum arabic solution, and diluting to 1 litre. From this more dilute standards are made containing 3·6, 3·2, 2·8, 2·4, 2·0, 1·6, 1·2, 0·8 and 0·4 mg. per 100 ml. respectively. Of each of these solutions, including the original undiluted liquid, 25 ml. are used for the colour standards, containing respectively 1·0, 0·9, . . . to 0·1 mg. of antimony. Hydrogen sulphide is passed through each until the liquid is saturated, a few minutes being sufficient. The antimony sulphide produced is held in colloidal suspension owing to the presence of the gum arabic and the liquids should appear to be clear orange-coloured solutions.

An aliquot portion of the acid solution of the ash or purified antimony sulphide is taken, mixed with the same proportion of the gum arabic solution as the standard, and, if necessary, diluted so that the volume is a simple multiple of 25 ml. A 25 ml. sample of this is measured out and saturated with hydrogen sulphide. If the colour is more intense than the strongest of the standards, a second sample is diluted to double the volume, and 25 ml. of this are treated with hydrogen sulphide. If necessary, this dilution process is repeated until a sample has been obtained which is approximately similar to one of the standards. The sample from the ash and the standard most nearly equal to it are then compared in a Duboscq colorimeter, and from the quantity of antimony thus determined in the diluted solution it is a matter of simple arithmetic to calculate the amount in the original material examined.

If, as frequently happens, the colour of the antimony sulphide obtained from the ash is not sufficiently pure for colorimetric comparison, the method of Schidrowitz and Goldsbrugh,[1] as modified by Beam and Freak,[2] should be used. This depends on the separation of the antimony by deposition on copper as in the Reinsch test. This deposit is afterwards dissolved in a boiling alkaline solution of potassium permanganate. The solution is then acidified and the excess of permanganate or manganate decomposed by means of

[1] *Analyst*, 1911, **36**, 101.
[2] *ibid.*, 1919, **44**, 196.

sulphur dioxide. The excess of sulphur dioxide is boiled off, and, after cooling, the liquid is mixed with gum arabic and made up to a standard volume. The quantity of antimony is then determined colorimetrically as sulphide.

This method has been used in our laboratory for the examination of hundreds of samples of excreta of patients who were being treated with antimony compounds for Bilharzia, and has been found very satisfactory. It can be applied directly to fluid or semi-fluid material like urine and faeces without preliminary treatment, which is a great advantage. Some amount of practice is usually necessary before the method can be used with complete assurance, as success depends largely upon the rapidity with which some of the operations are carried out, notably when the copper is being transferred from the reaction flask to the wash-water, and thence to the boiling permanganate solution; if there is any delay in this operation the antimony deposit tends to become passive and to resist solution. The permanganate solution must therefore be boiling ready for the immersion of the copper when the deposition is complete.

Strips of copper 10 cm. long and 1·5 cm. wide are prepared and coiled into spirals by winding round a glass rod about 5 mm. in diameter. The object of the spiral form is to facilitate the removal of the strips from the hot liquid; they can readily be taken out by means of a glass rod.

It is advisable to prepare beforehand a series of strips with known deposits of antimony varying from 0·1 to 0·5 mg. which can be dried, flattened and mounted between pieces of glass which are afterwards bound together with passe-partout binding. Mounted in this way they can be kept for many months, if not years, and they serve as a rough indication of the amount of antimony deposited from the material under examination. Indeed, it is possible to estimate the amount of antimony present in excreta with a degree of accuracy sufficient for many clinical purposes by simply carrying out the Reinsch test on a weighed or measured sample, using a copper strip of the same size and comparing the deposit visually with the standards.

In an actual determination it is not advisable to work with quantities of material containing more than 0·5 mg. of antimony as deposits heavier than this tend to form brittle scales which are liable to crack and become detached from the copper.

A preliminary test should be made on a weighed sample of the material under examination. The concentration of the hydrochloric acid, when mixed with the material, should be 1 in 5.

A strip of copper is put in and the mixture is boiled. If the quantity of antimony present is much greater than 0·5 mg. the copper usually blackens rapidly; otherwise the liquid should be kept steadily boiling for one and a quarter hours, the volume of the liquid being maintained by the addition of dilute hydrochloric acid as required. The copper is then taken out, washed in distilled water, and compared with the strips on which known quantities of antimony have been deposited. If the sample contains much more than 0·5 mg. or less than 0·1 mg. it may be necessary to repeat the preliminary test, decreasing or increasing the amount of material before deciding on the quantity to be taken for the actual determination.

The following reagents are required:

(1) Potassium permanganate solution of which 1 ml. corresponds to 0·01 g. of iron (i.e. 5·64 g. $KMnO_4$ per litre).

(2) Caustic potash solution; 1 per cent. (w/v).

(3) Standard solution of tartar emetic containing 0·2765 g. per litre. This contains 0·1 mg. of antimony per ml.; 1–5 ml. of it are taken for the colorimetric determination.

The weighed or measured sample is transferred to a large Erlenmeyer flask with the required amount of hydrochloric acid, the coiled strip of copper is put in and the liquid is boiled for one and a quarter hours. Before the end of this time the alkaline permanganate solution must be prepared and must be ready, boiling, for the copper to be transferred to it. The quantity of permanganate solution required varies with the amount of antimony; for deposits of less than 0·3 mg., 0·5 ml. is used, and for 0·5 mg., 1 ml. The amount of caustic potash is 15 ml. of the 1 per cent. solution in every case.

The copper is removed from the reaction-flask and transferred to a beaker containing distilled water. This water is poured off and the strip is rapidly washed two or three times with fresh distilled water. It is then dropped into the boiling permanganate solution, and the boiling is continued for one minute. This is usually sufficient for the complete solution of the antimony but the fact is not obvious because the copper is still dark-coloured. To test whether the deposit has been completely removed or not the copper is taken out and touched with a drop of 1 in 5 hydrochloric acid. The spot touched with the acid should be quite free from dark stain: if not, the copper must be treated a second time with alkaline permanganate; but strict adherence to the quantitative details usually ensures that this second treatment is not necessary.

The liquid is then filtered through a small filter into a 100 ml. Erlenmeyer flask. The copper and the beaker in which the permanganate has been boiled are washed twice with distilled water and the washings are poured through the filter. The filtrate is neutralized with hydrochloric acid and an excess equivalent to 0·2 ml. of concentrated acid is added. Sulphur dioxide is passed through the liquid for three to five minutes; or, alternatively, a slightly greater excess of hydrochloric acid may be used together with a sufficient quantity of sodium sulphite. The liquid is boiled until the last trace of sulphur dioxide has been expelled and the volume has been reduced to about 10 ml. When the liquid is cold it is mixed with 0·5 ml. of 10 per cent. gum arabic solution, and diluted to 25 ml. with distilled water. Hydrogen sulphide is passed through the liquid until there is no further intensification of colour and this colour is compared in a Duboscq colorimeter with that of a standard colloidal suspension of antimony sulphide prepared in a similar way from the required amount of tartar emetic solution.

MERCURY

The most poisonous compounds of mercury are those which are readily soluble in water, the insoluble compounds, such as calomel, and metallic mercury in the form of " grey powder " being relatively harmless. The commonest causes of acute mercurial poisoning are the mercuric salts, of which corrosive sublimate is the one responsible for the greatest number of deaths. An unusual case of fatal poisoning which came within our experience was one in which mercuric nitrate had been applied externally to remove warts. The salt was absorbed, possibly through cracks in the skin, and the patient died with many of the characteristic symptoms of mercurial poisoning. Mercury was afterwards detected in the liver and some of the other viscera.

The preliminary test for mercury, as for arsenic and antimony, is the Reinsch test. A silvery or grey deposit on the copper, yielding definite mercurial globules on heating, is a certain proof of the presence of mercury. There must, of course, be no doubt about the metallic nature of the globules, for the identification of which the technique already described on page 70 must be adopted. It is frequently possible to confirm the presence of mercury by breaking off the capillary portion of the ignition tube which contains the globules, transferring it to another ignition tube with a minute crystal of iodine and warming gently over a small flame, when a red sublimate of mercuric iodide may be formed. Before heating the tube the capillary tube should be crushed with a stiff platinum wire. A positive result in the Reinsch test does not prove that the mercury is present in toxic form. Metallic mercury forms an immediate deposit on copper even in the cold, and calomel yields a positive result on prolonged heating. Therefore, if the preliminary test shows that mercury is present, a fresh sample of the material under examination, mixed with water if necessary, must be filtered, and a portion of the filtrate used for a repetition of the Reinsch test.

If this second test also shows a positive result, a further portion of the filtrate is tested by adding a dilute solution of potassium iodide drop by drop; the formation of a red precipitate of mercuric iodide, soluble in excess of potassium iodide solution, indicates a mercuric salt. In the application of this test the fact that mercuric iodide is soluble in excess of potassium iodide solution is very important, and care must be taken not to add too much of the reagent at first. A convenient way of applying this test is to put a drop of the filtered liquid on filter-paper and a drop of dilute potassium iodide solution near to it so that, as the latter spreads, contact is made between the spots. In this way it is most unlikely that the red colour will be missed.

It sometimes happens that the preliminary Reinsch test applied to such material as the stomach or stomach-contents fails to yield satisfactory globules even when there is very good reason to believe that poisoning is due to mercury. In such cases the Reinsch test should be repeated, using as large a sample of the material as can be spared, bearing in mind the need for further tests; the heating also should be more prolonged. Should this test also fail to yield conclusive results a weighed portion of the material is destroyed by the Babo and Fresenius method. The liquid after filtration is diluted and treated with hydrogen sulphide and the resulting precipitate, collected on a filter or by centrifuging, is redissolved by warming with hydrochloric acid and a few drops of bromine. The excess of bromine is expelled by heat and the liquid is filtered. The application of the Reinsch test to this filtrate often shows the presence of traces of mercury when the preliminary tests have failed; but it must be remembered that the oxidizing action in the Babo and Fresenius process converts calomel and other insoluble mercury compounds into the soluble form, and that, therefore, the detection of mercury in the oxidized material is no proof of the presence of the more toxic mercury compounds in the original material; the finding is inconclusive.

In any case it would not be justifiable to diagnose mercury poisoning as the cause of death when the preliminary Reinsch test on the viscera fails to show the presence of the metal, unless a soluble mercury compound has also been detected in vomited or faecal matter.

The solution obtained after the destruction of the organic matter may be used, alternatively, for the electrolytic separation of metallic mercury. The sulphide of the metal is precipitated and redissolved in the usual way and the solution cooled and diluted. A direct current is then passed through the liquid, using platinum electrodes and an e.m.f. of about 6 volts. The cathode consists of a helix of platinum wire with an external diameter small enough for it to fit inside an ignition tube of the kind used in the Reinsch test. The electrolytic deposition is usually complete in about twelve hours, after which the cathode is detached and washed in distilled water, alcohol and ether successively; it is then dried in an oven at about 50° C. The helix is then put into an ignition tube and a portion of this tube is drawn out into a capillary, care being taken not to heat the wire during the drawing out. When the tube is cold the spiral is gently heated in a small flame so as to drive the mercury, if any, into the capillary portion of the tube which is thereafter examined under the low power of the microscope. The precautions described on p. 70 to ensure that drops of water or other liquid are not mistaken for mercury globules must be observed. Experience in our laboratory indicates that the delicacy of the Reinsch test for mercury is such that the electrolytic process is very rarely necessary as a qualitative test.

Determination of Mercury

If the quantity of mercury present is large enough to make gravimetric determination possible, the best method is the electrolytic one. The platinum cathode, after the deposition of mercury is complete, is washed, dried and weighed. The mercury is driven off by heat and the cathode is re-weighed, the difference giving the quantity of mercury. More usually the quantity found is so small that only colorimetric methods are possible.

The viscera or other material is treated in the manner indicated above, and the mercury precipitated as sulphide. The sulphide is re-dissolved and purified by again treating with nascent chlorine and this is repeated as often as is necessary to obtain a colourless solution. Finally, the sulphide is again produced in the presence of a colloidal substance, and the determination is made colorimetrically.

The following details recommended by Autenreith[1] for mercury in urine can be applied, *mutatis mutandis*, to the examination of faeces and viscera.

The urine is carefully measured into a capacious flask, using 800–1,200 ml. according to the amount of mercury expected, and mixed with 10–20 ml. of concentrated hydrochloric acid and 6–15 g. of potassium chlorate. This mixture is heated for four to six hours under a reflux condenser by means of a free flame, with frequent shaking, until the liquid is practically colourless, after which it is filtered. The filtrate is treated with considerably more than the calculated amount of sodium acetate in relation to the hydrochloric acid used; e.g. for 20 ml. of hydrochloric acid 35 g. of sodium acetate are recommended; 0·02–0·03 g. of zinc chloride is added, and hydrogen sulphide is passed into the mixture, kept at boiling-

[1] *Munchener Med. Wochenschr.*, 1920, p. 928.

point, for half an hour.   Sulphur is copiously precipitated since the liquid contains a certain amount of free chlorine.   With the sulphur is a mixture of zinc and mercury sulphides.   The precipitate is allowed to stand for several hours, after which it is filtered by suction through a pad of asbestos and well washed several times with hydrogen sulphide solution.   The precipitate, together with the asbestos, is transferred to a porcelain dish and dissolved in 5 ml. of hot dilute hydrochloric acid containing a little dissolved potassium chlorate.   The greater part of the liberated chlorine is driven off and the last traces removed by the addition of a little alcohol.   The liquid should now be completely colourless.   This colourless liquid is filtered through asbestos into a small measuring cylinder, the filter is washed and the remaining liquid well squeezed out by means of a glass rod.   The total filtrate should not amount to more than 10–20 ml.   After shaking and cooling the filtrate, 8 ml. of it are poured into a 10 ml. measuring flask and mixed with 1 ml. of 1 per cent. clear gelatine solution and 1 ml. of saturated solution of hydrogen sulphide.   The more or less intensely coloured solution (according to the whole amount of mercury) is compared with a solution of known mercury content prepared in the same way. Metals such as lead, bismuth, silver and copper must be absent. Arsenic does not interfere since it would be oxidized to arsenic acid by the potassium chlorate and this is not precipitated by hydrogen sulphide in the cold.   Also the organic matter must be completely destroyed; otherwise this may produce a yellow colour.   It is also recommended that the asbestos should be purified and this is best done by means of hydrochloric acid and potassium chlorate.   The gelatine solution must be clear and must give no colour with hydrogen sulphide.   Pure gum arabic solution may be substituted for gelatine.

Micro-tests for Mercury

Many organic reagents have been recommended for use in spot tests for the detection of mercury.[1]   Among them are diphenyl-carbazide, diphenylcarbazone, diphenylthiocarbazone (dithizone), di-β-napthylthiocarbazone   and   dimethylaminobenzylidine-rhodanine.

Dithizone is so generally useful that it merits a short general discussion.   The formation of coloured products when dithizone reacted with salts of heavy metals was noted as long ago as 1878 by Emil Fischer[2] but the systematic application of this observation to qualitative and quantitative analysis dates from the work of Hellmut

---

[1] FEIGL.   " Spot Tests ", p. 23.
[2] *Ann.* 1878, **140**, 118.

Fischer in 1925.[1] When a solution of dithizone in chloroform or carbon tetrachloride (green) is shaken with an aqueous solution of a salt of any one of some twenty metals, a complex salt is formed which is coloured (yellow, orange, red, or violet) and is usually soluble in the organic solvent. The action is usually reversible. The reaction can be made specific (or nearly so) for many metals (a) by carefully controlling the pH of the aqueous solution, (b) by adding a third reagent which will fix interfering ions, or (c) by selective re-extraction of the metallic ions. Thus (a) from a solution at pH 3·0 containing lead and bismuth, dithizone in carbon tetrachloride will extract practically all the bismuth but none of the lead ; (b) cyanide added to an alkaline solution prevents the formation of dithizonates of all metals except lead, tin (Sn″) thallium (T1′) and bismuth ; (c) if a carbon tetrachloride solution containing dithizonates of copper and lead is shaken with dilute acid, the lead goes into the aqueous solution whilst the copper remains as dithizonate in the organic solvent.

Two main procedures are available for using these reactions quantitatively. In the first, the desired metal is extracted completely into the dithizone solution (CCl_4 or $CHCl_3$), making successive extracts until the green colour of the reagent remains unchanged ; interfering metals are removed, if they have (or may have) been extracted : excess dithizone is removed by shaking with a very dilute solution of ammonia ; and the colour of the solution, which now contains only the desired metallic dithizonate, is measured. This method is the less preferable, because dithizone is difficult to extract from chloroform in which the metallic complexes are fairly stable, although it is easy to extract from carbon tetrachloride in which the complexes are relatively labile. However, it gives good results in suitable instances. The second, or mixed colour method, in which the excess dithizone remains along with the metal dithizonate, avoids these difficulties. For relatively crude work it may suffice to compare visually the colour of the solution with those of a series of standards, ranging from the pure green of the dithizone alone to the colour of the metal dithizonate alone ; if this is done the dithizone solution must be very dilute (about 0·001 per cent.). Much better results are obtained with a spectrophotometer or similar instrument, when it is possible, by adjusting the wave length of the incident light, to measure either the colour of the metal dithizonate or that of the excess dithizone. The strongest absorption of dithizone itself is at (about) 620 mμ, and at this wave length metal dithizonates in carbon tetrachloride absorb very little light ; this then gives good results when it is possible to depend on measure-

[1] *Wiss, Veröffentlich. Siemens-Konzern*, 1925, **4**, 158. *Angew. Chem.*, 1934, **47**, 685 : 1937, **50**, 919.

ment of excess dithizone—i.e. when there is a considerable excess and when the aqueous solution is not alkaline. Since dithizone is at least partly extracted into an alkaline aqueous solution, it is sometimes essential to measure the colour of the dithizonate itself. The approximate wave lengths (mμ) for maximum absorption are ; bismuth 500, cadmium 520, copper (Cu) 510, lead 525, mercury (Hg″) 530, silver 460, zinc 535. Both dithizone and metallic dithizonates in carbon tetrachloride obey Beer's Law so that a reference curve can readily be constructed from one or two standard solutions—provided the light is sufficiently nearly " monochromatic ", which is not always the case when filters are used.

A suitable stock solution of dithizone contains 10 mg. of the pure reagent in 1,000 ml. A.R. carbon tetrachloride (free from oxidizing agents) : it should be kept in the dark and stored for two weeks before use ; after shaking with dilute (metal-free) ammonia it should retain no more than a faint yellow colour. For quantitative work this solution should be freshly diluted with A.R. carbon tetrachloride to give a concentration of 1·0 mg. per 1,000 ml., and of this, 5 ml. may be used to determine 10-15 μg. of metal.

Mercury. In the case of mercury, the mercuric ion reacts with dithizone (to give an orange coloured complex) in strongly acid solution (1N mineral acid). Copper, silver, lead, zinc, cobalt, nickel, and bismuth (also gold, palladium and platinum, which, however, are not likely to be present) also react in acid solution. Bismuth, if present in considerable amounts, may interfere, and appreciable amounts of copper are to be expected in biological material. The other metals mentioned do not interfere unless they are present in very high concentration. To overcome interference, Lang and Nelson[1] proceed as follows.

Organic matter is destroyed by heating the sample (containing 10-100 μg. of mercury) with a 1 : 1 mixture of nitric and sulphuric acids. Any residual fat is filtered off, the solution (and washings) made up to a suitable volume of which 1/10 is taken for analysis. This aliquot, added to 50 ml. of 0·25 N HCl and 5 ml. of 20 per cent. aqueous hydroxylamine hydrochloride, is shaken vigorously with 10 ml. of dithizone solution (5.5 mg. per litre of A.R. chloroform). The chloroform layer is removed and a second similar extraction is made. The two chloroform extracts are combined and shaken with 50 ml. of 0·25 N HCl. The washed chloroform solution, containing mixed dithizonates and excess dithizone, is then shaken with a mixture of 50 ml. of 0·25 N HCl and 5 ml. of 40 per cent. (w/v) potassium bromide solution ; mercury passes into the aqueous phase, which is drawn off. (Copper remains in the chloroform layer.) The pH of this aqueous solution is adjusted to

[1] *J. Assoc. Off. Agr. Chem.*, 1942, **25**, 399.

about 6·0 by addition of 10 ml. of buffer solution (150 g. Na$_2$HPO$_4$ and 38 g. K$_2$CO$_3$ per litre), and the mercury is re-converted to dithizonate by extracting with 10·0 ml. of dithizone solution. In this solution it is determined by measuring the light transmittancy at 490 mμ. Mercuric dithizonate is somewhat light-sensitive, so the final stages should be carried out in subdued light. A reagent " blank " is required. As in all analyses using dithizone, the reagents should have heavy metals removed by shaking with dithizone, and then excess of dithizone removed by shaking with chloroform.

BISMUTH

Although bismuth salts are practically non-poisonous when taken by the mouth they may produce definitely toxic symptoms when introduced into the blood-stream by injection, or even when applied externally if the skin is broken.

At least one death[1] has been attributed to bismuth poisoning. The patient had received three injections of bismogenol (a 10 per cent. oily suspension of bismuth subsalicylate containing 60 per cent. bismuth) and one tablet of spirocid (4-hydroxy-3-acetylamino-phenylarsonic acid) daily. The treatment was stopped owing to inflammation of the skin, and the effect of calcium injections was only to aggravate the conditions; scabs and even ulcers formed. The stools were liquid. The patient developed fever and passed into a state of stupor. The hair began to fall out and there were scabs on the scalp. The pulse rate rose to 140 and death occurred three days after the admission of the patient to the hospital. At the autopsy the observations were: Necrotic ulcerative colitis, icterus, interstitial hepatitis and swollen spleen. Bismuth was detected in the liver. In spite of the fact that an arsenical compound had also been given, the bismuth was regarded as the cause of death.

If bismuth is suspected as a result of the Reinsch test, a portion of the material may be destroyed either by a wet or dry method and the residue, after dissolving in hydrochloric acid, treated with hydrogen sulphide. If a black precipitate is formed it may be due to bismuth, lead or copper. The possibility of the presence of the two latter metals must be excluded by the special tests to be described later.

If the quantity of the black precipitate is not too small the well-known oxy-chloride test for bismuth may be tried, though it is lacking in delicacy. A more sensitive test depends on the production of a characteristic yellow colour by treating a solution of bismuth with potassium iodide. When the presence of bismuth and the absence of lead, mercury and copper have been established the

[1] AERTZ. *Deutsch. Med. Wochenschr.*, 1938, **64**, 815.

quantity of the former may be determined colorimetrically by a method similar to that already described for mercury.

Determination of Bismuth

Iodide Method.[1] Heat 10 g. of the material with 20 ml. of concentrated nitric acid on the steam bath until a clear yellow-brown solution is produced. Cool and filter off any fat through glass wool. Wash the precipitate with a little nitric acid. Collect filtrate and washings in a Kjeldahl flask, add 3 ml. of concentrated sulphuric acid and heat until white fumes appear. Add, drop by drop, a nitric-perchloric acid mixture (1 : 2) with continued heating until the colour is destroyed. Add, drop by drop, $0 \cdot 5$ ml. of " 100 volume " (30 per cent.) hydrogen peroxide and again boil. Cool, add 5 ml. of water, heat until white fumes appear, re-cool, transfer to a 25 ml. graduated flask and make up to 25 ml. with water.

In the presence of considerable amounts of other heavy metals it is advisable to extract the bismuth with dithizone from the solution after making alkaline with ammonia and adding potassium cyanide. Otherwise, to a 10 ml. aliquot of the solution prepared as described aboved add $0 \cdot 1$ ml. of a freshly made 5 per cent. solution of SO_2 in water, 1 ml. of 30 per cent. hypophosphorus acid and 3 ml. of fresh 10 per cent. aqueous potassium iodide solution. Compare the yellow colour with that of a standard bismuth solution similarly treated (using a filter with maximum transmittance about 460 mμ).

If the sample contains coloured ions, extract the yellow bismuth complex with 2-3 ml. of a 3 : 1 mixture of amyl alcohol and ethyl acetate, repeating the extraction until the final extract is colourless. Make up the combined extracts to a suitable volume with the organic solvent for colour measurement.

Tompsett's Method. Another sensitive qualitative test[2] for bismuth consists in adding a 10 per cent. solution of thiourea to an acid solution of the bismuth salt. An intense yellow colour is produced if the bismuth concentration exceeds 10 mg. per litre. Other metals of Group II do not interfere. By carrying out the test in a Nessler glass, using defined volumes, and comparing with standard solutions similarly treated, it can be made roughly quantitative. It has been developed by Tompsett[3] in the following way.

The bismuth is extracted from alkaline aqueous solution in presence of a citrate (pH 8) by treating with diethyldithiocarbamate and shaking with ether to dissolve out the resulting compound;

[1] Autenrieth, *Munch. Med. Woch*, 1924, 601. Haddock, *Analyst*, 1934, **59**, 163. Sproull and Gettler, *Ind. Eng. Chem., Anal. Ed.*, 1941, **13**, 462.

[2] *Annali Chim. Appl.*, 1929, **19**, 392.

[3] *Analyst*, 1938, **63**, 250.

under these conditions phosphates are not precipitated and iron is not extracted.

Lead and copper, if present, will be extracted with the bismuth but they do not interfere with the final colour. The following reagents are required for the destruction of organic matter and the subsequent determination:

(1) Concentrated sulphuric acid.

(2) Perchloric acid.

(3) Sodium citrate solution, 20 per cent.

(4) Ammonia, sp. gr. 0·88.

(5) Sodium diethyldithiocarbamate solution, 2 per cent.

(6) Thiourea solution, 10 per cent.

(7) Standard solution of bismuth prepared in the following way: 1 g. pure metallic bismuth is heated with 20 ml. concentrated sulphuric acid and sufficient nitric acid to dissolve the metal. The nitric acid is driven off by heat and the solution, when cold, is diluted to 100 ml. with water. Of this solution 1 ml. contains 10 mg. of bismuth.

This method has been applied to urine, faeces and tissues.

For urine, 100–500 ml. are digested with concentrated sulphuric acid and perchloric acid in a Kjeldahl flask until all the organic material is destroyed and the excess of perchloric acid is eliminated. The residual liquid is diluted to 150 ml. with water, 100 ml. of the 20 per cent. sodium citrate solution are added and the pH is adjusted to 8 with ammonia. Ten ml. of 2 per cent. diethyldithiocarbamate solution are added and three successive extractions with ether are made. The united ethereal extracts are evaporated to dryness in a Kjeldahl flask and the organic matter in the residue is destroyed by heating with 1 ml. of concentrated sulphuric acid and 1 ml. of perchloric acid. When cold the liquid is diluted with water to 5 ml. and mixed with 5 ml. of the 10 per cent. thiourea solution. The colour is then compared with that of 5 ml. of a suitably diluted standard bismuth solution in 20 per cent. sulphuric acid, also mixed with 5 ml. of thiourea solution.

Hamence's Method. For the treatment of mixtures containing lead and bismuth, Hamence[1] recommends the extraction of the latter in the form of bismuth-pyridine-thiocyanate by shaking with a mixture of ether and amyl alcohol.

Another method is to dissolve the mixed sulphides of lead and bismuth in nitric acid and expel the excess of nitric acid by heating, after which the residue is dissolved in acetic acid. From this solution the metals are precipitated as chromates and the mixed chromates, after isolation and washing, are converted into hydroxides by the cautious addition of 10 per cent. caustic soda solution. The

[1] HAMENCE. *Analyst*, 1933, **58**, 461-4.

lead hydroxide rapidly re-dissolves, leaving the insoluble bismuth hydroxide, which can be filtered off. The mixed metals having been determined together colorimetrically as sulphides, the lead is re-determined in the filtrate. No great error is introduced by regarding the difference between the two determinations as a measure of the bismuth present, since, according to Hamence (*loc. cit.*), the colour given by 0·1 mg. of lead is very nearly the same as that produced by 0·1 mg. of bismuth.

SILVER

Silver is included among the " common metallic poisons " as previously defined, only because the metal is deposited from its solutions on a strip of copper in the Reinsch test.

Silver nitrate is the only toxic salt of silver which needs to be considered. It is a corrosive poison, but, apparently, it is seldom, if ever, used for criminal purposes. Silver nitrate blackens the skin and the black stain is not easy to remove; it also forms scabs on sensitive membranes and these local effects round the mouth and on the lips and tongue are of diagnostic importance.

It is stated that silver salts are not excreted by way of the kidneys but are likely to be found in the faeces, in which case the stools are black owing to the presence of silver sulphide.

If the method of Babo and Fresenius is used for the destruction of organic matter, silver must be sought in the fatty insoluble residue left on the filter-paper in the first filtration. This is an important distinction between silver compounds and those of thallium: in many other respects thallous salts and silver salts bear a striking resemblance to one another. The paper and the fatty residue, well washed with hot water, should be transferred to a basin and covered with sufficient sodium carbonate solution to make the whole definitely alkaline. The basin is heated on a sand-bath until its contents are dry and the organic matter begins to char. The basin is allowed to cool and its contents are intimately mixed with a further quantity of sodium carbonate and a smaller amount of potassium nitrate; the heating is continued until the oxidation is complete and a fluid melt is obtained. When cold, the melt is mixed with water and transferred to a flask. The liquid is boiled and then allowed to settle. The precipitate, which may contain traces of lead (if the washing with hot water has not been efficiently carried out), metallic silver, and possibly barium salts, is collected on a filter and then redissolved in hot 20 per cent. nitric acid. This solution is evaporated just to dryness, the residue is redissolved in water and the following tests for silver are applied.

(1) Hydrochloric acid is added to a portion of the solution;

if silver is present a white precipitate which becomes curdy on boiling and turns violet on exposure to light, is formed. This precipitate easily dissolves on the addition of ammonia and is reprecipitated on neutralizing the ammonia with nitric acid.

(2) A second portion is tested with potassium chromate solution; silver chromate, insoluble in nitric acid, is formed as an orange to red-coloured precipitate.

(3) A specially sensitive reagent for silver which is recommended by Feigl is p-dimethylaminobenzilidine-rhodanine. This reagent produces a violet coloration when mixed with a neutral or faintly acid solution of a silver salt. It is claimed that the test is capable of detecting 1 part of silver in 500,000 parts of solution. Mercury salts also give this reaction, but they can be distinguished from silver salts by carrying out the test in presence of a small quantity of potassium cyanide; under these conditions mercury salts give no colour. The reagent is used in the form of an alcoholic solution and the test can be carried out on filter-paper which has been impregnated with the solution and afterwards dried. In using this reagent as a test for *mercury*, the presence of sodium acetate is an advantage.

CHAPTER IV

OTHER METALS

LEAD

LEAD is seldom used for homicidal poisoning although the ingestion of lead preparations as abortifacients has been known to cause death. When death follows rapidly from an over-dose it is usually possible to detect the metal by ordinary analytical methods, using a solution freed from organic matter by oxidizing agents such as nitric acid, perchloric acid, etc. The four most useful tests are:

(1) Hydrogen sulphide gives a black precipitate of lead sulphide distinguished from other sulphides by being oxidized by concentrated nitric acid to white insoluble lead sulphate;

(2) Sulphuric acid gives a white precipitate of lead sulphate;

(3) Potassium iodide gives a yellow precipitate of lead iodide which dissolves in boiling water and crystallizes on cooling, in golden spangles;

(4) Potassium chromate gives a yellow precipitate of lead chromate.

A sensitive test, suitable for micro-work, consists in making the suspected solution neutral or slightly alkaline, adding potassium cyanide (which prevents interference by other metals except zinc) and shaking with a solution of diphenylthiocarbazone (dithizone) in carbon tetrachloride. Traces of lead turn the reagent from green to brick-red, whilst zinc gives a purple-red.

Chronic lead poisoning is much more common, and for the investigation of this special technique is required.

Wet methods for the oxidation of organic matter are preferable to dry ignition, since loss of lead occurs at temperatures above 550° C. For the isolation of lead free from other metals, many workers recommend electrolysis, lead being deposited at the anode as the peroxide. Another method which has come into use recently is the extraction of lead with a chloroformic solution of diphenyl-thiocarbazone.

In all determinations of minute quantities of lead, silica apparatus should be used, and all reagents must either be specially prepared or proved to be lead-free; even distilled water must be re-distilled in a lead-free still. The carrying out of blank tests is an essential part of the technique whichever process is used. Interpretation of the analytical results must take into account the normal occurrence of lead in tissues and excreta[2, 3].

Determination of Lead

Lead has been determined in biological materials by producing lead peroxide and using this to form malachite green[1] by the oxidation of tetramethyldiamino-diphenylmethane, and by converting the lead to a colloidal solution or suspension of the sulphide which could be measured colorimetrically.[2] In this laboratory, however, the dithizone method is preferred, the actual technique being a development of that described by Tompsett and Anderson and by Tompsett.[3]

Preliminary Treatment

For *urine*, 250 ml. are evaporated to dryness in a silica dish in a hot air oven (avoid frothing by controlling temperature) ; for *soft tissue*, 50-100 g. are minced, added to 100 ml. of 10 per cent. sodium phosphate solution (previously freed from lead by shaking with sodium diethyldithiocarbamate and ether, and dried as in the case of urine; for *blood*, 20 ml. are evaporated to dryness after addition of 100 ml. of lead-free 10 per cent. sodium phosphate solution; for *faeces* 10 g. of dried material is used, and for *bone*, 20 g.

The dried material is ashed by ignition over a bunsen burner, the process being assisted where necessary by grinding with a glass rod and/or the addition of a few drops of concentrated nitric acid.

Urine ash is dissolved in 75 ml. water containing 5 ml. concentrated HCl, 50 ml. of 20 per cent. sodium citrate[4] are added, the mixture rendered alkaline to litmus by the addition of ammonia and 5 ml. of 10 per cent. KCN are added. Then 5 ml. of fresh 2 per cent. sodium diethyldithiocarbamate are added and the mixture is extracted three times with ether, 25 ml. on each occasion. The ether extracts, which are separately washed with water, are transferred to a hard glass round-bottomed flask. The ether is evaporated off and the residue digested with 1 ml. concentrated H_2SO_4 and 1 ml. of perchloric acid to destroy organic matter. The residue is diluted with water, 1 ml. glacial acetic acid added, followed by 5 ml. of ammonia (0·880) and the mixture is diluted to 25 ml. with water.

[1] Seiser *et al.*, *Archiv für Hygiene*, **99**, 158.

[2] Roche Lynch, Slater and Osler. *Analyst*, 1934, **59**, 787.

[3] Tompsett, personal communication. *Biochem. J.* 1935, **29**, 1851 ; 1939, **33**, 1,231.

[4] The solution is stored over 0·1 per cent. dithizone in chloroform (50 ml. per litre) and is shaken and filtered before use.

Soft tissue Ash is dissolved in 100 ml. water containing 10 ml. of concentrated HCl and the solution is treated as described for urine.

Faeces or Bone ash is dissolved in 100 ml. of water containing 10 ml. of concentrated HCl, and the solution is diluted to 200 ml. with water. Of this, 50 ml. are mixed with 10 ml. of 2 per cent. sodium diethyldithiocarbamate, and the mixture is extracted three times with 25 ml. quantities of ether. The combined ether extracts are evaporated and the residue is digested with 1ml. of concentrated sulphuric acid and 1 ml. of perchloric acid. The digest is diluted with water, 1 ml. of concentrated hydrochloric acid is added, the mixture is heated to dissolve solid matter, and water is added to make the volume 50 ml. This solution, after addition of 5 ml. of 20 per cent. sodium citrate, is made alkaline with ammonia, 5 ml. of 10 per cent. potassium cyanide are added, and 5 ml. of 2 per cent. sodium diethyldithiocarbamate. The mixture is thrice extracted with 25 ml. of ether and the washed ether extracts are treated as described for urine.

Blood ash is dissolved in about 50 ml. water containing 5 ml. concentrated HCl. 5 ml. of 20 per cent. sodium citrate are added and the mixture made alkaline to litmus by the addition of ammonia (0·880). 5 ml. of 10 per cent. KCN are added followed by 2 ml. of 2 per cent. sodium diethyldithiocarbamate. The mixture is extracted three times with 20 ml. quantities of ether, and the ether extracts, which on each occasion are washed with water, are transferred to a 100 ml. hard glass round-bottomed flask. The ether is evaporated off and the residue digested with 0·2 ml. conc. H_2SO_4 and 0·5 ml. perchloric acid. To the digest are added 3·5 ml. water, 0·2 ml. glacial acetic acid and 1·5 ml. of ammonia (sp.gr. 0·880).

Determination.

The solution obtained at the end of the preliminary treatment contains the lead as $PbSO_4$ in an ammoniacal solution of ammonium acetate. That from urine, faeces, soft tissue or bone has been diluted to 25 ml., that from blood to 5 ml.

Into a glass-stoppered 50 ml. flask are measured 5 ml. of the lead-containing solution, 5 ml. of 1 per cent. potassium cyanide and 10 ml. of carbon tetrachloride. Dithizone solution, prepared as follows, is then added drop by drop with shaking.

5 ml. of a 0·1 per cent. solution of dithizone in carbon tetrachloride is shaken with 10 ml. of 0·5 per cent. ammonia (0·5 ml. 0·880 ammonia in 100 ml.), which extracts the dithizone but not the oxidation product usually present as an impurity. The ammoniacal extract is separated and used directly.

Addition continues until excess is present as shown by a greenish tint in the CCl_4 layer as well as the pink of the lead dithizone complex and a brownish tint in the aqueous layer.

Separate the carbon tetrachloride layer, remove droplets of water by centrifuging and read the light absorption at 620 mμ and 525 mμ (Unicam Spectrophotometer or similar instrument). At the former wave-length the lead dithizone complex gives little absorption, but the absorption of free dithizone is maximal ; at 525 mμ the absorption of the lead dithizone complex is maximal. The difference between these readings, *minus* the similar difference in a " blank " determination gives the amount of lead present on reference to a calibration curve constructed by determination of known amounts of lead (5, 10, 20 μg.) added to 5 ml. of the following solution which is also used as the " blank "; 1 ml. concentrated H_2SO_4, 1 ml. glacial acetic acid, 5 ml. concentrated ammonia (sp. gr. 0·880), water to 45 ml.

As a further check, shake the CCl_4 extract with 5 ml. of 20 per cent. HCl to convert the lead dithizone complex to free dithizone and again read at 620 mμ and 525 mμ.

The aliquot taken for the colorimetric determination should not contain more than 20 μg. of lead. A complete blank determination should be made on each batch of reagents.

COPPER

The soluble salts of copper are powerful emetics, and in sufficiently large doses they act as irritant poisons. No exact information as to the minimum lethal dose is available, but it is certainly large. In acute poisoning with copper the vomited matter is usually bluish or greenish in colour and there is no difficulty in the detection of the metal.

For the detection of copper in urine, blood, or tissues the organic matter may be destroyed either by wet or dry combustion without loss by volatilization. The residue is taken up in dilute nitric acid, filtered, and made alkaline with ammonia. If no blue colour is observed no considerable quantity of copper can be present, as a solution containing less than 1 part in 100,000 gives a strong colour.

A test of greater delicacy is the production of a reddish-brown colour with potassium ferrocyanide in neutral or faintly acid solution.

Montequi's reaction as carried out by Feigl is said to be capable of detecting less than 0·001 mg. of copper in 1 ml. of water. A neutral or faintly acid solution is treated with a few drops of dilute zinc nitrate solution followed by 1 or 2 ml. of a reagent consisting of 8 g. of mercuric chloride and 9 g. of ammonium thiocyanate in 100 ml. of water. A precipitate varying in colour from bright pink to deep violet according to the amount of copper present is formed.

(This test can also be used for the detection of zinc by adding a trace of copper salt followed by the mercuric thiocyanate reagent to the solution under examination.)

For the quantitative determination of copper the metal is first isolated as sulphide from the solution obtained after the oxidation of the organic matter. This is collected on a filter, washed, and thereafter dissolved in warm dilute nitric acid. Should there be any turbidity due to precipitated sulphur this is got rid of by boiling to coagulate the sulphur and filtering. The solution is neutralized with ammonia and if it is not then clear and blue it is again boiled and filtered. The liquid is then made very slightly acid with hydrochloric acid and a dilute solution of potassium ferrocyanide is added drop by drop until no further intensification of the colour occurs. For quantities of copper less than $0·3$ mg. the ferrocyanide solution should not be stronger than 1 per cent.; it is important to avoid too great an excess of the reagent as this may cause turbidity. The liquid is then made up to a definite volume and the colour is compared with a standard solution of known copper content treated in a similar way.

Tests of extreme delicacy are rarely useful, since traces of copper are found normally in tissues, blood and urine. One such test consists in adding a drop of the test solution (mixed with an equal volume of sodium potassium tartrate) to a filter paper previously soaked in a 5 per cent. alcoholic solution of benzoin-oxime and dried. Copper ($0·1\mu g.$) produces a green colour which becomes more distinct if exposed to ammonia.

CADMIUM

In the year 1923 a workman died in London as the result of inhaling fumes containing cadmium.[1] Subsequent experiments on rats showed that the admixture of 125 parts of cadmium per 1,000,000 in the daily diet caused death in fifty days. Half this quantity produced no toxic effects.

Cadmium may be detected in viscera after the destruction of the organic matter with potassium chlorate and hydrochloric acid. It is precipitated as the canary-yellow sulphide, which is distinguished from arsenic sulphide by being insoluble in ammonium sulphide solution. For complete precipitation of cadmium sulphide the solution of the cadmium salt should be dilute and only faintly acid. Cadmium salts in solution give a white precipitate, insoluble in excess, with sodium hydroxide (the precipitate dissolves in excess of ammonium hydroxide) or sodium carbonate. The test for cadmium recommended by Feigl[2] depends on the

[1] *Analyst*, 1923, **48**, 284.
[2] " Spot Tests ", p. 51.

formation of a brown colour changing to a bluish-green, when a solution containing the metal is treated with dinitrodiphenyl carbazide in the presence of formaldehyde. The colour effect is due to adsorption on cadmium hydroxide, and as the presence of alkaline cyanides favours the precipitation of cadmium rather than copper, a cyanide is added to eliminate the possible interference of the latter metal. The details of the tests are as follows: a drop of the test solution is mixed with a drop of alkaline cyanide solution, a drop of the reagent and 2 drops of formaldehyde solution. A bluish-green precipitate or colour indicates cadmium. A blank test should be made: the colour of the reagent alone in alkaline solution is red and this colour is changed to violet by formaldehyde.

The reagents required are: 10 per cent. caustic soda, 10 per cent. potassium cyanide solution, 40 per cent. formaldehyde solution, and a 0·1 per cent. alcoholic solution of dinitrodiphenyl carbazide.

A further test by which cadmium in 0·1 per cent. solution can be detected in the presence of ammonia or metals of the alkali and alkaline earth groups (although metals of the first and second groups interfere) has been described.[1] The reagent is thiourea. One or two drops of the test solution are evaporated to dryness on a slide and the residue is dissolved in one small drop of 1·2 N. hydrochloric acid and mixed with a large drop of a 1–1·5 per cent. solution of Rochelle salt; a drop of 5 per cent. thiourea solution is then added. The red cadmium-thiourea-tartrate forms rod-like crystals either at once or after a short time. When metals of Groups I or II are present the acidified test solution is added drop by drop with stirring, to a mixture of concentrated ammonia, hydroxylamine hydrochloride and sodium sulphite (the two latter reagents in 3–5 per cent. solution) and boiled. After standing for some time the mixture is filtered, acidified with hydrochloric acid, and heated. A drop of the filtrate is tested for copper with Rochelle salt and if a yellow precipitate is formed the whole is similarly treated and the yellow precipitate is filtered off. (This stage is omitted in the absence of copper, gold and platinum.) One or two drops of the filtrate are evaporated to dryness on a slide and ammonium salts are driven off by heating. The residue is treated in the manner above described. Lead salts also form crystals, but these are easily distinguished from those of cadmium.

MANGANESE

Acute poisoning by manganese is usually the result of swallowing potassium permanganate either accidentally or in attempting suicide. Both the salt and the concentrated solution in large doses

[1] MAHR. *Mikrochem. Akta.*, 1938, **3**, 300–3; *Analyst*, 1939, **64**, 141.

are powerfully irritant or even corrosive.   Death from manganese poisoning is fairly common among workers in manganese mines owing to the inhalation of dust.

According to Handovsky[1] the liver is the organ which suffers most in manganese poisoning.   He also states that manganese is excreted mainly through the intestines, traces only being found in the urine.

The specimens sent to the analyst usually consist of stomach washings, urine and faeces.

The most satisfactory method for the detection of manganese is its reconversion into permanganate, which can be carried out by oxidation in acid solution by means of potassium or ammonium persulphate in presence of a trace of silver which acts as a catalyst; chlorides must be absent.

It is frequently possible to carry out the test on samples of stomach-washings which are comparatively free from food without elaborate preliminary treatment.   The liquid is mixed with nitric acid, boiled and filtered, after which sufficient silver nitrate is added to precipitate the chloride and leave a small excess of silver in solution.   The silver chloride precipitate is coagulated by boiling and removed by filtration.   The vessel is then placed on a boiling water-bath and a large excess of solid persulphate is added little by little until the organic matter present is oxidized and the pink colour of the permanganate is seen.   As confirmation that the pink colour is really due to permanganate, it should be noted that the colour is discharged from a solution acidified with sulphuric acid by hydrogen peroxide or ferrous sulphate in the cold, and by oxalic acid on warming.

Urine or other excreta containing much organic matter must be evaporated to dryness, mixed with concentrated sulphuric acid and nitric acid and heated until oxidation is complete and chlorides are driven off by volatilization.

The residue is taken up in distilled water, 1 or 2 drops of silver nitrate are added, followed by excess of persulphate.   The liquid is then heated on the water-bath for fifteen to twenty minutes. Manganese has been detected in this way in the urine of people who habitually drink Nile water, which contains traces of the metal.

This reaction can be applied to the colorimetric determination of manganese by diluting the liquid, after the development of the permanganate colour, to a definite volume and comparing the colour with that of a freshly prepared standard solution of potassium permanganate.   As potassium permanganate solutions are not perfectly stable, Tillmans recommends the preparation of a series of solutions of alkaline phenolphthalein which can be matched

[1] *Arch. Exp. Path. Pharm.*, 1926, **110**, 265.   *Analyst*, 1926, **31**, 362.

against permanganate of known concentration and kept as permanent standards.

CHROMIUM

From a toxicological point of view chromium compounds strongly resemble those of manganese. Acute chromium poisoning is most likely to occur from the ingestion of the salts of chromic acid, but from excreta or tissues it is usually necessary to isolate the chromium as a salt of the metal, after which it is reconverted into chromate for the purposes of recognition and determination.

Two cases of fatal chromate poisoning which we investigated in the January of 1939 are of interest. In the first one the history of the affair was very uncertain but there was a suspicion of lead poisoning. As a preliminary test a drop of potassium iodide solution was added to a portion of the filtered stomach washings. Iodine was liberated, showing the presence of an oxidizing agent. The colour of the wash did not suggest chromium and therefore tests were made for manganese by the persulphate method above described. The colour which developed was not purple but yellow, and this yellow liquid, on treatment with hydrogen peroxide and ether, showed the characteristic blue colour of perchromic acid. After the destruction of the viscera by incineration with the aid of nitric acid, chromium was detected in all the samples. In the second case dichromate poisoning was suspected from the history of the case. Samples of the stomach, intestines, liver and kidneys were separately incinerated. The ash from the stomach and intestines was yellow, tinged with green; that from the other organs was intensely green. Both the yellow and the green residues were found to contain chromium by the tests above described.

We have never succeeded in converting chromium salts into perchromic acid in one operation. It appears to be necessary to use persulphate first to convert the chromium salt into a chromate and to treat the latter with hydrogen peroxide to obtain perchromic acid.

The persulphate oxidation may be used as the basis of colorimetric determination, using the same procedure as for manganese. If manganese is present in addition to chromium the permanganate colour will mask the yellow colour of the chromate; but whereas the former colour is discharged by boiling with hydrochloric acid the latter is not; therefore the interfering effect of manganese is easily eliminated.

As a confirmatory test the chromate solution can be reconverted into a solution of a chromium salt, the colour changing from yellow to green. This is effected by adding a small quantity of alcohol or formalin and mixing with a quantity of concentrated sulphuric acid

equal in volume to the test solution. The heat developed by the
dilution of the sulphuric acid is usually sufficient for the reduction
of the chromate but a little further heating is sometimes
necessary.

Diphenyl carbazide dissolved in alcohol and acetic acid (9 : 1)
is a sensitive reagent for chromates, producing a pink to violet
colour depending on the amount of chromate present. According
to Rosenthaler, 1 part of chromium in 6·7 million parts of solution
can be detected.

Heavy metals, if present, interfere with the test, but Gutzeit states
that this difficulty can be avoided by working in a solution strongly
acidified with hydrochloric acid.

ZINC

Although zinc chloride is a strong corrosive poison and the other
soluble salts of zinc are irritant, acute poisoning from zinc is
comparatively rare. The sulphate has sometimes caused dangerous
symptoms when taken in mistake for Epsom salts.

In the examination of stomach-washings or vomits the preliminary
test may be made by filtering a portion and making the filtrate
alkaline with sodium carbonate. The absence of a precipitate may
be taken as excluding any large quantity of zinc.

For the systematic examination of excreta or viscera the organic
matter may be destroyed by any of the usual methods and the
solution is treated as in ordinary inorganic analysis to remove metals
of the first and second groups and also phosphates[1]; particular care
must be taken to remove all traces of iron before proceeding to the
tests for zinc. The following tests should be made:

(1) Hydrogen sulphide is passed into the solution in presence of
ammonia and ammonium chloride. A white precipitate is formed
if zinc is present. The liquid is then boiled to coagulate the precipitate, which is collected on a filter and washed first with ammonium
sulphide solution and afterwards with distilled water. The residue
on the filter is dissolved by pouring hot dilute hydrochloric acid
several times through the paper. The solution so obtained is
boiled until all traces of hydrogen sulphide are expelled, after which
it can be used for subsequent tests.

(2) A portion of the solution is treated with 1 or 2 drops of
potassium ferrocyanide solution. The insoluble white ferrocyanide
of zinc is produced; this would, of course, be masked by the
strongly coloured ferrocyanides of iron and copper if these metals
had not been previously removed.

(3) The production of Rinmann's green is a very delicate test

---

[1] See p. 122 under " Thallium ".

for zinc if the micro-technique recommended by Emich is used. One end of a narrow strip of filter-paper is dipped into a 1 per cent. solution of cobalt nitrate and the other end into the solution to be tested in such a way that the two solutions meet. The paper is then carbonized by heating in a porcelain basin. A green deposit on the carbonaceous residue indicates zinc, but any green colour seen on the uncarbonized paper should be ignored.

(4) In the absence of lead, copper, cadmium, mercury and the metals of the platinum group a solution of diphenylthiocarbazone may be used as a test for zinc. The reagent dissolved in carbon tetrachloride is green in colour; when shaken with a solution of zinc the colour changes to reddish purple. Fischer and Leopold recommend the following method of applying the reaction. The faintly acid solution is treated with 5 per cent. sodium acetate solution, drop by drop, until the solution begins to turn acidified Congo paper red. The organic reagent is then poured into the test-tube so as to form a separate lower layer. If a reddish violet zone of contact is formed it may be due to zinc, cadmium or lead. The liquids are then shaken together in a separating funnel and the lower layer is separated and shaken with 5 per cent. acetic acid. If the colour is immediately changed to green, zinc is absent; if zinc is present the liquid remains more or less violet in colour.

Determination of Zinc

Several methods have been described for the determination of small quantities of zinc. The following process,[1] originally due to Breyer, and modified by Birckner, is said to give satisfactory results with quantities of zinc varying from 0·1 to 5 mg. The organic material is destroyed by means of sulphuric and nitric acids and the excess of acid vapours expelled by heat. The residue is repeatedly extracted with dilute hydrochloric acid and the extracts are poured through a filter and the solution evaporated to dryness. The residue is dissolved in 50 ml. of water acidified with 2 ml. of concentrated hydrochloric acid. The liquid is saturated with hydrogen sulphide and filtered and the residue is washed. The filtrate and washings are boiled until all traces of hydrogen sulphide are expelled; when cold the liquid is neutralized with ammonia and mixed with 10 ml. of 50 per cent. citric acid solution, after which it is heated to boiling point. If no calcium citrate separates, calcium carbonate is added gradually in sufficient quantity to produce about 1 g. of calcium citrate. The reason for this production of calcium citrate *in situ* is to ensure the subsequent complete precipitation of zinc as sulphide. A rapid stream of hydrogen sulphide is then passed through the

---

[1] *J. Biol. Chem.*, 1918, **38**, 191.

liquid continuously until the latter is cold. The liquid is allowed to stand until the precipitate coagulates and settles, rewarming on the water-bath if necessary. The precipitate is collected on a filter-paper and washed with a 2 per cent. solution of ammonium thiocyanate. The residue is dissolved in hot dilute hydrochloric acid, the solution being collected in the vessel in which the zinc was precipitated. If any red colour, due to iron, is seen the iron must be removed and the precipitation of the zinc in presence of calcium citrate repeated. Any turbidity due to the separation of sulphur is got rid of by boiling and filtering. When a clear and colourless solution has been obtained, either the whole or an aliquot part of it is transferred to a Nessler cylinder and made up to 45 ml. with water. A series of Nessler cylinders containing varying quantities of zinc dissolved in hydrochloric acid is prepared; 3 ml. of concentrated hydrochloric acid are added to each and each is diluted to 45 ml. with water. A solution of potassium ferrocyanide containing 34·8 g. per litre is added to each, making the total volume 50 ml.

The turbidities produced are compared by viewing the cylinders longitudinally over a dead-black surface. The standard which most nearly resembles the test sample, being slightly weaker than it, is adjusted by adding standard zinc solution from a burette until a satisfactory match is obtained.

It is claimed that this method involves an error of not more than 2 per cent. when the quantity of zinc is between 0·5 and 1 mg.; with quantities of the order of 10 mg. the error may be about 4 or 5 per cent.

Lott[1] has described a method in which zinc is precipitated from faintly acid solution with 5-nitro-quinaldinic acid. The precipitate is dissolved in hot hydrochloric acid containing 2·5 per cent. of stannous chloride. The reduction product so obtained is a deep orange solution suitable for colorimetric comparison. The details of the process are as follows: the zinc is isolated as sulphide and this is re-dissolved in hydrochloric acid. An aliquot portion of the clear solution (5–10 ml. containing 0·05–1 mg. of zinc) is made alkaline to methyl red with 3N ammonia and re-acidified with acetic acid. The liquid is then heated almost to boiling point and treated with a slight excess of the precipitating agent. The mixture is kept on a hot-plate below boiling point for half an hour and then filtered through asbestos and washed. The residue is dissolved in 5 ml. of the acidic stannous chloride solution, filtered to remove asbestos and allowed to cool. When cold the colour is compared with that of a standard solution of zinc which has been treated in a similar way. The precipitating reagent is a 0·75 per cent. solution in 95 per cent. alcohol.

[1] *Ind. Eng. Chem. Anal. Ed.*, 1938, **10**, pp. 331–3. *Analyst*, 1938, p. 626.

THALLIUM

Until twenty years ago thallium was regarded as one of the rare poisons, and the cases recorded were nearly all accidental. The acetate is sometimes given internally to cause the falling out of the hair of the scalp in the treatment of ringworm. The hair begins to fall ten to twenty days after the administration of the drug, but an accidental overdose may cause toxic symptoms within a day or two. Sometimes, however, no symptoms appear until about two weeks have elapsed.

In recent years reports of thallium poisoning have become increasingly common, especially in the German medical Press. Thallium salts are among the constituents of some of the pastes now on sale as rat poison, and such pastes have been used for homicidal and suicidal purposes[1][2][3][4][5][6]. Symptoms have varied considerably even between members of one family poisoned at the same time. Tendon reflexes were increased in some of the victims, diminished in others. Some of them had severe nervous symptoms and loss of sensation in the extremities. In other cases patients complained of pain in the feet. In one case (Oheim's) blindness was reported, in addition to incessant pain and insomnia. Another patient (Brumm's) had ulcerated tonsils. Böhmer reports ridges and fissures in the finger-nails. In one case typhus was first suspected and a later diagnosis of the same case was strychnine poisoning.

Thallium is a heavy metal in the third group of the periodic system. It forms two series of salts of which the most stable and characteristic are the thallous salts corresponding to the oxide Tl_2O. Thallous hydroxide resembles alkaline hydroxides in being soluble in water but it differs from them in that the solid substance loses water on heating to 100° C., being converted into the oxide.

The sulphide, Tl_2S, which is black in colour, is insoluble in water and in acetic acid, but it is not precipitated by hydrogen sulphide in presence of mineral acids.

The halides show analogies to those of silver. All except the fluoride can be readily precipitated from solution, the iodide being the least and the chloride the most soluble. Thallous chloride is white when freshly precipitated. The iodide is practically insoluble in water and in dilute acid and is bright yellow in colour like lead iodide.

[1] KOLODZIEFF. *Artz. Sachverst. Ztg.*, 1936, **52**, 115.
[2] KAMMLER. *Deut. Zeit. f. Gesmt. Gerichtl. Med.*, 1936, **27**, 202.
[3] PFLEGEL. *Ibid.*, 1937, **27**, 395.
[4] OHEIM. *Ibid.*, 1937, **29**, 95.
[5] BRUMM. *Munch. Med. Wochenschr.*, July 8th, 1938, **85**, 1024.
[6] BÖHMER. *Deut. Gesell. ger. soz. Med. u. Kriminol.*, September, 1938.
All abstracted in the *Medico-legal and Criminological Review.*

The sulphate is readily soluble and shows some resemblance to the alkali sulphates.

The isolation and identification of thallium depend on its conversion successively into sulphide and iodide, followed by the flame test, the spectroscopic test and certain colour reactions.

From tissues or other organic matter,[1] destroyed by the process of Babo and Fresenius, the solution must first be treated with ammonium chloride and ammonia and boiled to remove phosphates, calcium chloride being added if necessary to ensure the complete precipitation of the phosphates which are then filtered off. Thallous sulphide is precipitated by passing hydrogen sulphide through the liquid and this is collected on a filter and washed first with ammonium sulphide solution and afterwards with distilled water. The precipitate is dissolved in hot dilute hydrochloric acid and the solution is again made alkaline with ammonia and boiled. If any precipitate is formed at this stage it is filtered off and discarded. The solution is made just acid with hydrochloric acid and an excess of potassium iodide solution is added. The liquid is boiled and allowed to stand for about twelve hours to ensure the complete precipitation of the iodide, which may be collected in a Gooch crucible, washed successively with potassium iodide solution, distilled water and alcohol and dried at 120° C. until the weight is constant.

Thallous salts, moistened with hydrochloric acid, turn the non-luminous flame bright green and show a characteristic green line in the spectrum.

Berg and Fahrencamp[2] have described a reagent which is said to be a specific precipitant for thallium salts in alkaline tartrate solution containing cyanide. The reagent is the β-aminonaphthalide of thioglycollic acid $C_{10}H_7NHCOCH_2SH$ in which the hydrogen of the SH group can be replaced by metals. The thallium compound contains 48·6 per cent. of Tl.

A solution of thallium sulphate is neutralized with 2N caustic soda solution and treated with 2 g. of sodium tartrate, 3–5 g. of potassium cyanide and 10–20 ml. of 2N caustic soda. This mixture is then made up to 100 ml. with distilled water.

The reagent is a concentrated solution of the naphthalide in acetone and for complete precipitation of the thallium four to five times the theoretical quantity is required. The precipitate, which is at first amorphous, becomes crystalline on boiling and stirring. The vessel is cooled in water and the precipitate is collected in a sintered glass crucible. It is washed with cold water until free from cyanide and then with acetone until free from the reagent, after which it is dried at 100° C. and weighed.

[1] ROCHE LYNCH. *Lancet*, December 20th, 1930.
[2] *Zeit. Anal. Chem.*, 1937, **109**, 305–15. *Analyst*, 1937, **62**, 689.

A sensitive colour reaction is recommended by Picora for the detection of thallium. It is stated that 0·02 mg. can be detected in 1 ml. of solution. The solution is mixed with a few drops of carbon disulphide, a slight excess of ammonia and a little ammonium sulphide; on warming a reddish turbidity is produced.

According to Wenger and Rusconi,[1] thallous salts, treated in acid solution with 0·4 per cent. bismuth nitrate in 20 per cent. nitric acid and 10 per cent. sodium iodide, give a red precipitate. A single drop of each solution is used, and the test will detect 2 mg. thallium in 100 ml. Addition of a drop of concentrated sodium thiosulphate solution prevents the interference of platinum, iron, and cerium; rhodium and palladous salts slowly give a brown precipitate.

Thallium chloride can be extracted from aqueous solution with ether,[2] and a method has been devised, based on this fact, for the detection and determination of the metal.[3] The organic material (not more than 70 g.) is decomposed by treatment with hydrochloric acid and potassium chlorate. The liquid is filtered through glass-wool and the residue is washed with hot water. The combined filtrate and washings are made up to a definite volume and again filtered; 90 per cent. of the filtrate is shaken with ether until a colourless extract is obtained. The aqueous liquid is treated with chlorine and re-extracted with ether. The combined ethereal extracts are evaporated to dryness and the residue is treated with nitric acid and hydrogen peroxide until the organic matter is destroyed; the residual liquid is evaporated almost to dryness and diluted with water, after which it is again concentrated to a small volume on the water-bath. For small amounts of thallium this final volume may be as little as 0·3 ml. The solution is then made slightly alkaline with 25 per cent. ammonia and treated with 20 per cent. potassium iodide solution. The precipitate is allowed to settle overnight, after which it is collected in a Gooch crucible, the filtrate being used to transfer the last portion of the precipitate to the crucible. The precipitate is washed once with water and then with alcohol, after which it is dried at 100° C. and weighed. One part of thallium iodide corresponds to 0·6169 part of metallic thallium.

For quantities of thallium of the order of 1 mg. the colorimetric method of determination is preferable. The precipitation of the thallium iodide is carried out in a centrifuge tube in which it is washed by centrifuging with alcohol until free from potassium iodide. It is then treated with a few drops of concentrated sulphuric acid and, when the decomposition of the iodide is complete, it is

[1] *Helv. Chim. Acta.*, 1943, **26**, 2263.
[2] SHAW. *Ind. Eng. Chem. Anal. Ed.*, 1933, **5**, 93.
[3] KLUGE. *Zeit. Unters. Lebensm.*, 1938, **76**, 156–9.

diluted with 1 ml. of water, mixed with 1–3 drops of 10 per cent. sodium nitrite solution and 0·5 ml. of chloroform. After vigorous shaking, the chloroform layer is allowed to separate and its colour is compared with a series of standards of the same volume containing known amounts of iodine. The standards may be prepared from a solution of thallous sulphate containing 1 mg. of thallium per ml., by precipitating the metal as iodide and treating with nitrous acid and chloroform; or, alternatively, a solution of potassium iodide containing 0·8123 g. per litre, of which 1 ml. corresponds to 1 mg. of thallium, may be used. The ratio of 1 ml. of aqueous liquid to 0·5 ml. of chloroform must be maintained in all the comparison tubes. The limit of the colorimetric method is 0·05 mg. of thallium. The precipitated thallous iodide should be examined spectroscopically.

The distribution of thallium in the organs of a young dog weighing 3·77 kg. poisoned with 1 g. of thallous sulphate, corresponding to 0·81 g. of thallium, was investigated. Of the amount administered fifteen hours before death, 38·52 per cent. was recovered, the distribution being as follows:

Stomach	75·88
Intestines	14·25
Liver	5·32
Lungs	2·49
Kidneys	1·62
Spleen	0·27
Heart and blood	0·18

These figures represent the percentage of the recovered thallium in the various organs.

Mach and Lepper[1] recommend that thallium should be precipitated as chromate and not as iodide; potassium chromate solution is added in the presence of a slight excess of ammonia and the precipitate is collected on a filter and washed, first with 1 per cent. potassium chromate solution and afterwards with acetone.

NICKEL

The most toxic of the compounds of nickel is nickel carbonyl which is prepared by the action of carbon monoxide on the finely divided metal. It is a volatile liquid which decomposes on heating, depositing the metal in a chemically pure condition, this being the basis of the Mond Nickel Process. In the early days of this industry (1902) about twenty-five people were poisoned and three of them

[1] *Zeit. Anal. Chem.*, 1926, **68**, 36–45. *Analyst*, 1926, **51**, 367.

died.   According to Armit,[1] the toxic effects are due to the metal rather than to the carbon monoxide.   The symptoms include cyanosis, fever, coughing with bloody sputum, and giddiness. Death, in the fatal cases, occurred after four to eleven days.   The findings at the autopsies showed chiefly lesions of the lungs, such as haemorrhage and oedema.

For the detection of nickel the organic matter should be destroyed by one of the wet oxidation processes, and the metal separated from the resulting liquid by precipitation as sulphide in alkaline solution as in the ordinary method of inorganic analysis.   The sulphide is dissolved in hydrochloric acid and the liquid boiled to expel hydrogen sulphide, after which it is made alkaline with ammonia and then faintly acid with acetic acid.   To this solution are added a few drops of a 1 per cent. alcoholic solution of dimethylglyoxime after which it is again made alkaline with ammonia.   Traces of nickel are indicated by the formation of a red colour and larger quantities by a red precipitate.   The test is more sensitive if carried out on paper previously impregnated with the oxime solution and dried.   A spot of the test solution on such paper becomes red, if nickel is present, when the spot is exposed to ammonia fumes.

Other oximes may be used instead of dimethylglyoxime, α-benzil-dioxime being especially recommended.

If ferric iron is present the test solution must first be treated with a drop of a saturated solution of sodium tartrate followed by 2 drops of a saturated solution of sodium carbonate.[2]   The alcoholic glyoxime solution is then added and under these conditions it will reveal as little as 0·0005 mg. of nickel in the presence of one thousand times this quantity of iron.

Cobaltous salts interfere with the detection of nickel, and, if present to the extent of fifty times the amount of the latter the detection of nickel is impossible.   Cobaltous salts must therefore be converted into cobaltic oxide by the addition of equal volumes of hydrogen peroxide and saturated sodium carbonate solution. The cobalt will be precipitated if the quantity is sufficiently large ; and, in any case, the presence of nickel can be detected by allowing the alcoholic solution of the reagent to float on the surface of the test solution.

Dithio-oxamide (Rubeanic acid) gives a blue colour or precipitate with nickel salts in alkaline solution.   A drop of the suspected solution is placed on a filter-paper and exposed to ammonia vapour, after which a drop of a 1 per cent. alcoholic solution of the reagent is added.   Under these conditions cobalt gives a brown colour and copper an olive green.

[1] *J. of Hygiene*, 1907, p. 526.
[2] FEIGL.   " Spot Tests ", p. 87.

BARIUM

The soluble salts of barium are very poisonous. Dangerous symptoms have followed the ingestion of the chloride, the nitrate, the sulphide (in common use as a depilatory) and the carbonate, given by mistake instead of the sulphate in preparation for X-ray examination. The method of isolation of barium is that used in ordinary inorganic analysis. Oxidation of organic matter can be carried out either by means of nitric acid or nascent chlorine, but the use of sulphuric acid must be avoided. Metals other than alkaline earths and the alkali metals and also phosphates are removed by the usual methods and barium is precipitated as carbonate, filtered off and redissolved in acetic acid. The following tests are then applied :

(1) Solutions containing barium yield a white precipitate insoluble in nitric acid and hydrochloric acid when treated with dilute sulphuric acid. This precipitate of barium sulphate can be reduced to the sulphide, e.g. by heating on platinum wire in the reducing flame of the bunsen burner, and the residue tested for barium by test No. 5.

(2) Volatile barium salts colour the non-luminous flame green : so also do the salts of copper and thallium, which should have been removed before making the test. The flame spectra of copper, barium and thallium show the following characteristic lines :

Copper	· ·	λ 3247·5, 3274·0
Barium	· ·	λ 5535·5, 4554·9, 4900·0
Thallium	·	λ 3775·7, 2767·9, 3519·2, 5350·5

(3) A 5 per cent. solution of the sodium salt of 6-chlor-5-nitroto-luene-sulphonic acid added to a solution of a barium salt containing as little as 1 part in 2,000 produces a crystalline precipitate. The same reagent yields no precipitate with 10 per cent. solutions of calcium and strontium salts; the reagent may be used for the separation of barium from strontium and calcium in 1 per cent. solution. (Rosenthaler.)

(4) Feigl's test. A drop of a solution containing barium is spotted on filter-paper which has been treated with a freshly prepared solution of sodium rhodizonate. A reddish precipitate is formed which on treatment with hydrochloric acid becomes bright scarlet. Lead and strontium salts also produce red colours, but these are discharged, the former by acetic acid and the latter by hydrochloric acid.

(5) Barium salts in very dilute solution yield long crystals with a 1 per cent. solution of sodium tungstate. Calcium and strontium react only in much stronger solutions and yield spherical crystals.

MAGNESIUM SALTS

Normally, large doses of magnesium sulphate are tolerated when taken by the mouth, but cases of severe poisoning and even death have been reported. The first symptoms are those of a gastro-intestinal irritant; paralysis sometimes follows, and death is the result of respiratory failure. To a large extent the salt is excreted through the kidneys.[1] [2] [3]

Magnesium sulphate has the remarkable property of producing rapid anaesthesia when injected into a vein or one of the cardiac cavities.[4] A large dog, such as an Airedale, becomes unconscious within twenty-five to thirty seconds after the intravenous injection of 20 g. of the hydrated salt in 20 ml. of water. (Such a solution is supersaturated at ordinary temperatures and must be kept at about 40°–50° C. to prevent crystallization.) A muscular spasm follows and during the spasm the heart stops beating. A similar dose injected into the heart cavity often causes death before the completion of the injection.

The National Veterinary Medical Association recommends this method for the destruction of dogs and cats, and it has been used in Cairo for worn-out donkeys.[5]

A case of human poisoning after the intravenous injection of 2 ml. of 20 per cent. magnesium sulphate solution has been reported.[6] The patient, a twenty-one-year-old woman, was admitted to hospital suffering from severe cramp. There was no narcosis, and the diagnosis was tetany due to lack of calcium. The patient recovered after treatment with calcium salts.

For the detection of magnesium the organic matter is destroyed either by the method of Babo and Fresenius or by means of nitric acid, and the product is treated by the methods of ordinary inorganic analysis to eliminate all metals other than magnesium and the alkali metals, phosphates being removed before proceeding to the iron group.

If the quantity of magnesium is sufficiently large it can be precipitated as the triple phosphate, filtered, washed, dried, ignited and weighed as magnesium pyrophosphate.

In small quantities magnesium can be detected by the following tests,[7] but magnesium is normally present in animal tissues.

(1) The reagent is a dilute alcoholic solution of quinalizarin.

[1] SMITH. "Forensic Medicine", 5th ed., p. 468.
[2] *Lancet*, 24.4.09.
[3] *J. Amer. Med. Ass.*, 10.12.10. *Ibid.*, 20.10.28.
[4] Report of the Special Committee of the Nat. Vet. Med. Ass. to study the subject of small animal euthanasia.
[5] Private communication from Colonel Hodgkin of the Brooke Memorial Hospital, Cairo.
[6] ROLLER. *Wien. Klin. Woch.*, 1936, **1**, 241.
[7] FEIGL. "Spot Tests", p. 137.

One or two drops of the test solution are mixed on a spot plate with two drops of the reagent. Caustic soda (2N) is added until the colour changes to violet, the quantity of alkali being noted. Caustic soda is then added in excess, this excess being about one-quarter to one-half of the volume originally added. A blank test is made with the reagent alone; the colour of the blank test is violet, but if magnesium is present the colour is cornflower blue.

(2) The thiazol dyestuff, Titan yellow, is a sensitive reagent for magnesium, producing an orange or red adsorption compound with magnesium hydroxide. A drop of the solution is mixed with a drop of the reagent and a drop of N/10 caustic soda. Many common metals interfere with the reaction and should be removed beforehand, although the interference of metals which form complex cyanides may be made non-effective by the addition of potassium cyanide.

Minute quantities of magnesium may be determined by an indirect colorimetric method which depends on the treatment of magnesium ammonium phosphate with ammonium molybdate to produce the phospho-molybdate.[1] This compound is reduced with hydroquinone, whereby molybdenum blue is produced, and the colour is compared with a standard solution of magnesium which has been treated with the same reagents.

GOLD

Since the introduction of gold compounds into medicine several fatalities have been reported following their use. Fatzer[2] has reported two cases of death following the use of such gold compounds. In the first case a sixty-five-year-old patient was treated with one injection of 0·05 g. and five injections of 0·1 g. of " Allochrysin ". The other patient, sixty years old, received during one month a total quantity of " Solganol " amounting to 3 g. Both deaths were due to hypersensitiveness towards gold preparations. Nevertheless, these and other similar examples have shown that gold therapy is not free from danger.

The usual test for the presence of gold in solution is the reduction of the compound to metallic gold which, except in special circumstances, separates in the colloidal form known as " purple of Cassius ". The organic material is oxidized and the ash is extracted with a solution of potassium cyanide in presence of air. The filtered solution containing potassium aurocyanide is treated with a reducing agent, such as stannous chloride or metallic zinc. A method for the determination of minute quantities of gold in biological fluids has been described by Pollard;[3] it appears to give very satisfactory results.

[1] DENIS. *J. Biol. Chem.*, **52**, 411.
[2] *Schweitzer Med. Wochenschr.*, 1936, **1**, 120.
[3] *Analyst*, 1937, **62**, 597–603.

The principle of the process is to precipitate the gold along with tellurium from a solution acidified with HCl, by means of sulphur dioxide. The tellurium solution is made by dissolving 5 g. of the metal in a mixture consisting of 20 ml. of hydrochloric acid and 5 ml. of nitric acid and evaporating to a thick syrup to get rid of nitric acid. The syrup is diluted with 25 ml. of hydrochloric acid and the volume is made up to 50 ml. with distilled water.

To separate 0·1 mg. of gold from 10 litres of fluid, Pollard uses 2 ml. of the tellurium solution. A quantity of concentrated hydrochloric acid not less than $\frac{1}{10}$ th of the total volume of the liquid is added and sulphur dioxide is passed through until the liquid is saturated with the gas. After standing on the water-bath overnight it is filtered through paper in a small Buchner funnel. The paper and the precipitate are transferred to a porcelain crucible and heated, gently at first, and finally very strongly for a few minutes. The residue contains the whole of the gold and the unvolatilized portion of the tellurium. The cooled residue is dissolved in 6 drops of hydrochloric acid and 2 drops of nitric acid with the aid of a small stirring rod, the crucible being heated gently on a water-bath, away from direct steam. The liquid is then diluted with water. A gentle stream of air is blown on to the surface of the liquid through a capillary tube for a few minutes to remove nitrosyl chloride and free chlorine; this is an essential part of the process.

The pH is adjusted by the use of a buffer consisting of acid potassium fluoride which neutralizes the excess of either alkalinity or acidity. The gold is in the form of chloroauric acid and is determined by titration with an organic reducing agent such as hydroquinone. The indicator is o-dianisidine (now preferred to o-tolidine, which was formerly used), which forms an intense red colour with chloroauric acid discharged on reduction.

The solutions required are:

(1) Standard hydroquinone solution made by dissolving 0·4186 g. of the pure substance in about 200 ml. of water, adding 10 ml. of hydrochloric acid and making up to 500 ml. (1 ml. = 1 mg. of gold).

(2) o-dianisidine solution: 0·5 g. dissolved in 200 ml. of water, mixed with 2 ml. of hydrochloric acid and made up to 500 ml.

(A micro-burette graduated in hundredths of a ml. is used. The end-point is shown by the disappearance of the red colour.)

Substances which interfere with this process are: mercury, platinum, palladium, selenium, titanium, tin, antimony, bismuth and molybdenum.

In presence of metals of the platinum group other reducing agents are substituted for the hydroquinone; p-phenylenediamine or " metol " (p-methylaminophenol) may be used.

CHAPTER V

CORROSIVE ACIDS AND ALKALIS

POISONOUS SALTS OF ALKALIS. HALOGENS

Mineral Acids

THE examination of specimens for free mineral acids in cases of poisoning is not always as simple a matter as might be supposed. The question is complicated by the fact that alkaline antidotes may have been given and that exact information as to the quantity of antidote and the conditions under which it has been administered is often lacking. The analyst should insist on having the fullest possible information on the history of the case before beginning his work.

Moreover, nitric and sulphuric acids are more or less completely decomposed by prolonged contact with animal tissues so that the results of analysis, especially quantitative analysis, need very careful interpretation. A further complication is that the stomach normally contains chlorides and very often sulphates. Finally, free hydrochloric acid is a normal constituent of the gastric juice and is usually present in the stomach contents.

Diagnosis of poisoning by mineral acids depends largely on the post-mortem appearance, especially the appearance of the lips and the skin about the lips, the mouth, throat, oesophagus and the stomach (see p. 21).

If washings of these parts, made before the administration of any antidote, are available the chief difficulties of the analyst are eliminated.

The first step is to prove the presence of free mineral acid. The reddening of blue litmus is not a sufficient indication, but if the washings do not give an acid reaction to litmus it is useless to go further. Congo red paper should be used; in presence of any considerable quantity of free mineral acid the red colour changes to pure blue. Small traces of mineral acids or larger quantities of vegetable acids change the colour to reddish purple. Methyl violet also indicates free mineral acid, the colour changing to green. Another indicator which is sometimes used is Günzburg's reagent, which is prepared by dissolving 1 part of phloroglucinol and 1 part of vanillin in 30 parts of alcohol. The test is made by evaporating a few drops of the reagent, with about 1 ml. of the liquid to be tested, to complete dryness. In presence of sulphuric or hydrochloric acid the residue has a definite red or reddish yellow colour. Nitric acid also yields a colour, which is usually more yellow. Organic acids do not react.

Portions of the liquid should then be tested for the sulphate, chloride and nitrate ions, using the barium chloride test for the sulphate ion, the silver nitrate test for the chloride ion, and for the nitrate ion first the diphenylamine test and afterwards the brucine-sulphuric acid reagent.

Sulphuric Acid

If the sulphate ion is present, as shown by a precipitate of barium sulphate insoluble in hydrochloric acid, the liquid must be tested for free sulphuric acid after the elimination of metallic sulphates. An aliquot part is evaporated as far as possible on the water-bath. The basin is washed out with absolute alcohol and the whole of the residue is thereby transferred to a beaker and allowed to cool. When cold the liquid is filtered and again evaporated to dryness, as nearly as possible, on the water-bath. The basin is now washed out with distilled water and the liquid is boiled in order to hydrolyze ethylsulphuric acid. The liquid is again tested with Congo paper and a portion of it with barium chloride. If these tests give positive reactions the presence of sulphuric acid should be confirmed by the following tests.

(1) If the quantity of the barium precipitate is sufficient it should be collected, dried, mixed with an excess of sodium carbonate and fused on charcoal. The residue is tested for sulphide by dissolving in water and placing a drop of the solution on a piece of metallic silver. A dark stain on the silver indicates the presence of sulphide produced by reduction of the sulphate.

(2) A portion of the liquid is concentrated to a small bulk by evaporation on the water-bath; a small piece of copper wire is put in and the liquid is heated over a small flame. In the presence of sulphuric acid, sulphur dioxide is evolved, which is recognized by its odour.

Hydrochloric Acid

Before testing for free hydrochloric acid the concentration should be increased by distillation. When a very dilute solution of hydrochloric acid is distilled the first runnings contain very little of the acid. It is advisable therefore to collect the distillate in fractions. The distillation is carried out in an ordinary distillation flask, the side-tube being connected to a Liebig's condenser. The flask should be heated in an oil-bath and the receiver should be immersed in iced water. The first fraction collected may be conveniently 50 per cent. of the original volume, the second 20 per cent., and the third and fourth 10 per cent. each. The distillation is continued as far as possible, the fifth fraction containing the last portion of the distillate. Each fraction is then tested by mixing 1 or 2 drops with a drop of silver nitrate solution in a capsule of black glass. Any fraction which shows no more than a barely perceptible turbidity may be rejected. The fractions which give definite reactions for the chloride ion are united and the total volume measured. The reaction of the liquid to Congo paper should be observed. A portion of the distillate is titrated with N/10 sodium hydroxide using phenolphthalein as indicator, and the amount of chloride in the remainder is determined either volumetrically using Volhard's method, or gravimetrically by precipitating with silver nitrate in the presence of added nitric acid, collecting the silver chloride in a Gooch crucible containing asbestos, washing with distilled water, alcohol and ether and drying at 100° C. to constant weight.

Nitric Acid

The examination for free nitric acid, as for free hydrochloric acid, should be made after concentrating the liquid by distillation, the first portion of the distillate being rejected and the more concentrated portion tested first with Congo red to prove the presence of a volatile mineral acid. Portions of the distillate are then subjected to the following tests.

(1) A solution of diphenylamine is made by adding a drop or two of water to a few crystals of the substance and then mixing with about 5 ml. of concentrated sulphuric acid. If the sulphuric acid is quite pure and the test-tube absolutely clean the reagent will be colourless; it becomes blue on exposure to the laboratory atmosphere and is best freshly prepared as required. About 1 ml. of the distillate in a white porcelain basin is treated with the reagent by running a few drops of the latter down the side of the basin. If nitric acid is present a bright blue colour will be seen at the junction of the two liquids. The test is not specific for nitric acid, but it is useful as a negative test, the absence of colour proving the absence of the nitrate ion. Before making the test it is necessary to apply a few drops of the reagent to the empty basin to ensure that it is free from substances such as nitrates, chlorates and chromates, which also produce a blue colour; if it is not absolutely clean it must be repeatedly rinsed with distilled water until it gives a blank test with the reagent. This is particularly necessary owing to the custom of cleaning apparatus with a solution of dichromate.

(2) The brucine-sulphuric acid test may be applied in various ways. Autenrieth recommends that the solution to be tested should be mixed with an equal volume of 1 per cent. brucine sulphate

solution in a test-tube and sulphuric acid poured down the side of the tube so as to form a lower layer. An orange-red zone of contact indicates the presence of the nitrate ion.

(3) A solution of pure ferrous sulphate is mixed with the test solution in a test-tube and sulphuric acid is poured in to form a lower layer; in the presence of the nitrate ion a brown ring between the two layers is seen. Emich recommends the carrying out of this test under the low power of the microscope. A portion of the distillate, evaporated to dryness with nitrate-free alkali, is transferred to a slide and moistened with concentrated sulphuric acid. A particle of ferrous sulphate is introduced into the drop by means of a platinum wire and the brown colour is observed.

(4) This test depends upon the reduction of nitric acid to nitrous acid by metallic magnesium. The resulting solution is tested for the nitrite ion, either with the Griess-Ilosvay reagent (p. 139) or by the test of Baumgarten and Marggraff. In the latter test the neutralized solution is treated with amino-sulphonic acid and barium chloride. The nitrite reacts with the amino-sulphonic acid to produce a sulphate which yields the usual precipitate with barium chloride.

$$KNO_2 + NH_2SO_3H = KHSO_4 + H_2O + N_2$$

(5) A portion of the distillate is evaporated to dryness with a minute piece of copper. Red fumes of nitrogen peroxide and a green coloured solution indicate that free nitric acid is present. This test, although not the most delicate, is probably the most satisfactory.

If, in fatal poisoning with a mineral acid, washings of the mouth and gastro-intestinal tract are not available for analysis and samples of the viscera have to be examined, an aqueous extract is made from the minced tissue, and this, after filtration, is treated in the manner above described.

Quantitative determination is of little value in sulphuric and nitric acid poisoning, but in the case of fatal hydrochloric acid poisoning a quantitative determination on the whole stomach or an aliquot part of it is essential. The hydrochloric acid content of the stomach is normally from 0·2 to 0·3 per cent., and unless a considerably larger quantity than this can be proved to be present the diagnosis, by chemical analysis, of hydrochloric acid poisoning fails.

ALKALINE HYDROXIDES AND CARBONATES

The lesions due to caustic alkalis show certain points of resemblance to those due to mineral acids, the main difference being that tissue corroded by alkalis is usually slimy whereas corrosions due to acids may be hard and brittle.

As in acid poisoning the problem of the analyst is complicated by the fact that the gastro-intestinal tract normally contains salts of alkali metals; and, therefore, in order to diagnose alkali poisoning it is necessary to prove the presence of the hydroxide or the carbonate.   Again the question of the administration of antidotes is obviously of fundamental importance and the chemist should have all the information possible about the history of the case.   Stomach washes made before treatment with acidic antidotes present no difficulty.   The chief difficulty arises from the fact that if the material to be examined is putrefied the reaction is almost sure to be alkaline owing to the presence of ammonia.   If ammonia is present the quantity of it should be determined.   Fluid material should be measured and distilled, the flask being heated in an oil-bath and the lower end of the condenser should dip into a measured quantity of standard hydrochloric acid.   When the distillation has been carried on as far as possible, aliquot fractions of the distillate should be tested for ammonium salts and the remainder should be titrated with N/100 or N/10 caustic soda, using methyl red as indicator.

The residue in the distillation flask may contain hydroxides or carbonates of potassium or sodium.   The flask is washed out with a little distilled water and the washings tested with litmus or phenolphthalein.   If the reaction is alkaline it is still necessary to distinguish between alkalinity due to caustic alkalis and that due to alkaline carbonate.   This is done by adding a drop of phenolphthalein solution and excess of barium chloride to the liquid; in presence of caustic alkali the red colour persists, whereas in presence of carbonate ion this is precipitated as barium carbonate and the solution is colourless.   The ordinary tests for sodium and potassium are then made.

For the examination of tissues an aqueous extract is made from the minced material and this, after filtration, is treated in the manner above described.

OXALIC ACID AND OXALATES

Oxalic acid and the soluble oxalates produce toxic symptoms and sometimes death in a remarkably short time.   The acid not only acts as a corrosive poison on the mucous membrane but it is very rapidly absorbed.   According to Bischoff[1] as much as 0.285 g. has been found in the liver of a person who died within fifteen minutes.   Dr. Sydney Smith,[2] quoting Christison, agrees with the latter's statement that if a person swallows a white crystalline substance which has a strongly acid taste, produces a burning sensation in the throat and stomach and causes vomiting, especially

~er., 1883, p. 1337.
~rensic Medicine ", 5th Edition, p. 434.

if there is blood in the vomit, and if the pulse is imperceptible and there is extreme languor followed by death in ten, twenty or thirty minutes, the diagnosis of oxalic acid poisoning may be taken as almost certain.

Less than 4 g. of oxalic acid has been known to cause death within four hours. Fifteen g. is likely to cause death in most cases. If life is prolonged there is usually diarrhoea, although death very often occurs before the bowels are moved.

Oxalic acid differs from most of the mineral acids in that its toxicity depends less on the concentration of the acid, and that the soluble salts are almost equally toxic. Naturally, the post-mortem lesions are not so pronounced when the solution is dilute.

Elsdon and Stubbs[1] have submitted the methods commonly used for the isolation of oxalic acid and oxalates from stomach contents to critical examination. They found:

(1) That evaporation to dryness and extraction of the dry residue with alcohol, again evaporating to dryness, and shaking an aqueous extract of this residue with ether is an inefficient method.

(2) That dialysis has some advantages as a qualitative method but that it is too slow for quantitative work and that the dialyzed solution is not, as a rule, free from substances which interfere with the subsequent tests.

(3) Precipitation with lead acetate solution, separation of the lead oxalate, decomposition of the latter with hydrogen sulphide, filtration and reprecipitation of the oxalic acid as the calcium salt is a method which may give good results, but it involves slow filtration and very tedious washings of precipitates. The precipitation with lead very often has to be repeated and although the filtrate thus obtained yields fairly pure calcium oxalate on treatment with calcium chloride solution, the method is considered cumbersome, and is not recommended.

The method they recommend is to centrifuge the liquid, diluted with water if necessary, for some minutes. The clear liquid is decanted and the residue is broken up, mixed with water and again allowed to settle, and the clear liquid decanted. The decanted liquid and the washings are mixed with 15–20 per cent. of concentrated hydrochloric acid and heated on the water-bath for about two hours. The liquid is now in such a condition that it can be easily filtered and the precipitate washed. The mixed filtrate and washings are made alkaline with strong ammonia and then acidified with acetic acid. Calcium chloride solution is added and the precipitated calcium oxalate is collected on a filter. It may be necessary to redissolve the precipitate in hot hydrochloric acid, filter and repeat the treatment with ammonia, acetic acid and

[1] *Analyst*, 1930, **55**, 321.

calcium chloride. When a pure white precipitate has been obtained it is collected on a filter, washed, dried at 100° C. and weighed as calcium oxalate (CaC_2O_4, H_2O).

The gravimetric determination should be controlled by redissolving the precipitate in hot hydrochloric acid and titrating with N/10 permanganate solution.

Elsdon and Stubbs also point out that an organic acid which reduces permanganate and gives a precipitate with calcium chloride insoluble in acetic acid is not necessarily oxalic acid. It may be tartaric acid for example. But whereas a solution containing 1 per cent. of oxalic acid acidified with acetic acid gives an immediate precipitate in the cold with calcium chloride solution, a solution of tartaric acid of similar concentration yields no precipitate until the solution has been shaken or allowed to stand for some time.

Paget and Berger[1] have described a qualitative test for oxalic acid which depends on its conversion to glyoxylic acid by reduction with metallic zinc. The glyoxylic acid is recognized by the red colour produced when it is treated with phenylhydrazine and potassium ferrocyanide. The following is a description of the test. About 5 ml. of a solution containing approximately 0·01 per cent. of oxalic acid are mixed with 1–2 ml. of concentrated hydrochloric acid and a strip of pure zinc (1–2 g.) is immersed in the liquid. The solution is boiled for one minute and after waiting for two minutes the liquid is transferred to a test-tube containing 5 drops of a 1 per cent. solution of phenylhydrazine. This mixture is heated almost to boiling and then thoroughly cooled. An equal volume of pure concentrated hydrochloric acid is added to prevent the precipitation of zinc ferrocyanide on adding 5 drops of a 5 per cent. solution of potassium ferrocyanide. The latter reagent serves as an oxidizing agent and, in presence of iron, hydrogen peroxide may be substituted for it. A red colour appears on shaking. It is stated that under the specified conditions glyoxal is not formed and that acetic, formic, succinic, lactic, tartaric, malic and citric acids do not interfere.

In the presence of acids such as nitric acid, which are readily reduced by nascent hydrogen, the period of reduction with zinc should be prolonged by about five minutes. Sulphuric, hydrobromic, hypobromous and phosphoric acids do not interfere.

Another colour reaction of glyoxylic acid may be used as a test for oxalic acid and according to Pesez,[2] it is capable of detecting 1 part of oxalic acid in 10,000 parts of solution. The oxalic acid (5 ml.) is mixed with 1 ml. of sulphuric acid (1 : 2) and 2 drops of 10 per cent. copper sulphate solution; about 1 g. of zinc is then put

[1] *J. Pharm. Chim.*, 1938, **27**, 577–9. *Analyst*, 1938, **63**, 620.
[2] *Bull. Soc. Chim.*, 1936 (5), **3**, 2072–4. *Analyst*, 1937, **62**, 145.

into the liquid so as to form a zinc-copper couple. After three minutes 0·2 ml. of the reduced solution is added to 2 ml. of concentrated sulphuric acid and 0·1 ml. of a 2 per cent. aqueous solution of resorcinol. A pale blue colour develops and this is intensified by warming.

Nitric, nitrous, chromic, bromic, perchloric and hypochlorous ions do not interfere, but if bromides or iodides are present the test should be modified in the following way: 2 ml. of sulphuric acid and 2 drops of the resorcinol solution are mixed together in a test-tube and 4 drops of the glyoxylic acid solution are run down the side of the tube. A blue zone of contact is formed between the two liquids.

Tartaric acid, in the absence of oxalic acid, yields a rose-violet zone when treated in the same way.

POTASSIUM CHLORATE

Although this salt is commonly used as an antiseptic for the mouth and throat it is definitely poisonous. A dose of 15–30 g. may prove fatal to an adult, and a case has been reported in which a child three weeks old died after swallowing 1 g.

Not only are chlorates local irritants, but they act directly on the blood, converting oxyhaemoglobin into methaemoglobin, which may be recognized by its chocolate-brown colour and by its absorption spectrum, converted into that of reduced haemoglobin by such reducing agents as sodium hydrosulphite.

The usual method of extraction from vomited matter, stomach-contents and tissues is dialysis. The material to be examined, minced and mixed with water if necessary, is placed in the inner compartment of a Graham's dialyzer. The surface of the membrane should be large enough for all the material to be spread over it in a thin layer and the outer vessel should contain plenty of distilled water. Dialysis is continued for five or six hours, after which the liquid in the outer vessel, which should contain the greater part of the chlorate, is evaporated to dryness on the water-bath. The residue is taken up in distilled water, filtered if necessary, and tested for chlorates.

The following qualitative tests may be used:

(1) *The Indigo Test.* The solution is acidified with dilute sulphuric acid, sufficient indigo-carmine solution is added to give a distinct blue colour and sulphurous acid is added. In the presence of a chlorate the blue colour of the indigo is changed to green or greenish yellow.

(2) *The Silver Nitrate Test.* Silver nitrate, added to a solution of chlorate, yields no precipitate. If any chloride is present the

precipitate produced by the addition of silver nitrate must be filtered off. The filtrate is then mixed with nitric acid and a reducing agent such as formaldehyde, when the silver chlorate in solution is converted into the insoluble chloride. The precipitate should be allowed to settle and, after decanting the clear liquid, the solubility of the precipitate in cold ammonia solution should be tested.

(3) A particle of the dry residue is mixed with 1 drop of concentrated hydrochloric acid in a test-tube and heated on the water-bath; if a chlorate is present there is effervescence with the evolution of chlorine which may be recognized by its odour and yellow colour. After the mixture has been warmed for one or two minutes it may be shaken with a few drops of potassium iodide solution and a drop of chloroform; the chloroform is coloured violet by the liberated iodine. This test is not specific, as nitrites behave in the same way, nitrogen peroxide being first liberated and afterwards setting free iodine from the potassium iodide.

(4) A solution of a chlorate heated with a drop of aniline and a little hydrochloric acid yields a blue to green colouration, and under certain conditions, a precipitate of a similar colour.

(5) Chlorates react with the diphenylamine reagent, producing a blue colour.

Roy[1] tests for chlorate in the presence of halides, perchlorate, persulphate, nitrate, or phosphate by evaporating the solution to be tested, in a porcelain dish, and adding to the dry residue a few drops of a reagent prepared by adding 9 ml. of concentrated sulphuric acid slowly and with constant shaking, to 3 ml. of pyridine, cooling the liquid. Chlorate gives a permanent violet colour (·01 mg. detectable). Bromate and iodate give a similar colour; chromate and other coloured ions mask the colour. The test can be made roughly quantitative.

For *quantitative determination* the solution is made up to a definite volume and divided into two equal parts. The first portion is used for the determination of chlorides already existing as such, by adding nitric acid and excess of silver nitrate solution. The liquid is boiled and the precipitated chloride is collected in a Gooch crucible, washed with distilled water, alcohol and ether, dried and weighed. From the weight of the precipitate the amount of chloride is calculated; 143·5 g. of silver chloride corresponding to 74·5 g. of potassium chloride.

In the second portion of the liquid the chlorate is reduced to chloride by heating on the water-bath after adding acetic acid and excess of metallic zinc. After heating for half an hour the liquid is filtered and treated with nitric acid and silver nitrate as before. The difference between the two weighings gives the amount of

¹ *J. Indian Chem. Soc.*, 1941, **18**, 165.

silver chloride corresponding to the potassium chlorate originally present, 143·5 g. of silver chloride being equivalent to 122·5 g. of potassium chlorate. According to Bischoff,[1] potassium chlorate is completely and very rapidly reduced to chloride by putrid organic matter.

NITRITES

Small traces of nitrites occur normally in stomach and intestinal contents owing to the reduction of the nitrates in food by bacterial action; and by specially sensitive reactions, these traces can be detected in saliva and some other secretions. In large doses nitrites, like chlorates, act as irritant poisons on the mucous membranes and also act on the blood pigment, converting oxyhaemoglobin into methaemoglobin.

Kobert[2] regarded sodium nitrite as a relatively mild poison. He reported a case in which a patient took several hourly doses of 0·5 g. without dangerous symptoms, although he mentioned nausea, diarrhoea, cyanosis, faintness and increased diuresis.

Scholes[3] has reported three deaths in one family by poisoning with sodium nitrite, the symptoms being vomiting, cyanosis, difficulty in breathing, stupor and collapse. He found the following quantities of nitrite, estimated as sodium nitrite, in the three stomachs: (a) 4·275 g., (b) 1·284 g., and (c) 0·005 g. In the third case the stomach, that of a child, had been washed out before death.

For the detection of nitrites the material may be acidified with dilute acetic acid and distilled in a current of carbon dioxide, the nitrous fumes being collected in aqueous solution by allowing the end of the condenser to dip into water, thereby regenerating the nitrous acid decomposed by heating with acetic acid. The qualitative tests should include the following:

(1) The starch-iodide test. Starch-potassium iodide paper is turned blue by a solution of a nitrite in presence of dilute acid.

(2) The diazotization test. In presence of a nitrite and free mineral acid an aromatic amine is diazotized, and the resulting compound can be converted into an azo dye by coupling with a phenol or another aromatic amine. This is the basis of the Griess-Ilosvay reaction, in which a mixture of α-naphthylamine and sulphanilic acid is used. This test is both delicate and specific (cf. p. 66).

The *quantitative determination* of nitrites can be effected by titration with permanganate in the absence of interfering organic matter. The diazo reaction, which is quantitative under properly controlled conditions, can be used as a volumetric method, the

[1] AUTENRIETH'S " Detection of Poisons ", 6th Edition, p. 318.
[2] *Ibid.*, p. 321.
[3] *Analyst*, 1936, **61**, 685.

nitrite being run from a burette into an ice-cold solution of sulphanilic acid mixed with excess of dilute hydrochloric acid. Starch-potassium iodide paper is used as an external indicator. However, the most suitable method in poisoning cases is probably the gravimetric one of treating an aliquot part of the extract or distillate with silver bromate in acetic acid solution and weighing the silver bromide formed: 62·7 g. of silver bromide corresponding to 69 g. of sodium nitrite. The chloride content of another aliquot part must be determined and allowed for.

POTASSIUM BROMIDE AND BROMINE

Liquid bromine or its vapours cause asphyxiation and also staining and blistering of the mucous membranes, and even of the skin.

Poisoning by alkali bromides may be acute, or, when the drugs have been administered over a long period, chronic.

The acute symptoms are those of an irritant poison together with giddiness, headache and in severe cases, coma. Chronic poisoning shows itself most usually in rashes resembling acne on the face and head.

Bromides are not quickly excreted by the kidneys. Autenrieth has shown experimentally that a healthy adult after taking two doses of sodium bromide, 8 g. in all, may excrete the drug continuously in the urine for six or seven weeks. The same author has reported the examination of the viscera of an adult who had not taken bromide for at least twenty-eight days before death; considerable quantities of bromine were detected in the liver and kidneys and also in the blood and brain.

If stomach washings have to be examined for free bromine, distillation in steam should be attempted, using a portion of the liquid, but success is not very likely as the bromine immediately combines with organic matter. Free hydrobromic acid may be present, this being produced at the same time as the organic bromo-derivatives. The distillate should be tested both for free bromine and hydrobromic acid, using the following tests.

(1) A dilute solution of phenol, treated with an aqueous solution of free bromine, yields a precipitate of tribromphenol. This is not a very delicate test for bromine, as the precipitate is only formed when the quantity of the latter, relatively to the phenol, is in considerable excess.

(2) The liquid is shaken with chloroform; free bromine colours the chloroform yellow.

(3) A dilute solution of fluorescein (less than 1 per 1,000) in 35 per cent. acetic acid is spotted on to thick filter-paper and dried.

When this is treated with free bromine the colour changes to pink owing to the formation of eosin.

If negative results are obtained in the above tests for free bromine, the distillate may be neutralized with sodium carbonate and evaporated to dryness on the water-bath, after which the following tests are applied to portions of the residue.

(1) A solution of 2·5 g. of copper sulphate in 50 ml. of water is mixed with 100 ml. of concentrated sulphuric acid. A drop of this reagent with a trace of bromide gives a brownish-violet colour or precipitate (Emich).

(2) The fluorescein test is applied to bromides according to Pavlinowa in the following manner. A piece of filter-paper is soaked in an alkaline solution of fluorescein and dried. A drop of a 5–10 per cent. sodium nitrite solution mixed with 3 per cent. hydrogen peroxide is placed close to a drop of dilute sulphuric acid and between the two a drop of the solution to be tested. A rose-pink colour which can, if necessary, be intensified by means of ammonia fumes, is formed.

If the first distillate does not yield satisfactory results a second sample, strongly acidified with sulphuric acid and mixed with excess of potassium permanganate may be distilled and the distillate, made alkaline with sodium carbonate, evaporated to dryness. The same tests for bromide are applied to the distillate, but, obviously, positive results do not necessarily indicate the presence of free bromine in the material under examination.

Determination of Combined Bromine

(1) Samples of blood, urine or viscera can only be examined for combined bromine, and must first be reduced to ash by heating in a nickel basin with pure sodium hydroxide. The charred material is then heated with excess of pure potassium nitrate until a white melt is obtained. The basin should be heated from the side and from above to avoid loss by spurting. The heating must not be unduly prolonged, nor must a blow-pipe be used. When cold the melt is extracted with a small quantity of water and the solution is poured through a filter into a separating funnel; the basin is washed with a further quantity of water which is poured through the same filter. Excess of dilute sulphuric acid is added and, when the evolution of carbon dioxide has ceased, a concentrated solution of permanganate is added drop by drop until all traces of nitrite are completely oxidized and a slight excess of permanganate is present. The solution is then repeatedly extracted with chloroform until the last extract is colourless. The combined extracts are filtered, and the filter-paper is afterwards washed with a little more chloroform.

The filtered solution is made up to a definite volume and the colour compared with that of a chloroformic solution of bromine made in the same way from a 1 in 1,000 solution of potassium bromide.

Blank tests must be made on the caustic soda and potassium nitrate used.

(2) Brodie and Friedman[1] have published a method for the determination of quantities of bromine of the order of 0.06–2 mg. in 200 mg. of tissues. The dried tissue is weighed in a 30 ml. nickel crucible and covered with 3 g. of sodium hydroxide. The crucible is placed in a larger nickel crucible of 100 ml. capacity, the bottom of which is covered with a layer of sand 0.5 cm. thick. The larger crucible is supported by metal cross-bars in an iron cylinder and the temperature is gradually raised to a red heat. When bubbling has almost ceased, potassium nitrate is added, a few mg. at a time, until all organic matter is destroyed, as is shown by the absence of bubbling when more nitrate is added. The crucible is rotated until the melt has solidified on the sides. It is then cooled almost completely and 15 ml. of warm water are added, after which the crucible is placed in an oven maintained at 100° C. for fifteen minutes. The solution is transferred to a beaker and thence to a conical flask, using sufficient wash-water to make the total volume 30 ml. When the liquid is cold, 2 ml. of concentrated sulphuric acid are added cautiously, drop by drop, down the side of the flask, after which it is again cooled. After the further addition of 0.3 ml. of concentrated sulphuric acid, sodium carbonate is cautiously added until the liquid is alkaline. This is followed by 2 g. of sodium dihydrogen phosphate and 6 ml. of a normal solution of sodium hypochlorite. The flask is then immersed in a boiling water-bath for ten minutes after which the excess of hypochlorite is destroyed with 5 ml. of 50 per cent. sodium formate solution, the flask being again heated for five minutes. When cold the liquid is transferred to a 500 ml. wide-mouthed conical flask and diluted to 160 ml. To this are added 10 g. of sodium dihydrogen phosphate and 40 ml. of 6N sulphuric acid. Three drops of 10 per cent. ammonium molybdate solution and 1 g. of potassium iodide are next added; when the iodide is dissolved the liberated iodine is titrated with N/200 thiosulphate solution.

(3) Hahn[2] states that the liberation of bromine by excess of chlorine is not quantitative but that it may be made so by substituting chloramine-T for chlorine; the liberated bromine is then determined by the conversion of fluorescein into eosin. The reagents used are:

(a) Five g. of pure fluorescein in 5 ml. N/10 caustic soda diluted to 1 litre.

[1] J. Biol. Chem., 1938, **124**, 511–18. Analyst, 1938, **63**, 671.
[2] Mikrochem., 1935, **17**, 222–35. Analyst, 1937, **62**, 153.

(b) Buffer solution (pH 5·6–5·5), prepared by neutralizing N/10 caustic soda with acetic acid and adding $\frac{1}{9}$th to $\frac{1}{10}$th extra acetic acid.

(c) Chloramine-T; 0·01–0·1 molar.

(d) Five per cent. caustic soda containing 0·5 per cent. sodium thiosulphate.

For amounts of bromine up to 0·002 mg. 3 drops of the buffer solution, 1 drop of fluorescein and 1 drop of chloramine-T are used. After one to one-and-a-half minutes the reaction is stopped by adding alkaline thiosulphate solution. If the original bromide solution is not neutral it must be made so, using methyl-red, before carrying out the test.

(4) Conway[1] describes a micro method, using micro-diffusion, in which bromine is liberated by dichromate-sulphuric acid and, after diffusion, is determined iodometrically.

As Dr. Roche Lynch has pointed out, the detection of bromine may be the only evidence that can be obtained of poisoning by such ureides as adalin and bromural.

IODINE

The commonest cause of iodine poisoning is attempted suicide by swallowing the tincture. Such attempts are very common in Egypt, but, up to the present, fatal results have not been recorded. If any considerable quantity of the tincture has been swallowed it is usually possible to detect iodine in the stomach-washings or the urine by simply acidifying the filtered liquid with sulphuric acid, adding excess of sodium nitrite and shaking with chloroform. The chloroform is coloured violet. If the direct test fails to show the presence of iodine the liquid is evaporated to dryness with a little caustic soda and the carbonaceous matter in the ash is oxidized with the aid of a little potassium nitrate. The ash is dissolved in water, acidified with dilute sulphuric acid and shaken with chloroform, more sodium nitrite being added if required. As in the determination of bromides, blank tests must be made on the caustic soda and the potassium nitrate. This is, of course, absolutely necessary in view of the fact that iodides are commonly present as impurities in saltpetre.

FLUORIDES AND SILICOFLUORIDES

Hydrofluoric acid is a powerful corrosive poison causing painful blisters on the skin and loss of finger-nails if these come in contact with the acid. If the fumes are inhaled the respiratory passages may become corroded. The wounds on the skin sometimes become gangrenous.[2]

[1] Micro Diffusion Analysis, 1947. p. 177 ff.
[2] " Industrial Poisoning ": Rambousek. Arnold, p. 38.

Chronic fluorine poisoning manifests itself in mottled teeth, a symptom which may be produced by as little as 1 mg. per litre of a fluoride in drinking water. Fluorides were not recognized as the cause of mottled teeth until 1931.[1] A year later, in Denmark, a much more serious symptom, osteosclerosis, was traced to fluoride poisoning. In one cryolite factory fifty-seven out of sixty-eight workers suffered from this disease.

Fluorides sold for the destruction of vermin have been responsible for a number of deaths.

In 1937, Roholm[2] published an exhaustive dissertation on the subject, dealing with both acute and chronic poisoning. In a list of 34 recorded fatal cases he mentions the following symptoms: vomiting (31 cases), pains in the abdomen (17 cases), diarrhoea (13 cases), and convulsions (11 cases).

Hydrofluoric acid and hydrofluosilicic acid may cause death within a few minutes, five, ten and fifteen minutes having been reported. The alkali salts act a little more slowly, the lethal periods varying from forty-five minutes to several days.

Signs of deep corrosion are almost invariably found at the autopsy, both with the free acids and the alkali salts. Roholm (op. cit., pp. 12–23) gives full details of these lesions and (pp. 24 and 25) details of symptoms in non-fatal acute cases.

The lowest recorded lethal dose of sodium fluoride for an adult is about 4 g. But of the silicofluoride, less than 1 g. has caused death.

Chronic poisoning of cattle is common in the neighbourhood of cryolite factories, the teeth and the bones of the animals being particularly affected. Cattle have also been poisoned by being fed on the waste matter from distilleries where, formerly, fluorides were used to disinfect the fermentation mashes. Experiments on rats have shown that distinct deterioration of the dental enamel was produced by 0·0014 per cent. of sodium fluoride in the diet, and some of the rats were affected by much less. Definite thickening of the bones has been noted in sheep which have been fed on hay containing 2–2·5 parts of fluorine per 1,000,000. For the isolation of fluorides from tissues and from bones and teeth, three methods have been recommended. Brüning and Quast[3] used a lime-fusion process; Willard and Winter[4] destroyed organic matter with perchloric acid in the presence of silica and distilled off the resulting hydrofluosilicic acid, and Fabre[5] used an electrodialyzer.

The qualitative tests used for the identification of fluorides are:

[1] B.M.J., 21.1.39, p. 120.
[2] " Fluorine Intoxication; A Clinical-hygienic Study." Lewis, 1937.
[3] Zeitsch. Angew. Chem., 44 (1931), p. 656.
[4] Ind. Eng. Chem. Anal. Ed., 1933, 5, 7. Analyst, 1933, 58, 242.
[5] J. Pharm. Chim., 1938, 27, 467–76. Analyst, 1938, 63. 615.

(1) the etching test, (2) the hanging-drop test as modified by Feigl and Crumholtz,[1] (3) the flame test, and (4) the zirconium-lake test.

The Etching Test. The ordinary way of carrying out this test is to liberate gaseous hydrofluoric acid from a fluoride by means of concentrated sulphuric acid in a platinum or lead capsule covered with a watch-glass, the under side of which is coated with a very thin layer of paraffin wax which is scratched to expose portions of the glass to the acid fumes. This test has been investigated by Caley and Ferrer[2] who found that, to ensure a high degree of sensitivity, it was necessary to take special precautions against leakage of the gas and to heat the mixture to 150° C. At 110°–115° C. the time required for the reaction was excessive and by raising the temperature to 175° C. difficulties were caused by the volatilization of the sulphuric acid. Moreover, they recommend that no wax should be used, having found that etching effects produced on a clean microscope cover-slip were quite easily visible when the glass was moistened by breathing on it. Their apparatus consisted of a hollow leaden cylinder with a flange to facilitate handling with tongs, and a heavy leaden cover. The cover-slip was placed between the top of the cylinder and the cover. They found that very definite etching was produced by 1 mg.

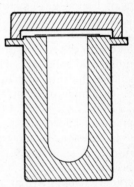

FIG. 17. Etching test for fluorides (Caley and Ferrer).

of calcium fluoride in half an hour and that 0·05 mg. produced perceptible effects in the same time, the temperature being maintained at 140°–150° C. This smaller quantity required twelve hours to produce the same effect at 110°–115° C.

The Hanging Drop Test. In this test, the fluoride is converted into the volatile silicon tetrafluoride by warming with quartz sand and concentrated sulphuric acid, and the liberated gas is taken up in a hanging drop of water. The precipitate formed may not be obvious when the quantity of fluorine is small but the test can be made more sensitive by converting the silicic and hydrofluosilicic acids into silicomolybdic acid and reducing the latter with benzidine.[3] The drop is washed into a micro-crucible, mixed with 1 or 2 drops of ammonium molybdate solution and warmed until the bubbles appear. A slight excess of sodium acetate and a solution of

[1] FEIGL. " Spot Tests ", p. 164.
[2] Frick Chemical Laboratory, Princetown Univ., 30.11.36.
[3] FEIGL. " Spot Tests ", p. 164.

benzidine in acetic acid are then added. The benzidine is oxidized to benzidine blue and the silicomolybdate is simultaneously reduced to molybdenum blue. The ammonium molybdate solution is made by dissolving 15 g. of ammonium molybdate in 300 ml. of water and pouring this solution into 100 ml. of nitric acid of specific gravity 1·42. The benzidine reagent is a 1 per cent. solution in 10 per cent. acetic acid. The sodium acetate, which is added with the benzidine, is used in the form of a saturated aqueous solution. Feigl gives the limit of sensitivity as 0·001 mg. of fluorine, and Roholm had no difficulty in detecting 0·005 mg.

Flame Test. A mixture of a fluoride, boric acid (or sodium borate) and potassium hydrogen sulphate (or concentrated sulphuric acid) heated on a platinum wire in the bunsen flame colours the flame grass-green. Copper or barium salts mask the colour.

The Zirconium-lake Test.[1] Zirconium compounds form a colour-lake with the sodium salt of alizarin sulphonic acid, which is red in dilute acid solution. The colour is discharged by the addition of a soluble fluoride, and this reaction may be used as a spot test for either simple or complex fluorides, though many radicals interfere including sulphates, thiosulphates, phosphates, silicates, chlorides, arsenates and oxalates.

Filter-paper is impregnated with zirconium-alizarin solution and dried. A spot is moistened with 50 per cent. acetic acid, the paper becoming red. On adding a solution containing fluorides the colour changes to yellow.

Isolation of Fluorides

The Lime-fusion Method. Brüning and Quast[2] have described a method for the detection of fluorides after the destruction of organic matter by fusion, the details being as follows.

About 35 g. of the material are minced and well mixed in a nickel basin with 10 ml. of milk of lime containing 50 g. of lime per litre. Copper sulphate solution (10 ml. of 10 per cent.) is then stirred in the mixture and it is evaporated to dryness and converted to ash, heat being applied from above as well as from below. The residue is transferred to a platinum crucible and moistened with about 1 ml. of dilute sulphuric acid. When this paste is cold 5 ml. of concentrated sulphuric acid are cautiously added. Hydrofluoric acid is liberated and detected by the etching test.

Quantitative Determination

For quantitative determination Roholm uses the method of Willard and Winter[3] in which the fluorine is liberated as hydro-

[1] FEIGL "Spot Tests", p. 161.
[2] *Zeitsch. angew. Chem.*, 1931, **44**, 656.
[3] *Ind. Eng. Chem. Anal. Ed.*, 1933, **5**, 7. *Analyst*, 1933, **58**, 242.

fluosilicic acid by means of perchloric acid, and this is titrated with a standard solution of thorium nitrate using the zirconium compound of alizarin as indicator. The decomposition of the organic matter is carried out in a Claisen Pyrex distillation flask fitted with a rubber stopper through which passes a tap-funnel the lower tube of which is drawn out to a capillary, and also a thermometer reading to 200° C. The flask rests on an asbestos sheet in which there is a hole large enough to allow one-third of the flask to be exposed to the flame. The end of the condenser dips into an Erlenmeyer flask of 300 ml. capacity. The material is put into the distillation flask together with five or six small pieces of glass tubing, and a little water is added, followed by 5 ml. of perchloric acid. The stopper is then fitted. The tip of the funnel must not dip into the mixture but the bulb of the thermometer is immersed. The mixture is heated with a large flame and water is added carefully so as to produce at first a liquid boiling at 110° C. After a time the temperature is allowed to rise to 135° C., and thereafter a continuous addition of water is made from the funnel so that boiling continues regularly between 130° C. and 135° C. The quantity of material used by Roholm varied from about 0·2 g. to 2 g. of bone ash, and the total quantity of water added was 70 ml. Distillation is usually complete in a little over half an hour.

The volumetric determination depends on the precipitation of the fluorine as thorium tetrafluoride.

$$Th(NO_3)_4 + 4HF = ThF_4 + 4HNO_3.$$

The indicator is the zirconium-alizarin lake, the colour of which, discharged by the soluble fluoride, reappears when the fluoride is completely thrown out of solution.

The distillate is mixed with an equal volume of rectified spirit and 5 drops of a 0·05 per cent. solution of sodium alizarin sulphonate and an equal amount of zirconium nitrate solution (also 0·05 per cent.). Sufficient N sodium hydroxide solution is added to produce a red-violet colour with the indicator, and then dilute (1 : 50) hydrochloric acid, drop by drop, until this colour is discharged. The liquid is then titrated with thorium nitrate solution which has been previously standardized with sodium fluoride. The thorium nitrate solution is made from Merck's *Thorium nitricum siccum* $(Th(NO_3)_4 + ca.4H_2O)$ and the sodium fluoride (also Merck's) contains 45–46 per cent. fluorine.

BORIC ACID AND BORATES

Fatal poisoning by boric acid and its alkaline salts has been reported on a number of occasions. Children have died from doses as small as 3 g. In acute poisoning the symptoms are those of a gastro-intestinal irritant. The use of boric acid as a food preservative is forbidden.

In the absence of oxidizing agents boric acid or borax can be detected by the turmeric test. The substance to be tested is acidified with dilute hydrochloric acid and the piece of turmeric paper is dipped into the liquid. The paper is carefully dried and is then treated with 1 per cent. caustic soda solution. In the presence of boric acid the colour of the paper changes from reddish brown to greenish blue, but is restored to the original tint by dilute hydrochloric or sulphuric acid.

Boric acid forms volatile esters with methyl and ethyl alcohols and when the vapours are ignited the flame is coloured green. The test can be made in a small corked vessel with an inlet tube passing through the cork nearly to the bottom of the vessel and an outlet tube drawn out to form a jet. The sample mixed with concentrated sulphuric acid and methyl alcohol is put into the vessel which is then heated to 55°–65° C. in a water-bath and air is bubbled through the liquid at the rate of three bubbles per second. The issuing vapour is ignited at the jet and the flame is viewed against a black background. Metallic chlorides should be absent, as they may produce ethyl or methyl chloride which also gives a green flame. See p. 146 for an alternative procedure.

Boric acid causes colour changes in some of the polyhydroxy anthraquinones of which quinalizarin (1 : 2 : 5 : 8-tetrahydroxy anthraquinone) is the most sensitive. The reagent is a $0 \cdot 01$ per cent. solution of the anthraquinone compound in concentrated sulphuric acid. A trace of boric acid changes the colour of quinalizarin from violet to blue and purpurin from orange to wine-red. The colours should be compared with the reagent, free from boric acid. It is important to note that many commercial samples of hydroxyanthraquinones contain traces of boric acid, which is sometimes used in their manufacture. Pure reagents are essential.

For the qualitative examination of stomach-washings it is often sufficient to make the liquid alkaline and filter, and apply the above tests to the residue obtained by the evaporation of the filtrate.

When destruction of organic matter is necessary this must be done by ashing in presence of alkali, since free boric acid is volatile even in steam.

The quantity of boric acid in the ash can be determined gravimetrically by the Rosenbladt-Gooch method[1] which depends on the distillation of the acid in the form of its methyl ester and the saponification of the latter by means of lime.

For a quantity of material containing not more than $0 \cdot 2$ g.

[1] *Z. Anal. Chem.*, 1887, **18**, 316. TREADWELL. 8th American Edition, **2**, 386.

of boric acid, about 8 g. of lime, which should be the purest obtainable, is ignited over a blow-pipe in a platinum crucible until the weight is constant and this weight is noted. The lime is then transferred to an Erlenmeyer flask which is to serve as a receiver for the distillate, and slaked by the gradual addition of 10 ml. of water ; and the crucible is returned to the desiccator. A weighed portion of the ash containing boric acid is transferred with a little water to a retort the outlet of which is bent upwards and connected by means of glass tubing to the top of a vertical Liebig condenser, the lower end of which passes through a cork in the neck of the Erlenmeyer flask containing the lime. A vent is cut into the cork to serve as an outlet for air. The other opening of the retort is fitted with a tap-funnel. The alkali borate in the retort is mixed with a few drops of litmus solution and is made first slightly acid with hydrochloric acid, then just alkaline with caustic soda and is finally acidified with acetic acid. Distillation is carried out by heating in an oil-bath maintained at 140° C. and when the retort is dry it is allowed to cool a little by temporarily removing the oil-bath. Methyl alcohol, free from acetone, is then run into the retort through the tap-funnel in three successive portions, each of 10 ml. and each portion is distilled off. During this process the residue becomes alkaline. Water (2–3 ml.) and sufficient acetic acid to reacidify the residue are added. Three more successive portions of methyl alcohol are run in and distilled off, after which the oil-bath is removed. The receiver-flask is allowed to stand for several hours and thoroughly shaken from time to time in order that the saponification may be completed. The contents of the flask are then transferred to a platinum dish and evaporated to dryness at as low a temperature as possible : the alcohol must on no account be allowed to boil. The flask is then washed out with the minimum quantity of dilute nitric acid and the washings transferred to the basin. The liquid is again heated on the water-bath and, after the last trace of alcohol has been removed, the water in the bath may be allowed to boil and the evaporation continued to dryness. The basin is heated until the calcium acetate is decomposed. When cold the residue is transferred with the aid of a little water to the crucible in which the lime was weighed. The liquid is again evaporated to dryness on the water-bath after which the crucible is heated gently at first and then more strongly, until the weight is constant. The gain in weight is due to boric anhydride, B_2O_3.

Volumetric Determination of Boric Acid

Boric acid does not show an acid reaction to methyl orange. Towards phenolphthalein it is acidic, but titration with caustic soda can only be carried out to the exact end-point in presence of large quantities of glycerol or other poly-hydroxy alcohol, such as mannitol. Carbon dioxide must be absent.

A mixture of boric acid and sulphuric acid is titrated in the following way. The volume is noted and an aliquot portion is titrated with caustic soda using methyl orange as indicator. The titre is noted. To a second aliquot portion, equal to the first, the same volume of standard caustic soda is added, without the methyl orange. Phenolphthalein added to the mixture should remain colourless. Caustic soda is run in from the burette until a pink colour appears. If boric acid is present this is not the end-point. Neutral glycerol is added to the titration mixture. As much as 100 ml. is needed for 1 g. of boric acid. The colour of the indicator disappears. The titration is continued until the colour reappears. This may or may not be the end-point ; to decide the question more glycerol must be added, and if the colour again disappears the titration is again continued, and this process is repeated until the addition of more glycerol no longer discharges the colour. The quantity of N/10 caustic soda used, after neutrality to methyl orange was reached, is the measure of the boric acid present. One ml. of N/10 caustic soda is equivalent to 2·063 mg. of boric acid.

This process can be applied to viscera in the following manner. The tissues are reduced to ash[1] in the presence of excess of alkali, as in the Strzyzowski process (see Arsenic). The alkaline ash is washed into a flask and dissolved in dilute hydrochloric acid or sulphuric acid. Phenolphthalein is added and then caustic soda until the indicator is just pink. Phosphates are removed by filtration ; the precipitate is washed and the washings added to the filtrate, which is then made up to a standard volume. To an aliquot part of this liquid, normal sulphuric acid is added until the pink colour just disappears. Methyl orange is added and the titration is continued until the reaction is faintly acid to this indicator. The liquid is then boiled under a reflux condenser to expel the carbon dioxide and the condenser is washed down with hot water so that any volatilized boric acid is returned to the flask. The liquid is again made neutral to methyl orange with caustic soda.

A second aliquot part of the ash solution is treated in exactly the same manner, the quantities of caustic soda and acid added in each stage of the process being identical but the methyl orange is omitted. The titration in presence of glycerol is then carried out as above described.

---

[1] cf. *Analyst*, 1918, **43**, 138.

CHAPTER VI

THE ISOLATION OF NON-VOLATILE ORGANIC POISONS

THE poisonous substances which are readily volatile in steam have already been discussed. There remains an enormous number of non-volatile substances, usually of relatively high molecular weight and complex structure, to which steam-distillation as a process of isolation is not applicable.

Many of these substances are derived from plants, but the number of synthetic drugs which come into the same category is large and is constantly increasing.

For the purposes of analysis the non-volatile poisons are divided into two main groups, basic and non-basic ; of the latter group some have acidic or phenolic properties, while others are neutral. The basic group includes all the vegetable alkaloids and the synthetic drugs which have come into use as substitutes for natural alkaloids, e.g. the cocaine substitutes. The non-basic group includes glycosides ; synthetic ureides (which are either simple or complex derivatives of urea) ; purgative drugs, many of which are natural hydroxy- or methoxy-derivatives of anthraquinone, sometimes also glycosidal in character ; hypnotics like sulphonal ; substances like picrotoxin which do not fit into any larger group ; poisons of animal origin like cantharides ; some anthelmintics like santonin ; and many plant products of unknown constitution, common especially in India and farther east, such as the active principle of madar juice, marking nuts, etc.

The separation of these organic poisons is the most difficult of the toxicologist's analytical problems, partly because of the diversity of their chemical nature and partly because of the small amounts of them to be sought in the presence of relatively vast quantities of other organic matter.

The principles underlying the methods used are simple enough but the actual technique of obtaining the organic substances in the state of purity which is required for absolute identification can only be acquired by experience and almost infinite patience.

The method which has been in use for about a century for the isolation of these poisons was first devised by Stas for the extraction of nicotine from viscera. It has been modified by Otto and many other workers, and is known as the Stas-Otto process.

The essential facts on which the process is based are these:

(1) Almost without exception, the substances in question are

soluble in alcohol, and to a greater or less extent in acidified water or hot neutral water.

(2) From aqueous solutions the substances may be extracted by repeatedly shaking with an immiscible organic solvent, the solution being acidified for the extraction of neutral or acidic substances, and made alkaline for the extraction of basic substances.

The Stas-Otto Process

1. Extraction with Dilute Alcohol

It is absolutely essential that the samples of viscera should be thoroughly minced, and a little experience in the use of a mincing machine with viscera containing much fluid, especially if putrefaction has begun, soon convinces one of its impractibility. Daubney and

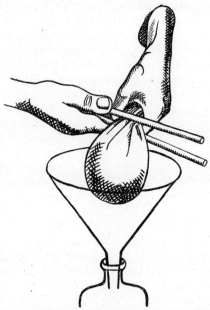

FIG. 18. Method of squeezing the alcohol from the residue after the first extraction in the Stas-Otto process.

Nickolls[1] solved the problem by freezing the samples in the ice-drawers of a refrigerator and mincing them while frozen.[2] Our own practice is to postpone the mincing to a later stage. The weighed samples are cut into small pieces with large sharp scissors and the first extraction is made by covering the pieces with rectified spirit in large Erlenmeyer flasks. If the reaction to litmus is not

---

[1] *Analyst*, 1937, **62**, 851.
[2] It can also be solved by use of a " Waring Blendor ".—EDITOR.

acid it is made so by adding tartaric or citric acid solution.   It may be worth mentioning that the litmus paper should be moistened with water before making this test.   The flasks are loosely stoppered with cotton wool and the temperature is raised to about 40°–50° C., after which they are allowed to stand for some hours, preferably until the following day.   The liquid is poured through a doubled piece of muslin spread over a large funnel and the solid matter is afterwards thrown on to the same muslin.   As much of the fluid as possible is squeezed out in the manner shown in Fig. 18, and the residue is transferred to a powerful screw-press in which it is pressed into a hard, dry cake.   This cake is put through the mincing machine, and the mincing of this dry matter presents no difficulty. The minced material is now returned to the flask, again covered with rectified spirit, warmed, allowed to cool and strained through muslin. The residue is again squeezed as thoroughly as possible by hand, but the use of the press is not usually necessary.   A third extraction is made and this should be clear and colourless; the residue from the liver and kidneys should resemble coffee-grounds, and that from the alimentary organs should be like coarse meal.   The three extracts are mixed and allowed to stand for some hours, after which they are filtered through thick filter paper (Schleicher and Schull, No. 572, or similar quality).   The paper should be fluted; suction-filtration seldom works well at this stage.

2.   Evaporation of the Alcoholic Extract

The filtrate is evaporated at a low temperature.   There are certain advantages in carrying out this evaporation in open dishes instead of by vacuum-distillation.   The latter process may be accompanied by troublesome frothing which, however, can usually be controlled by octyl alcohol.   In our laboratory the dishes are placed on the bench in a room kept exclusively for the purpose and a current of compressed air is allowed to play on the surface of each. The temperature of the liquid falls below that of the room and to counteract this the basin may, in most cases, be placed on the water-bath from time to time for short periods.   It is generally found that after the liquid has been standing in the basin under the air-current overnight considerable quantities of fat and proteins have separated in a form which admits of rapid filtration and when this occurs it is an advantage to remove this animal matter before completing the evaporation.   One of the big difficulties in the Stas-Otto process is the presence, in this first extract, of much fat, protein, etc., which is soluble in dilute alcohol and forms a very bulky residue when the extract is evaporated.   It is therefore highly desirable to remove as much as possible by filtration after partial evaporation.

3. *Extraction with Absolute Alcohol*

The residue, in the classical process, is taken up in absolute alcohol which dissolves the organic poison and leaves the greater part of the animal matter undissolved. This step is not always necessary, but it is advisable if the residue is still very bulky. If cold absolute

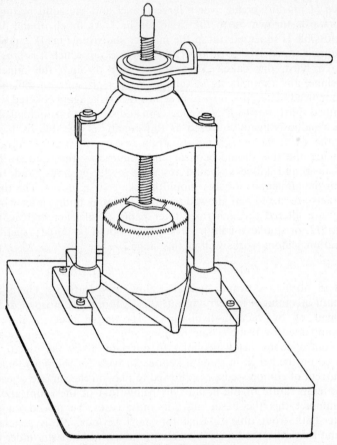

Fig. 19. Screw press used in Stas-Otto process.

alcohol is used it is difficult to prevent the animal matter from forming greasy masses which are probably not penetrated by the alcohol, and in any case cause trouble in the subsequent filtration. With practice it is possible to convert this animal matter into small, hard, granular particles which can be readily filtered off, but this result is achieved much more easily by using hot absolute alcohol. The alcohol is pre-heated almost to the boil in a flask and is added little by little to the fatty residue. As each portion is added the dish is moved in such a manner that the fluid rotates; the residue begins to break up, and when no further change is seen the alcohol is poured off into a flask or stoppered jar which has been previously washed out with alcohol. The addition of fresh quantities of hot alcohol is continued until the whole of the residue has been transferred in a granular form to the other vessel. If there is any remnant which does not respond to this treatment it is mixed with sand or powdered glass and rubbed with a pestle until it breaks up into a powder which can be washed into the bottle with alcohol. Occasionally the fat does not separate from the alcohol in a solid form but sinks to the bottom of the vessel in a fluid or semi-fluid condition; in such cases the material should be allowed to stand in the refrigerator overnight. In any case, several hours should elapse before the alcoholic extract is filtered. The residue is washed with absolute alcohol and the combined filtrate and washings are again evaporated to dryness. Vacuum distillation seldom presents any difficulty at this stage.

4. Further Purification

The residue obtained by the evaporation of the absolute alcohol is now ready to be taken up in acidified water and filtered, but the exact procedure may have to be modified according to the condition of the material. Usually, it is only necessary to add hot water, little by little, and as the residue breaks up to transfer it to a filter. The last vestiges remaining in the dish are covered with hot water and rubbed with a piece of cotton-wool on the end of a stout glass rod to remove them from the dish. The liquid is poured through the filter and the pad of cotton is thoroughly squeezed against the side of the dish, the rod being used as a roller. This rubbing and squeezing process is repeated as often as necessary, using fresh small quantities of hot water.

If the residue is still very fatty it is sometimes better not to attempt filtration at this stage but to transfer the whole of it with the aid of hot water to a separating funnel, and, after allowing it to cool, to remove the fat by shaking with successive portions of light petroleum. The aqueous liquid must be made distinctly acid with mineral acid (preferably sulphuric), otherwise there may be a partial extraction of alkaloids by the petroleum. This shaking out with light petroleum is not an ideal process as there is often a tendency to form emulsions which separate very slowly. If such emulsions do form, various expedients may be adopted to break them down. Adding a little alcohol and shaking is sometimes successful. Another method is to add a strong solution of a salt such as sodium chloride or sodium sulphate and to shake again. If the upper layer does not become completely clear it may be filtered into a second separating funnel through a layer of sand supported by a plug of glass-wool. The petroleum extract should be shaken with acidified water and the aqueous washings added to the main bulk of the aqueous liquid. If these expedients have been found necessary and the liquid is loaded with mineral salts, it is advisable to evaporate to dryness once more, again at a low temperature, after neutralizing with sodium carbonate. The residue thus obtained is taken up in absolute alcohol and again evaporated to dryness. The petroleum extract is preserved for further examination if necessary.

It should be emphasized that the two steps described above, taking up in absolute alcohol and treatment with light petroleum, are only essential if the residue from the first extraction is very bulky and greasy.

5. *Extraction of Toxic Substances*

The aqueous liquid thus obtained, with or without treatment with absolute alcohol and with or without washing with petroleum, should be free from turbidity and may be treated with immiscible solvents without further purification. However, if the analysis is limited to a search for (*a*) alkaloids, or (*b*) barbiturates or glycosides, further purification by treatment with lead salts is recommended. This is effected by adding a solution of lead acetate. A precipitate usually forms at once and the gradual addition of lead solution is continued until precipitation ceases. For alkaloids the lead solution must first be acidified with acetic acid, but for barbiturates and glycosides basic lead acetate solution is used. The flask may be warmed on the water-bath, if necessary, to accelerate the coagulation and sedimentation of the lead precipitate which is then filtered off, washed and preserved, since it may have to be examined for meconic acid if morphine is subsequently detected. The filtrate is freed from lead either by passing a current of hydrogen sulphide through it or by very cautiously adding dilute sulphuric acid until the liquid is just acid to Congo-red. This second precipitate is also removed by filtration and washed, the washings being added to the filtrate and the residue discarded.

This filtrate is usually sufficiently pure to yield a fairly clean extract of the alkaloid by shaking with the appropriate immiscible solvent after making alkaline, but it is nevertheless advisable to shake out with ether first in presence of dilute sulphuric acid to extract any non-basic poisons which may be present. The presence of sulphuric acid and the choice of ether as the extracting solvent at this stage are important. Some of the less strongly basic alkaloids are partially extracted by chloroform from aqueous solution even in presence of hydrochloric acid, and some of the hydrochlorides of alkaloids (notably heroin) are readily soluble in chloroform. At least three extractions with ether should be made and the combined extracts transferred to a second separating funnel in which they are washed by shaking with water. The aqueous washings are added to the main aqueous liquid and the ether extract is preserved.

For the extraction of alkaloids after making the aqueous liquid alkaline, chloroform is the best general solvent. Of the common alkaloids the only one which remains dissolved in the water is morphine, which can be extracted with a mixture of alcohol and chloroform, or hot amyl alcohol or ethyl acetate. This alkaloid, moreover, having phenolic properties, forms a soluble compound with caustic alkali which is not extracted from aqueous solution even by the best solvent. The procedure, therefore, is to make the aqueous liquid alkaline with caustic soda and shake out with three or four successive portions of chloroform. The collected chloroform extracts are filtered through a small plug of cotton-wool into another separating funnel and shaken with a little water, the aqueous washings being returned to the first funnel. This first chloroform extract is to be tested later for alkaloids other than morphine. (N.B.—It may contain heroin, and possibly other opium derivatives.)

The aqueous liquid is made just acid to litmus and then just alkaline with ammonia. It is then mixed with at least half its volume of alcohol, methyl alcohol being better than ethyl alcohol, and again shaken out with five or six successive portions of chloroform. The mixed chloroform and alcohol is liable to be turbid, and filtering through cotton-wool does not clarify it; it should be filtered through thick filter-paper (Schleicher and Schull, No. 572, or similar quality).

Three extracts are thus obtained, or four if the fat has been extracted with petroleum. The last two will be considered first, viz. the general alkaloidal extract, made with alcohol-free chloroform in presence of caustic soda, and the extract which is to be tested for morphine, made with alcoholic chloroform in presence of ammonia.

6. Purification of the Extracted Poisons

The residues obtained by evaporation of the extracts should be, in general, pure white in colour ; and if they are not, further purification may be necessary. This may be effected in various ways. The simplest is to leave the residue exposed to the air in an open dish for twenty-four hours, which causes some of the impurities to become insoluble in acidified water. The residue is taken up in acidified water with the aid of a piece of cotton-wool on the end of a glass rod in the manner already described, using several successive small portions of water and pouring them through a filter into a small separating funnel, after which the liquid is made alkaline with ammonia and the extraction process is repeated. For morphine, ethyl acetate should now be chosen as the extracting solvent ; it dissolves morphine less readily than alcoholic chloroform but it yields a cleaner extract, and since the bulk of the aqueous liquid is now reduced to a few ml., the relatively low solubility of morphine in this solvent is less important.

In very stubborn cases in which pure alkaloidal extracts have not been obtained by any of the methods above described, the residue is taken up in a little distilled water acidified with hydrochloric acid and transferred to a small flask, if necessary through a filter. The alkaloid is then precipitated with one of the double iodides, of which Mayer's reagent is the one most generally useful. The reagent is added drop by drop until precipitation ceases, and the flask is allowed to stand until the precipitate has coagulated or crystallized. It is then collected on an asbestos filter in a Gooch crucible and washed with a little acidified water. The asbestos with the precipitate is transferred to a small stoppered bottle and mixed with excess of hydrogen sulphide solution. The stopper is inserted and the bottle is thoroughly shaken from time to time until the sulphide of the metal is completely precipitated. After making sure that the reaction is still acidic, the liquid is filtered and the residue washed with acidified water. The filtrate is then made alkaline and the shaking out process is repeated.

The one alkaloid to which a thoroughly drastic purification process can be applied is strychnine, which is so stable that it does not decompose even when heated on the water-bath for two hours with concentrated sulphuric acid. Under these conditions almost any organic matter present as an impurity will be charred, and strychnine can be extracted by diluting the acid, when cold, with water, filtering, making alkaline and shaking out with chloroform. Obviously this treatment must not be applied if it can be avoided, since any other alkaloid present would be destroyed, and in any case only a portion of the material available should be used.

Tests for the identification of alkaloids will be described later; here, it is emphasized that the extract should be as nearly as possible chemically pure before identification is attempted.

The Stas-Otto process is, by common consent, long and tedious; but all the steps above described are not invariably necessary. Sometimes, as in the examination of the viscera of dogs poisoned with strychnine, a relatively rapid extraction can be made by washing the stomach with alcohol and evaporating the filtered washings to dryness on the water-bath. The residue, taken up in acidified water, filtered and treated with lead acetate, often yields a clear liquid from which the alkaloid can be extracted in a comparatively pure state, giving quite convincing chemical and physiological reactions. In such cases the whole process can be carried out in about three hours. A full analysis of large samples of the principal abdominal viscera usually takes four or five days.

Alternative Processes

Various suggestions have been made for shortening and simplifying the work by the use of solvents other than alcohol for the initial extraction.

Acetone has been recommended,[1] especially for the extraction of derivatives of barbituric acid. It is claimed that acetone dissolves these substances very readily, but extracts very little animal matter from the tissues. We also have found that the addition of acetone to the absolute alcohol extract causes the precipitation of much animal matter which can be filtered off.

Stewart, Chatterji and Smith[2] in a preliminary note, give details of a process which has yielded excellent results with morphine, quinine, nicotine and aconitine ; the extraction of atropine has been less satisfactory, but this may have been due to partial decomposition of the atropine before the extraction was made. The process is also recommended for barbiturates and some glycosides.

The minced tissues are made into a paste with 10 per cent. trichloracetic acid and this is filtered and sucked dry on a Buchner funnel. The treatment is repeated on the residue, after which it is washed with water. The filtrate is said to be clear and colourless and to contain the whole of any alkaloid present. The alkaloid is separated from the filtrate by adsorption on kaolin which has been previously washed with alcohol, chloroform and ether ; 10 g. of kaolin are sufficient for 800 ml. of fluid obtained by two extractions from 400 g. of animal matter. From the kaolin the alkaloid is dissolved out in one of two ways.

(a) The dry way : the wet kaolin is made alkaline with 10 per cent. sodium carbonate solution which is then ground up with anhydrous sodium sulphate until a dry powder is produced. This powder is transferred to a Soxhlet apparatus and thoroughly extracted with dry chloroform.

(b) The wet way : the wet kaolin, mixed with dilute sodium carbonate solution, is shaken repeatedly with hot chloroform and the united extracts are filtered to remove traces of kaolin.

More recently, Stolman and Stewart[3] have described the isolation

[1] *Analyst*, 1935, **60**, 50–2.
[2] *B.M.J.*, October 23rd, 1937, p. 793.
[3] *Analyst*, 1949, **74**, 536, 543.

of morphine, heroin, codeine and certain barbiturates from tissue extracts by an adsorption process. They used the orthodox Stas-Otto extract with alcohol and tartaric acid, to which, however, they then added trichloracetic acid to remove further amounts of protein. Alternatively they were able to use the trichloracetic acid extract of Stewart, Chatterji and Smith, adding alcohol to prevent the adsorption of various extracted impurities. In either case the final extract was so adjusted that 125 ml. of fluid contained 5 g. of trichloracetic acid, 25 ml. of (95 per cent.) alcohol, and had pH in the range 6·0 to 8·0. The alkaloid in this was completely adsorbed by a suitably prepared column, 14 mm. diameter and about 100 mm. long, of the synthetic magnesium silicate *Florisil* from which, after washing, it was quantitatively eluted by methyl alcohol for identification or colorimetric determination. Quantities of 1·0 to 5·0 mg. of any one of the three alkaloids could be accurately determined and by modification of the conditions, mixtures were successfully separated. Barbiturates were not adsorbed by the Florisil but, after removal of alkaloids (i.e. in the filtrate from the Florisil column) they could be absorbed on coconut shell charcoal and eluted with ethyl acetate. The method is useful for the three alkaloids with which it has been tested, but its main importance perhaps lies in the possibility it raises of developing a general method shorter and simpler than the Stas-Otto.

Two papers have been published by Daubney and Nickolls[1] recording their experiments on the extraction of alkaloids. They discarded, after trial, adsorption on kaolin and similar substances, having formed the opinion that the adsorbing power of such materials was slight in the presence of strong electrolytes. This, however, as the work of Stolman and Stewart[2] has shown, can be overcome by a suitable adsorbent and the optimal conditions. They also dislike the use of trichloracetic as a precipitant for proteins as they find that the coagulated protein has a rubber-like consistency and is not suitable for thorough washing.

In their first paper they recorded experiments on morphine which they found could be extracted from tissues by saturated ammonium sulphate solution which by coagulating the protein yielded a clear filtrate. They found later that some of the other alkaloids were not so extracted and they therefore modified their process, using acidulated water as the extracting solvent.

The following are the details of the process finally adopted by these workers :[3]

The material is frozen in the ice-drawer of a refrigerator and

[1] *Analyst*, 1937, **62**, 851.
[2] *Ibid.*, 1949, **74**, 536, 543.
[3] *Ibid.*, 1938, **63**, 560.

minced, while still frozen, through a cooled machine. The minced material is weighed and mixed with water and glacial acetic acid so as to form a thin paste. Sufficient ammonium sulphate to form a saturated solution is added and the mixture is stirred at 65° C. until the protein coagulates and the paste becomes fluid. It is then filtered on a large Buchner funnel and washed with warm water. The residue is returned to the casserole in which it was previously heated and macerated with warm water containing 1 per cent. of acetic acid until a smooth thin paste is obtained. This process is repeated until about 1-1½ litre of extract has been obtained, 1 litre being the minimum obtained from 200 g. of tissue and 1½ litre from 400 g. The filtrate is extracted five times with chloroform using 100 ml. for each extraction. The alkaloid is extracted from the chloroform by shaking successively with 25, 15 and 10 ml. of 3N sulphuric acid, after which the chloroform is shaken with 25 ml. of water which is added to the previous extracts, and the mixed aqueous liquid is filtered, made alkaline with ammonia, and extracted with five portions of chloroform, each 20 ml. The chloroform is filtered into a small flask and evaporated to dryness. The residue is weighed. Afterwards this residue is dissolved in dilute acid and filtered through paper; the flask and paper are well washed with dilute acid and any insoluble residue is washed back into the flask, first with acetone and then with chloroform. These washings are evaporated to dryness and the flask is reweighed; the difference between the two weighings is taken to be the weight of pure alkaloid. If morphine is present 200 ml. of alcohol are added to the aqueous extract before shaking out with chloroform.

In the first edition (1940) of this book, Bamford wrote :
" These experiments show results which are full of promise, but our experience is in agreement with that of Roche Lynch,[1] who says, ' I have never had any difficulty in isolating morphine in quantity from viscera by the ordinary Stas-Otto process ', and ' any process used must be capable of finding any alkaloid which may be present. The analyst may start with the knowledge that he may expect morphine, but unless his process is capable of detecting other alkaloids, he may find himself in great difficulties at a later stage.' "

Alcohol as an initial solvent has the great advantage that it does extract practically all organic poisons, and for this reason it should not lightly be discarded. Moreover, both of these groups of workers have discarded or ignored the use of lead salts for the purification of extracts; our own belief,[2] based on experimental work and long experience, is that they are very valuable indeed.

[1] *Analyst*, 1938, **63**, 237–50.
[2] BAMFORD. *Analyst*, 1938, **63**, 645–9.

We are of the opinion that the case for the abandonment of the modified Stas-Otto process has not yet been proved."

The editor (1950) agrees that the Stas-Otto process is still to be preferred as the standard general procedure. Simplified methods may, however, be used when a specific substance alone is being sought, and there is no doubt that efforts should be made to discover a method less laborious than the Sta-Otto but equally reliable.

Separation of Barbituric Acids from Biological Material

It is often the case that, whilst barbituric acids are the suspected cause of poisoning, other toxic substances may have to be sought as well ; in such circumstances the general, Stas-Otto, method of isolation must be employed. Where, however, barbiturates are known to have been employed, and the problem is to identify the particular substance or to make a quantitative estimation, other methods may be used with economy of time and trouble.

Thus Valov[1] brings the barbiturates into solution and precipitates protein by a rapid method. He shakes together (5 mins.) 60 g. of blood or minced tissue, 410 ml. of distilled water and 10 ml. of 10 per cent. sodium hydroxide solution ; to this he adds 60 ml. of 10 per cent. sodium tungstate, then 60 ml. of 0·67N sulphuric acid slowly and with continuous shaking. He then acidifies the mixture (to Universal indicator paper) with 18N sulphuric acid and filters. An aliquot of the filtrate, 450 ml., is shaken for five minutes with an equal volume of redistilled ether. The extract is separated and evaporated. For rough work, or when much barbiturate is present, the weight of the residue, minus the amount of material extracted from normal material (average 3 mg. from 60 g. of liver) gives the amount of barbituric acid present. For more accurate work and with small amounts colorimetric determination is used. In any case the presence of barbituric acid should be confirmed by qualitative tests. In practice, Valov finds up to 3 mg. per 100 g. liver after secanol ingestion, up to 16 mg. after pentobarbitone and up to 39 mg. after phenobarbitone ; quantities of extracted material over 40 mg. per 100 g. liver are rare and indicate the presence of other ether soluble acids (salicylic acid etc.).

Adsorption as a means of extraction from a crude blood, urine or tissue filtrate has been advocated by various authors. Thus Brundage and Gruber[2] shook the filtrates with activated charcoal which was then filtered off, dried by mixing with Plaster of Paris and extracted with a mixture of, equal volumes of ether and petrol ether. Stolman and Stewart[3] adsorbed the barbiturates on a

[1] *Ind. Eng. Chem. (Anal. Ed.)*, 1946, **18**, 456.
[2] *J. Pharmacol. Exp. Ther.*, 1937, **59**, 379.
[3] *loc. cit.* cf. p. 160.

column of activated coconut shell charcoal after removal of interfering substances on a synthetic magnesium silicate, and eluted with ethyl acetate.

Other workers have omitted the protein precipitation, extracting acidified blood, urine, or macerated tissue with chloroform or ether. Thus Raventos[1] acidifies urine to pH5 with hydrochloric acid, or blood, diluted with an equal volume of water, by addition of an equal volume of 10 per cent. sodium dihydrogen phosphate ; the liquid is then extracted with peroxide-free ether in a continuous extractor at 45-50° C. for 8-10 hours; the extract is evaporated to dryness and the residue taken up in a little alcohol-free chloroform which is dried over sodium sulphate. Tissue, ground with one-tenth of its weight of sodium dihydrogen phosphate is de-hydrated by mixing with twice its weight of anhydrous sodium sulphate and is then extracted with benzene ; the extract is concentrated to a small volume *in vacuo*. The barbituric acids so extracted are further purified by adsorption on activated alumina. Elution with 50 ml. of 2 per cent. pure methanol in chloroform yields the thiobarbituric acids, and further elution with 50 ml. of 10 per cent. methanol in chloroform removes the remaining barbituric acids.

This method is convenient and suitable for dealing with small quantities of blood. It is, however, long, and this may militate against its value when the less stable barbituric acids are being sought. Especially in such cases (although he has no evidence that Raventos' method is unsatisfactory) the editor prefers the procedure described by Valov.

Basic Animal Products

It occasionally happens that basic products of putrefaction are found in the material extracted from viscera by the Stas-Otto process, and it is perhaps convenient to consider these interfering substances here. They are known as **ptomaines** and were at one time commonly believed to be very poisonous. Symptoms of poisoning which have been traced to the use of decomposed food are now attributed to bacteria rather than to the decomposed food itself, and, in fact, not all ptomaines are toxic; nevertheless, the question has many times been raised in the Courts, whether it is possible for the analyst to mistake basic substances of animal origin for vegetable alkaloids; and, obviously, it is a question to which an answer must be given.

Some of these products are gases, viz. ammonia and methylamine. Others, e.g. dimethylamine and trimethylamine, ethylamine, diethylamine, normal and iso-propylamine, are liquids of low

[1] *Brit. J. Pharmacol.*, 1946, **1**, 210. *Analyst.*, 1949, **74**, 126.

boiling point.   All these substances, besides being volatile, are very soluble in water.   They are most unlikely to be extracted with immiscible solvents from water and if they are so extracted they volatilize with the solvent.   Moreover they have characteristic ammoniacal or fishy odours which would be noticed in the residue if any of them remained.   To a less extent these considerations apply to triethylamine (B.P. 89° C.), which has a pleasant odour, and isoamylamine (B.P. 97° to 98° C.).   **Neurine,** $CH_2 : CH.N : (CH_3)_3OH$, is very toxic but it is also very soluble in water.

Neuridine $(C_5H_{14}N_2)$ is one of the most abundant of the basic products of putrefaction but it is non-toxic.

Putrescine (tetramethylenediamine, $NH_2(CH_2)_4NH_2$) and **cadaverine** (pentamethylenediamine, $NH_2(CH_2)_5NH_2$) are not volatile but they are very soluble in water and are non-toxic.

Choline or bilineurine (hydroxyethyltrimethylammonium hydroxide) is a product of hydrolysis of lecithine and is only toxic in large doses.

Ethylidene diamine is toxic, causing convulsions and muscular tremors, but it is seldom found in more than the most minute traces.

It will be seen that the presence of any of these putrefactive bases in the extract, made as described above, is in the highest degree unlikely; almost without exception they volatilize or remain in the aqueous liquid.   Moreover, none of them gives reactions which exactly simulate those of the vegetable alkaloids, and if chemical tests are supplemented by physiological tests it is impossible for a careful worker to go wrong.   Nevertheless, in the past, reports have been made of the extraction of ptomaines resembling vegetable alkaloids so closely that experts have been deceived.   On scrutinizing these reports it appears that in some cases impure reagents had been used, and in others the chemical tests were old fashioned and inadequate.   In no case, as far as is known, has any basic animal matter been extracted by the Stas-Otto process, properly carried out, which exactly simulated a vegetable alkaloid in all its chemical reactions; and where there has been some apparent resemblance, this has never been confirmed by physiological tests.

The following are some examples of alleged simulation of vegetable alkaloids by ptomaines:—

Liebermann extracted a substance which resembled colchicine in certain respects but differed in others.   No details of chemical or physiological tests are available.

Baumert, from animal matter which had been putrefying for twenty-two months, extracted a substance which gave precipitates with seven of the ordinary alkaloidal precipitants and which, he believed, resembled colchicine.   After purification it gave a carmine colour with nitric acid.   Colchicine dissolves in nitric acid forming a dirty violet solution which changes to red and finally to yellow, but the most characteristic test is made by dissolving it in concentrated sulphuric acid and drawing a rod moistened with nitric acid through the liquid. The initial yellow colour changes to greenish blue in the middle and violet at the edges; on stirring, the whole liquid changes through blue to violet which rapidly fades to a dull yellow. This test was apparently not tried. Moreover, the substance was physiologically inert, whereas colchicine is a powerful irritant which usually produces very severe symptoms, although sometimes their onset is delayed.

Otto extracted a substance with an odour resembling coniine which was precipitated by solutions of the chlorides of gold, mercury and platinum, but it was only slightly toxic compared with coniine; 70 mg. were required to kill a frog.

Selmi reported a similar case but did not record any physiological tests.

Selmi also reported on a morphine-like ptomaine, but since the only positive reaction was the reduction of iodic acid this report is singularly unconvincing.

In a case quoted by Witthaus, which was much discussed at the time (1893), it was admitted that impure amyl alcohol had been used as the extracting solvent. Tests for morphine which were accepted at that time but which would be considered inadequate nowadays were the iodic acid test, Fröhde's test and Lafon's test.

Vaughan in the following year reported the presence of morphine as a result of colours obtained with nitric acid, Fröhde's reagent and Pellagri's test. The colour with Fröhde's reagent was blue. This test will be discussed more fully later, but it may be said here that a blue colour, unless preceded by a very definite violet colour, is not evidence of morphine.

Several observers have found nicotine-like substances in extracts but these cases also do not withstand scrutiny. No really characteristic reactions of nicotine were obtained.

Ciotti and Selmi from a slightly decomposed body extracted a substance which showed colours similar to but not identical with those given by strychnine in the dichromate test (q.v.). The substance was also toxic but did not produce tetanic spasms.

Lombroso and Dupré extracted from decayed cornmeal a substance which gave blue to dirty yellow colours in the dichromate test and also caused tetanic spasms.

It is now universally agreed that when confusion has occurred between the basic products of putrefaction and the vegetable alkaloids it has been due to one or more of three causes:—

(1) Insufficient care in purifying extracts.

(2) Insufficient strictness in applying chemical tests, i.e. being

satisfied with reactions which are not identical with those of the known alkaloids; also the use of tests which are now obsolete.

(3) Failure to confirm chemical reactions by physiological tests.

Ptomaines and the Mydriatic Test

The significance of the mydriatic test as applied to extracts from viscera has been discussed in the Courts, notably in the trial of Crippen when Sir W. H. Wilcox described it as part of the proof of the detection of hyoscine in extracts from the viscera. The question which is always raised is whether the basic products of putrefaction may have a mydriatic effect. Apart from the general question which we have already discussed, as to whether such substances may be present in properly purified extracts from viscera, the valuable experience recorded by Chatterji[1] enables one to give a definite negative answer. He collected the reports on fifty-five samples of viscera, all more or less putrid, to the extracts from which the mydriatic test had been applied. Forty-nine of the extracts produced no mydriasis at all. Of the six which gave positive results, three showed the characteristic colour in the Vitali test (q.v.); two failed to give this colour and the other sample was not examined by chemical methods. We, in Cairo, have also applied the mydriatic test to numerous extracts from putrid viscera and our results agree very closely with those of Chatterji. This experience points to the conclusion that mydriatic substances are not found in properly purified extracts from viscera unless a mydriatic vegetable alkaloid is present. The two samples which failed to respond to Vitali's test probably contained minute traces of an alkaloid of the atropine group, the quantity being sufficient to affect a cat's eye but not sufficient to produce the violet colour.

A positive result in the cat's eye test must always be considered significant, but the presence of a vegetable alkaloid should never be positively affirmed unless positive reactions can be obtained in both chemical and physiological tests.

Stability of Alkaloids

The converse question to the one just discussed is whether alkaloids resist putrefaction and whether they can be detected in highly putrid viscera. The answer is that alkaloids vary; some, like strychnine, are apparently quite unaffected by the presence of putrid animal matter. Others, like cocaine, atropine and aconitine, are more or less rapidly decomposed; but atropine has frequently been detected in viscera and excreta in the middle of the Egyptian summer, and cocaine has been isolated in a pure condition from

[1] *Analyst*, 1926, **51**, 344–5.

urine which had been standing for twenty-five days and was to a large extent decomposed.[1] Morphine has been very definitely detected in our laboratory in samples of viscera which were in such an advanced stage of decomposition that the stoppers of the jars had been blown out before they reached us. Naturally, the work ought to be begun as soon as the samples reach the analyst, or if that is impossible, alcohol should be added at once.

It is, however, the common experience of toxicologists that they have failed to detect certain alkaloids when there has been strong evidence of their administration; this occurs in the case of addicts whose ability to tolerate large doses is possibly due to the acquired power of the organs to destroy the drugs. Lewin has a different theory to account for drug-tolerance, which is discussed in the last chapter of this book.

[1] *Analyst,* 1938, **63**, 648.

CHAPTER VII

NON-BASIC ORGANIC POISONS

Toxic substances which can be extracted from acidified aqueous solution by shaking with appropriate immiscible solvents do not form a single group like the alkaloids. Some of them are violent purgatives like croton oil, colocynthin and jalap; others are hypnotics and soporifics such as the barbituric acid derivatives.

Glycosides, other than those containing cyanogen, are also included; convulsant poisons like picrotoxin, anthelmintics like santonin and extract of male fern; many substances derived from coal-tar, like dihydric phenols, nitro-phenols, salicylic acid and its derivatives; and many others which are not easily classified into groups, and may therefore escape detection if the attention of the analyst is not clearly directed to them by the known circumstances of the cases, the ante-mortem symptoms and post-mortem observations. Moreover, a few of the alkaloids may be so extracted.

POISONS SOLUBLE IN LIGHT PETROLEUM

The Toxic Oils. Some of these which are volatile in steam have already been discussed. If steam distillation has been omitted they may be extracted with petroleum ether from an acidified aqueous extract.

Among the non-volatile oils are the purgatives croton oil and castor oil.

Croton Oil is extracted from the seeds of *Croton tiglium* (euphorbiaceae), which are similar in general appearance to castor seeds, but are somewhat larger and are marked with longitudinal striations, whereas castor seeds are mottled.[1] The seeds are very poisonous, but the toxicity is not entirely or even mainly due to the oil; the chief toxic principle is the albuminous substance **crotin,** one of the class of toxalbumins which will be considered later. Four crushed seeds have proved sufficient to cause death. The oil is powerfully vesicant and this property is used for identification (see p. 190). Croton oil applied to the skin may produce bloody stools.

According to Modi (" Text-book of Medical Jurisprudence and Toxicology ") the root is used as an abortifacient drug in the Malay

---

[1] For further similarities and differences between croton and castor seeds, see p. 205.

Peninsula and the oil has been used as an arrow poison by tribes on the North-Western Frontier.

Castor Oil, from *Ricinus communis*, of the same natural order as croton, is not itself a dangerous drug; but the seeds are poisonous owing to the presence of the toxalbumin, **ricin.** Two seeds have proved fatal, but recovery has been known after the swallowing of twenty-four. The detection of the oil may be contributory evidence in the diagnosis of ricin poisoning.

Marking Nut Oil. The common Indian marking nut *Semecarpus anacardium*, weighing about $1 \cdot 6$–$3 \cdot 2$ g., contains a fleshy pulp from which can be expressed a brownish, oily, acrid juice. This turns black when it is mixed with lime and exposed to air, and is used by Indian washerwomen for marking linen. There is some uncertainty about the composition of the juice. Naidu[1] claims to have isolated catechol and a monohydric phenol, anacardol; whereas Pillay and Siddiqui[2] state that it contains a monohydroxy phenol, semecarpol, a dihydroxy compound, bhilawanol, and a tarry residue. In India the juice is used in the treatment of some skin diseases. Applied externally it is a very powerful vesicant; and the blisters produced contain a serum which causes eruptions on the surrounding skin. These eruptions sometimes develop into ulcers. It is stated that death has been caused by the application of the oil to the skin of the scrotum. Bruised nuts are sometimes used in India to cause abortion by application to the *os uteri*.

Another variety of marking nut is *Anacardium occidentale*. This also contains an acrid juice with vesicant properties. Tests for the oils will be described later.

POISONS SOLUBLE IN ETHER

The following groups of non-basic substances are readily soluble in ether and can be extracted from acidified aqueous solutions by shaking with this solvent.

The readily volatile phenols have already been discussed. The others are the dihydric and trihydric phenols, *m*- and *p*-nitrophenols, dinitrophenols, and picric acid.

Pyrocatechin, or **catechol** (*o*-dihydroxybenzene), is usually obtained by heating guaiacol, a constituent of beechwood-tar, with hydriodic acid, and it also occurs in catechu, from the tree *Acacia catechu*. It is a crystalline substance, not used in medicine; but, taken internally, it is poisonous, being a gastro-intestinal irritant and a stimulant of the central nervous system. It melts at 104° C.

Resorcinol, *m*-dihydroxybenzene, is prepared by the alkaline

[1] *J. Indian Inst. of Science*, 1925, **8.**
[2] *Ibid.*, 1931, p. 517.

fusion of the corresponding benzenedisulphonic acid. It is less toxic than carbolic acid and the other dihydroxyphenols; it is less irritant and has much less effect on the central nervous system. Externally it has been used in ointments and internally, combined with quinine, in the treatment of tonsillitis. It is an almost white crystalline compound, melting at 110° C.

Hydroquinone, *p*-dihydroxybenzene, is the product of reduction of benzoquinone, which is itself prepared by the oxidation of aniline. It is used in photography as a developer, and most of the cases of poisoning with it are accidental. Physiologically, its action resembles that of catechol.

Pyrogallol, 1 : 2 : 3 trihydroxybenzene, is obtained by heating gallic acid, either alone or with glycerine. In alkaline solution it has powerful reducing properties, and it is in common use as a photographic developer. It is a white crystalline solid, melting at 115° C., which, like resorcinol, is used as a constituent of ointments. It is an irritant poison and is dangerous even externally if applied freely over large areas.

Phloroglucinol, 1 : 2 : 5 trihydroxybenzene, is obtained by fusing certain resins, such as gamboge and dragon's blood, with potash. It is one of the constituents of the glycoside phloridzin (or phlorhizin) which is found in the bark of many common fruit trees (apple, pear, cherry, plum, etc.). This glycoside causes glycosuria if taken internally, but does not increase the amount of blood sugar. In other respects the symptoms of poisoning by phloridzin closely resemble those of diabetes mellitus. Substances of the acetone type may be found in the urine ; but these effects are largely due to changes in the excretory power of the kidney and not to the impairment of the functions of the pancreas.

Phloroglucinol forms colourless prisms melting at 218° C. It is one of the products of hydrolysis of filicic acid and the resinous constituents of male fern (*vide infra*). The anthelmintic drug Cusso or Kousso, from the flowers of *Brayera anthelmintica*, contains a toxic principle which, on reduction with zinc dust and caustic soda, yields the trimethyl ether of phloroglucinol.

The **nitrophenols** are chiefly important as intermediate products in the dyestuff and explosives industries. They produce symptoms of chronic poisoning owing to the breathing in of dust by workmen. The para-compound is said to be the most toxic of the three isomers (Rambousek[1]), although it is less volatile than the ortho. In acute poisoning, according to Leymann,[2] the onset of symptoms may be very sudden; the workman collapses, with pain in the chest, vomiting, respiratory difficulty, rapid pulse and convulsions.

[1] " Industrial Poisoning ", p. 213.
[2] RAMBOUSEK. *Op. cit.*

The commonest dinitro-phenol, the 2 : 4 isomer, is not only important in the explosives industry but is used in the manufacture of the photographic developer " Amidol ". It has been the cause of both severe chronic poisoning and fatal acute poisoning. Moreover, it had, for a time, a reputation as a remedy for obesity, owing to its property of causing profuse sweating and markedly raising the metabolic rate. Its efficacy is now doubted; and its use is certainly very dangerous.

Picric acid, symmetrical trinitro-phenol, is a yellow crystalline solid melting at $122 \cdot 5°$ C.

It has the property of dyeing silk and wool in bright yellow shades. It is a strong acid, readily decomposing alkaline carbonates and forming yellow crystalline salts which are highly explosive. It is still used occasionally in the treatment of burns in spite of the severe symptoms which frequently follow its use. It may be absorbed into the blood-stream through the skin. It forms yellow stains on the mucous membranes; the urine is yellow and contains casts. Sometimes convulsions are caused.[1]

Salicylic Acid and its Derivatives

Salicylic acid, o-hydroxybenzoic acid, was formerly obtained almost exclusively by the hydrolysis of its methyl ester, oil of wintergreen. Another possible source of it is saligenin, o-hydroxybenzyl alcohol, which is obtained by the hydrolysis of salicin, the glycoside of the willow-bark. This alcohol yields on oxidation, in two successive stages, salicylaldehyde and salicylic acid.

The modern method of preparation is to treat sodium phenate with carbon dioxide, under pressure. Sodium phenyl carbonate is produced, and this yields, on further heating, sodium salicylate.

Salicylic acid crystallizes from hot water in needles which melt at 156° C. It is used as an antiseptic, and its sodium salt as a remedy for rheumatism. As a rule, salicylates are well tolerated, but some patients who are unusually sensitive suffer from nausea, vomiting, diarrhoea and some nervous symptoms. Occasionally injury to the kidneys has been observed, and the urine may contain cylinders, epithelial cells and white blood corpuscles.[2]

Aspirin, acetylsalicylic acid, is a white crystalline powder which melts at 137° C. In very large doses it produces unpleasant symptoms, such as vomiting, lethargy and even coma; acetone may be noticed in the breath.[3] Taylor[4] states that about twenty fatal suicidal cases occur in England and Wales every year. Acetyl-

---

[1] CUSHNY. " Pharmacology and Therapeutics ", 10th ed., pp. 146–7.
[2] AUTENRIETH. " Detection of Poisons." Sixth American Edition, p. 132.
[3] Op. cit., p. 136.
[4] " Medical Jurisprudence ", 10th ed., Vol. II, p. 587.

salicylic acid passes through the stomach unchanged, but is partially hydrolyzed in the intestines.

Salol, the phenyl ester of salicylic acid, melts at about 42° C. It is hydrolyzed in the intestines and is used as an intestinal disinfectant.

Autenrieth[1] describes several cases of poisoning by salol, with one death. The autopsy in the fatal case revealed severe degeneration of the kidneys.

Phenacetin, acetylphenetidine, is a white crystalline substance, melting at 135° C. It can be prepared by the ethylation of acetyl-p-aminophenol. It is much less poisonous than either antipyrine or acetanilide. We have had no experience of severe acute poisoning with phenacetin, but Autenrieth[2] has recorded several cases in which unpleasant symptoms occurred. There was deep blue colouration of the skin, cold sweat, and in some cases, swelling of the eyelids. Snapper[3] has also reported chronic poisoning, in which cyanosis and sulph-haemoglobinaemia were the symptoms; these disappeared after treatment was stopped.

Derivatives of Barbituric Acid and Urea

Of all the poisons which can be extracted with immiscible solvents from acid solution, the commonest, especially in Western countries, are the derivatives of barbituric acid, malonyl urea.

$$\begin{array}{c} O{:}C{-}NH \\ \diagup \qquad \diagdown \\ H_2C \qquad \quad C{:}O \\ \diagdown \qquad \diagup \\ O{:}C{-}NH \end{array}$$

The parent substance is practically inactive physiologically, but powerful drugs are obtained by the substitution of alkyl and aryl radicals for the hydrogen atoms of the malonic acid fraction of the molecule with, in some cases, replacement also of a hydrogen atom attached to nitrogen. Very large numbers of such compounds have been put on the market (with a very confusing multiplicity of proprietary names), not all of which are in common use. The barbituric acid derivatives are used in medicine as hypnotics (soporifics), sedatives, anticonvulsants (e.g. in eclampsia, epilepsy, etc.), and as anaesthetics (either in combination with other drugs or, for certain operations of brief duration, alone). For this last purpose pentothal and evipan are usually employed.

The barbiturates are all toxic, and reactions may occur during their therapeutic use either because of individual susceptibility or through over dosage. Hypersensitivity may be shown by mental or

---

[1] AUTENREITH. " Detection of Poisons." Sixth American Edition, p. 136.
[2] *Op. cit.,* p. 127.
[3] Merck's " Annual Report ", 16–648, 1927, p. 274.

emotional disturbances, by skin eruptions, or by pyrexia, but fatal results are almost unknown so long as the dosage normally employed for sedation has not been exceeded. Most cases of barbiturate poisoning are suicidal but some, it has been suggested, may be due to " automatism ", the patient continuing to take the drug while in a dazed condition. In general, 5-10 times the full oral dose of a barbiturate may be expected to produce toxic symptoms and fifteen times the full dose is likely to be fatal.[1] However, there is great individual variation and other drugs (e.g. alcohol[2] and morphine[3]) may have a synergistic effect. The barbiturates are removed from the body partly by renal excretion and partly by destruction in the liver. The former route is the more important for the slower acting members of the group (e.g. barbitone, phenobarbitone), the latter for the short acting members (e.g. amytal). This has an important bearing on the safety of the drugs in the presence of renal or hepatic disease, and also on the likelihood of their detection in the urine after moderate dosage.

The common symptoms of barbiturate poisoning are drowsiness, mental confusion and headache, sometimes preceded by mild excitement with ataxia and slurred speech, and proceeding to profound sleep or coma. The pulse is weak and rapid, respiration is decreased to the point of anoxia with cyanosis ; blood pressure and temperature fall (though the latter may later rise above the normal) ; the pupils are contracted at first but dilate later ; there is usually oliguria.

The barbiturates are frequently regarded as drugs of addiction but it seems likely that they are more correctly described as habit forming.[4] Although true addiction—increased tolerance paralleling continued use—may occur to some extent[5], the habitué, taking larger and larger doses, often shows toxic symptoms.

The names, synonyms, chemical structure and melting point of the commoner barbituric acid drugs are given in the table below. The melting points are fairly sharp, but complete identification depends on the observation of mixed melting points. Crystallization can often be obtained by sublimation under normal pressure.

Barbituric acids are more or less soluble in ether and can be extracted from the acidic aqueous solution by shaking with this solvent. Some of them, like dial and prominal, which are less soluble in ether than the others, must be shaken with many small portions of ether to ensure complete extraction. The *dry* ethereal

[1] Goodman and Gilman. *The Pharmacological Basis of Medicine*, 1941.
[2] *J. Pharm. Exp. Ther.*, 1937, **61**, 385; 1946, **88**, 313. *Arch. Path.*, 1943, **36**, 113.
[3] *Physiol. Rev.*, 1939, **19**, 472.
[4] Tatum. *Physiol. Rev.*, 1939, **19**, 472. Editorial *Med. J. Austral.*, 1940, **2**, 411.
[5] Robinson. *J. Missouri Med. Assoc.*, 1937, **34**, 374.

extracts can be decolorized and purified when necessary by shaking with a *small* quantity of animal charcoal and filtering. They can, moreover, be removed from ethereal solution by shaking with very dilute caustic soda solution, which distinguishes them from certain

Usual or Official Name	Chemical Structure	Synonyms	Melting Point of free acid
Allonal	isopropyl-allyl-barbituric acid +pyramidone		138–141°
Amytal	isoamylethyl-barbituric acid		155–157°
Barbitone	diethyl-barbituric acid	Veronal, Barbital	191°
Barbitone-soluble	sodium salt of barbitone	Veronal-sodium, Medinal	
Barbitone +Amido-pyrine		Veramon, Veropyron	
Buto-barbital	ethyl-butyl-barbituric acid	Neonal, Soneryl	123–124°
Dial	diallyl-barbituric acid	Curral	179°
Hebaral	free acid of ortal-sodium		126°
Hexobarbitone	N-methyl-cyclohexenyl-methyl-barbituric acid	Evipan, Evipal, Cyclonal, Hexano-stab-oral	144–145°
Hexobarbitone-soluble	sodium salt of Hexobarbitone	Evipan-soluble, cyclonal-sodium, Hexanostab	
Ipral	ethyl-iso-propyl-barbituric acid		203°
Narconumal	sodium methyl-isopropyl-allyl-barbiturate		50°
Noctal	isopropyl-bromallyl-barbituric acid	Nostal	176–177°
Ortal sodium	sodium ethyl-n-hexyl-barbiturate		
Phanodorm	cyclo-hexenyl-ethyl-barbituric acid		174°
Phemitone	N-methyl-ethyl-phenyl-barbituric acid	Prominal	176°
Phenobarbitone	ethyl-phenyl-barbituric acid	Gardenal, Luminal, Sominal, Pheno-barbital	177°
Phenobarbitone + Theobromine		Theoba, Theogar-denal, Theominal	
Pentobarbital	sodium ethyl-methylbutyl-barbiturate	Nembutal	130–132°
Pentothal-sodium	sodium ethyl-methylbutyl-thio barbiturate		155–157°
Pernoctal	isobutyl-bromallyl-barbituric acid	Pernoston	130–132°
Rutonal	methyl phenyl barbituric acid		226°
Sandoptal	iso-butyl-allyl-barbituric acid		138–141°
Seconal	sodium *sec*.amyl-allyl-barbiturate		122°
Thioethamyl	sodium isoamyl-ethyl-thiobarbiturate		

other hypnotics, e.g. sulphonal, trional and the open-chain ureides adaline and bromural.

Some derivatives of urea which are not barbituric acid compounds are also used as hypnotics. Some of them are simple substituted ureas. Adaline, or uradal, is brom-diethyl acetyl urea, a white crystalline powder, melting at 115°–117° C. The pure substance contains 33·7 per cent. of bromine. Bromural, uvaleral or dormigene is α-brom-isovaleryl urea. It also is a white powder, melting at 154° C. and containing 35·7 per cent. of bromine.

Sedormid, allyl-isopropyl-acetyl urea, is a white crystalline substance melting at 194° C. It is said to have no harmful effects on the heart or kidneys and to be completely destroyed in the body so that no cumulative effects need be feared.

Nirvanol differs from all the other hypnotics of this type, being ethyl-phenyl-hydantoin.

$$\begin{array}{c}
C_2H_5 \\
\diagdown \\
\diagup \\
C_6H_5
\end{array}
C
\begin{array}{c}
C:O{-\!\!-}NH \\
\diagdown \qquad | \\
\diagup \qquad \\
NH{-\!\!-\!\!-}C:O
\end{array}$$

Nirvanol

It is a white crystalline substance which melts at 199°–200° C. It has been used in the treatment of chorea minor (St. Vitus's dance). Often, its administration is followed by the appearance of a rash and sometimes febrile symptoms, after which the chorea symptoms begin to disappear.[1]

Ureides differ greatly in their stability. Some, such as veronal and luminal, are almost unchanged in the animal body. Others, especially those containing the allyl or phenyl radical, are to a very great extent decomposed. The simple ureides and the thio-barbiturates (pentothal, e.g.), adaline and bromural, appear to be almost entirely destroyed. Roche Lynch reports five cases, three of them fatal, in which he failed to find these drugs in the urine or viscera, although in every case bromine was detected. In another case a person committed suicide by opening an artery after taking a mixture of adaline and bromural. The mixed drugs were detected in the stomach contents but bromine only could be detected in the liver, kidneys and urine.

Sulphonal, Trional and Tetronal

Sulphonal is prepared by oxidizing the condensation product of acetone and ethyl mercaptan and is therefore the diethyl sulphone of dimethyl methane. Trional and tetronal are the corresponding sulphones of methylethyl methane and diethyl methane, i.e. they form a homologous series. These drugs are hypnotics which produce long sleep, but not immediately. They are, to some extent, retained in the body and one dose may induce sleep more than once. In large doses, or after long-continued administration, they cause toxic

---

[1] Merck's " Annual Report ", 1927, pp. 202–3.

symptoms which include gastric pains, vomiting, irritation of the kidneys and stupor. Sometimes the patient passes into a state of coma and during the coma bronchial pneumonia may develop. A patient sometimes dies of sulphonal poisoning long after the administration of the drug has ceased, and even after its complete elimination from the body (Sydney Smith, Godamer). Trional and tetronal produce effects similar to sulphonal but less severe.

One of the characteristics of sulphonal poisoning is the appearance of haematoporphyrin in the urine, rendering it claret-coloured. This substance can be isolated by making the urine alkaline and shaking with amyl alcohol. The extract so obtained can be identified by its absorption spectrum. In acid solution a very strong, narrow band is seen on the red side of the D line, a wider and weaker band on the yellow side of it and also a wide, weak band in the blue. In alkaline solution the band on the red side of the D line moves still farther towards the red; the band in the yellow divides into three, while that in the blue remains unchanged.

Sulphonal, trional and tetronal are white crystalline substances which can be sublimed under normal pressure without decomposition. They melt at 126°–127° C., 76° C. and 86°–89° C. respectively. They are slightly soluble in cold water, more soluble in hot water, and very readily soluble in alcohol and ether.

Other Ether-Soluble Poisons

Capsaicin is one of the ether-soluble constituents of capsicum. Lapworth and Royle[1] have devised a method for the extraction of it from the fruits. An aqueous ammoniacal suspension of the alcoholic extract is treated with finely powdered barium chloride on the water-bath. The insoluble deposit is filtered off; both the liquid and the solid are extracted with ether and the united extracts are evaporated to dryness. The dry residue is dissolved in methyl alcohol and the hot solution is treated with powdered barium hydroxide. The solution is boiled for several hours under a reflux condenser and sufficient baryta is added to keep the liquid alkaline. The liquid is then made acid to phenolphthalein with acetic acid and the methyl alcohol is distilled off. The residue is extracted with dry acetone and the filtered extract evaporated. To purify the residue it is dissolved in caustic soda and shaken with ether, the ether extract being discarded. The liquid is then saturated with carbon dioxide and shaken again with ether to extract the pure capsaicin, which is a crystalline solid, melting at 64°–65° C. It is a skin irritant, but not actually a vesicant. One of the most revolting of the sexual crimes in the East is to insert capsicum fruits into the

[1] *J.C.S.*, 1919, **118**, 1109. EVERS. " Chemistry of Drugs ", p. 211.

vagina of the victim during sleep. The fragments of the fruit can be identified by microscopic examination.

Male fern, *Aspidium Felix mas*, is one of the commonest of the drugs used in the treatment of tape-worm. *Felix mas* is a perennial fern the rhizome of which contains 6–15 per cent. of an oleo-resin. The liquid extract is said to contain 20 per cent. of the active principles. The nature of the active principles is in dispute, but filicic acid is regarded as the most important. The oleo-resin normally should pass through the bowel with no other effect than the expulsion of the worms, but sometimes alarming symptoms occur. It has been suggested that these symptoms may be due either to overdose or the administration of castor oil with or shortly after the anthelmintic. The symptoms are: vomiting, diarrhoea, acute abdominal pains, somnolence, twitching (sometimes convulsions), headache, fever, collapse; sometimes coma and death. Blindness, either temporary or permanent, is not uncommon. The minimum lethal doses are said to be: for children, 4–8 ml., and for adults, 18–22 ml. The therapeutic dose for adults is 3–6 ml. Death has occurred in some cases in six hours and in others as late as twenty hours after the administration of the drug.

Filicic acid and some other constituents of the resin are decomposed by hydrolytic agents into phloroglucinol and butyric acid.

Madar Juice. This is a milky liquid which is obtained by crushing the leaves and stalks of the plants *Calotropis gigantea* and *C. procera* which grow on waste land in India, where it is a very common poison. It is a powerful irritant; applied externally to the skin it causes vesication, and when administered internally it is a cerebrospinal poison. Death has been known to occur one hour after drinking madar juice. In Madras alone 14 cases of madar poisoning were reported in one year.

The juice is used as a depilatory by tanners, and it is one of the many Oriental drugs used for criminal abortion: for this purpose it is sometimes given by the mouth and sometimes by way of the vagina.

The juice, which is a liquid of sp. gr. 1·021, contains 14·8 per cent. of solids, and has an acid reaction. On standing, a white coagulum separates leaving a straw-coloured serum which contains 3 per cent. of solids. This serum is highly toxic, 1 drop being sufficient to kill a frog in a few minutes.

Extraction from Viscera and Identification. An alcoholic extract of the viscera is made and divided into two parts, (*a*) and (*b*).

(*a*) This is saponified with absolute alcoholic potash and then extracted with petroleum ether; the extract is evaporated to dryness. The residue is taken up in chloroform and treated with a slight excess of digitonin dissolved in ether. This mixture is evaporated to dryness and extracted with ether. The ethereal extract yields a crystalline precipitate if madar juice is present. A little of the solution, treated with concentrated sulphuric acid on a porcelain plate, gives a red colour which changes to purple on adding chloroform and acetic anhydride. The alkaline alcoholic solution which has been extracted with petroleum ether is evaporated nearly to dryness, taken up in absolute alcohol, and filtered. The filtrate is treated with concentrated hydrochloric acid and allowed to stand. A characteristic ester-like odour is observed if madar juice is present.

(b) The second portion of the alcoholic extract is evaporated to dryness and the residue is taken up in water acidulated with acetic acid, and filtered. The filtrate is mixed with lead acetate and the precipitate is filtered off. Excess of lead is removed from this filtrate by passing a current of sulphuretted hydrogen and the lead sulphide is filtered off. The filtrate so obtained is evaporated to dryness on the water-bath and the dry residue is extracted with absolute alcohol. This extract is again filtered and evaporated, and a portion of the residue, taken up in water, is injected into a frog. The symptoms produced are: convulsions, paralysis and death. The frog usually has a bloated appearance.

Two other methods of extracting the active principles of madar juice have been described.[1]

Narjudu's Method. The alcoholic extract from the juice leaves on evaporation a yellow, bitter, poisonous resin which gives a bluish colour with concentrated hydrochloric acid and a green colour with concentrated sulphuric acid. With dilute acids the colour is pink.

Black's Method. The material is heated with absolute alcohol under a reflux condenser until extraction is complete. The liquid is filtered and allowed to evaporate spontaneously. Characteristic cauliflower-like masses separate, which are easily recognized.

Plumbagin, a crystalline glycoside, is the active principle of *Plumbago rosea* and *P. zeylanica.* Unlike most glycosides it is freely soluble in ether.

It is obtained in golden-yellow needles or prisms, from alcoholic or ethereal solution. In small doses it causes contraction of the muscles of the heart, intestines, and uterus, and in large doses death from respiratory failure.

The minimum lethal dose for rabbits is stated to be 10 mg. per kg. of body weight.[2]

The extract from the root has a vesicant action. It is made by taking up the residue from the evaporated alcoholic extract with dilute caustic potash: this liquid is filtered, acidified and shaken

---

[1] MODI. "Textbook of Medical Jurisprudence and Toxicology."
[2] MODI. *Op. cit.*

out with ether. The ether extract is evaporated to dryness and the tests described later are applied to an aqueous suspension of the residue.

POISONS SOLUBLE IN CHLOROFORM

Picrotoxin is a non-nitrogenous substance, $C_{30}H_{34}O_3$, and is neither an alkaloid nor a glycoside. It is obtained from " fish berries " or Levant nuts (*Cocculus indicus*), the dried seeds of *Animirta paniculata*, a woody climbing plant indigenous to South-eastern Asia. The berries, which are very toxic, are used by the natives of India and Malay to stupefy fish.

The seeds contain from 1 to 1·5 per cent. of picrotoxin which is extracted from the powdered seeds by boiling with alcohol. The residue from the evaporated extract is taken up with hot water, filtered and purified with lead acetate. The lead-free solution is concentrated until crystals begin to separate. Alternatively it may be extracted from aqueous solution by means of chloroform. It is almost insoluble in petroleum ether, which may be used if necessary to remove fat. An alcoholic solution may be boiled with a little animal charcoal to effect further purification. The crystals melt at 199°–200° C. The minimum lethal dose of picro-toxin is not known, but 20 mg. may produce symptoms of severe poisoning and it is said that death has been caused by 2·4 g. of seeds. The symptoms of picrotoxin poisoning are: a burning pain in the throat with vomiting, salivation and diarrhoea. Giddiness, stupor and unconsciousness follow, then a series of convulsions, the later ones being similar to those caused by strychnine. Death is due to asphyxia or heart failure, and recovery is rare (Sydney Smith). Usually death is very sudden (from thirty minutes to six hours), although Taylor has recorded a case of survival for nineteen days.

Santonin, which is used as an anthelmintic, is derived from worm-seeds (*Artemisia maritima*), the unexpanded flowers being used. The flowers are treated with milk of lime, which produces calcium santinonate, and this is afterwards converted into the soluble sodium salt by means of caustic soda and carbon dioxide. This salt is decomposed with sulphuric acid and the free acid is recrystallized from boiling water. Santonin melts at 170° C. It consists of white crystals which become yellow on exposure to light.

The symptoms of santonin poisoning are vomiting and diarrhoea with severe abdominal pains, disturbances of the central nervous system, headache, dizziness, trembling, unsteady gait, mydriasis, convulsions, loss of consciousness and fall of temperature. Another remarkable symptom is the so-called yellow sight in which illumin-ated objects appear to have a yellow fringe: complete temporary blindness has also been known.

The minimum lethal dose is probably about 0·15 g. for a child, although adults have recovered from as much as 1 g.

Santonin is partly decomposed in the body. One constituent which passes into the urine turns red on the addition of caustic potash. Rhubarb-urine gives a similar colour, but this can be distinguished from the colour due to santonin by digesting with zinc dust. The colour due to santonin fades, but that due to rhubarb persists.

Isolation of Santonin. The material is made into a paste with dilute caustic soda solution, mixed with three volumes of rectified spirit and allowed to stand for twenty-four hours. The mixture is filtered and the alcohol distilled off. The residual alkaline liquid is shaken with benzene to remove fatty matter, after which it is acidified and shaken out with chloroform.

Glycosides

Glycosides are substances which on hydrolysis yield a sugar and one or more other substances (termed the *aglycones*). A substance which yields glucose is termed a glucoside. The structure is that of the simple methyl glucosides, so that there are two series, α and β, with the general structures:

$$R\text{—}O\text{—}C\text{—}H \quad \text{and} \quad H\text{—}C\text{—}O\text{—}R$$

$$\beta\text{-glycoside} \qquad\qquad \alpha\text{-glycoside}$$

where R' represents the rest of the sugar molecule and R the non-sugar part.

Most glycosides are hydrolyzed by enzymes which accompany them in the plant tissues, though in different cells. When, therefore, the glycosides are to be extracted, a process which would allow the enzyme to gain access to its substrate, the enzyme should first be inactivated by heating to 100° C.

Most glycosides have a bitter taste and an acid reaction, and can be extracted from acidified aqueous solution. Ether is not a good solvent for this purpose, chloroform being much more useful; and for some glycosides ethyl acetate is better. In Allen's " Commercial Organic Analysis ", fifth edition, Vol. viii, a list of about 300 glycosides is given. The chemistry of most of them is still obscure, and only a few of them can be dealt with here.

For toxicological purposes it is convenient to classify glycosides as:

(*a*) Cardiac poisons, which are usually free from nitrogen; toad poison is an exception.

(*b*) Cyanogenetic glycosides which liberate hydrocyanic acid on hydrolysis. In these the nitrogen is often present in the form of mandelic nitrile which may be an intermediate product of hydrolysis.

(*c*) Glycosides which are associated with anthraquinone derivatives in vegetable purgatives.

The cyanogenetic glycosides have already been discussed and the purgative compounds will be treated separately.

The Cardiac Glycosides

The chief glycosides which act on the heart are:

(1) The digitalis group, from *Digitalis purpurea*, the common foxglove.

(2) The strophanthin group, including strophanthin itself and ouabain from *Strophanthus kombé* and *S. gratus* respectively. The latter glycoside is also obtained from various species of ancocanthera.

(3) Squill glycosides from *Urginea scilla* (of the British Pharmacopoeia) and *U. maritima* (of the United States Pharmacopoeia).

The literature on these glycosides has been very confusing in the past owing to the unsystematic nomenclature which has been used. More systematic names have been adopted in recent times, but even now there is some confusion.

Chemical Structure. The digitalis glycosides isolated by the usual extraction processes are degradation products of the native glycosides. The native glycosides of *Digitalis lanata* leaves are termed digilanids A, B, and C, and these, by hydrolysis, lose glucose and acetic acid, forming respectively **digitoxin** (M.P. 252° C.), **gitoxin,** and **digoxin.** The leaves of the common foxglove, *Digitalis purpurea*, contain deacetyldigilanids A and B (from which extraction, involving loss of glucose, gives digitoxin and gitoxin) along with **gitalin** (M.P. 150°–155° C.), whilst the seeds contain still another glycoside, **digitalin** (M.P. 229° C.) (not the commercial "digitalin", which is a mixture). In addition to these cardiac glycosides which have a similar specific action on the myocardium, digitalis contains other glycosides which are saponins—**digitonin** (softens at 225° C., melts at 235° C.), **gitonin** (M.P. 272° C.), etc.—but have no action on heart muscle. Of the five cardiac glycosides mentioned above, four (digitoxin, gitoxin, digoxin, gitalin) contain a methyl-deoxypentose, digitoxose, as the sugar moiety; digitalin contains glucose and a methoxy-methyl-pentose, digitalose. The aglycones of all five, as of other less important glycosides from these plants and the digitalis saponins, are steroids and have attached to the nucleus a lactone ring and other groups—methyl, hydroxyl, or aldehydic. They are named by substituting the ending " -igenin " for the " -in " of the corresponding glycoside, e.g. digitoxigenin from digitoxin.

The seeds of various strophanthus species of the *Apocyanaceae* contain glycosides of structure and pharmacological activity similar to those of the digitalis glycosides. From *S. kombé* are obtained (1) **K-strophanthin-β** (the ordinary strophanthin, M.P. 180°-183° C.) in which the steroid aglycone strophanthidin is combined with glucose and the methyl-methoxy-hexose cymarose (i.e. " strophanthobiose "), and (2) **K-strophanthoside** which is K-strophanthin-β condensed with another glucose molecule. *Strophanthus gratus* (*Acocanthera ouabain*) contains **ouabain** of which the sugar is rhamnose and the aglycone is named ouabagenin. Canadian hemp (*Apocyanum*) yields **cymarin**, containing cymarose strophanthin. The principal glycoside of squill, with a digitalis-like action, is **scillaren-A** which is of the usual structure, consisting of a steroid aglycone, scillaridin-A, combined with glucose and rhamnose.

Separation

1. *Digitalis*. Digitoxin is obtained from an alcoholic extract of the plant which has been evaporated to dryness, taken up in water and treated with lead acetate solution. The precipitate produced by the lead is filtered off, the excess lead is removed by means of hydrogen sulphide and the filtrate from the latter is evaporated to dryness. The residue is extracted with chloroform. This chloroform extract is shaken with water to remove gitalin; the digitoxin remains in solution. The dry residue which has been treated with chloroform is then shaken with chloroform and water. The chloroform contains part of the digitoxin. The watery liquid contains digitalin (*vide infra*); the chloroform extract is dried over anhydrous sodium sulphate and evaporated to dryness. The residue is impure digitoxin which can be purified by taking up again in chloroform and adding petroleum ether which precipitates digitoxin in a purer form, though it is still not pure. It can be recrystallized from ether and afterwards from absolute alcohol. This product is known in France as digitaline crystalisée.

The mother liquor, i.e. the aqueous liquid mentioned above, is saturated with sodium chloride and treated with acetone, which extracts digitalin.

Gitalin is obtained by shaking a cold water extract of digitalis leaves (purified with lead acetate and afterwards freed from lead with hydrogen sulphide) with chloroform. From this extract it is precipitated with petroleum ether in the manner already described in the extraction of digitoxin. The product is recrystallized from dilute alcohol.

Digitonin is extracted from mother-liquors, especially from seeds, after digitoxin and digitalin have been removed. The liquors, after saturating with salt and extracting with acetone, are extracted with alcohol. Digitonin is precipitated from the alcoholic extract by the addition of ether.

The preparations of digitalis which are on the market contain various mixtures of the above glycosides. Digitalin Nativelle is a solution containing mainly digitoxin. The German " pure powdered digitalin " contains digitalin, gitalin and digitoxin. Homolle's digitalin is largely digitoxin with a little digitalin.

2. *Strophanthus.* The plant *Strophanthus kombé,* a creeper which grows in the tropical parts of East Africa, has seeds characterized by long silky hairs called " awns " attached to one end.

The glycoside is extracted from the powdered seeds with absolute alcohol after first removing oil with petroleum ether. The residue from the evaporated extract is taken up in water and clarified with basic lead acetate. The aqueous liquid, after the elimination of the excess of lead, is treated with sufficient ammonium sulphate to induce crystallization without precipitating amorphous matter. The crystals are collected and dissolved in alcohol which is afterwards diluted with an equal quantity of water and evaporated *in vacuo* until crystals separate. When pure the crystals melt at 180°–183° C.

Ouabain from *S. gratus,* long used as an arrow-poison in East Africa, is separated by similar methods.

3. *Squill.* The bulbs of squill contain glycosides which have a physiological activity similar to that of digitalis. The red variety is used in England as rat poison, but it is employed medicinally in France. The principal glycoside can be extracted from the dried and powdered bulbs with alcohol and the dried extract is taken up in dilute alcohol. Tannin is added to this solution, which precipitates the glycoside. The precipitate is dissolved in chloroform and evaporated to dryness. This tannin compound, again dissolved in dilute alcohol, is decomposed by treatment with lead acetate; the filtrate, freed from excess of lead, is concentrated *in vacuo* and finally purified with methyl alcohol or chloroform. It yields a red colour with concentrated hydrochloric acid.

Symptoms of Digitalis Poisoning. In large doses the cardiac glycosides cause nausea, vomiting, abdominal pains, diarrhoea, headache, muscular weakness and collapse. They may also cause burning pain in the larynx. The pulse-rate falls to 40 per minute or even lower. In fatal cases coma supervenes and the patient dies. Before death, the pulse may be temporarily accelerated.

The active principles of digitalis are to some extent destroyed in the body, especially in the intestines; but the decomposition is not complete, as is proved by the fact that when repeated doses are administered the drug accumulates, and symptoms of poisoning may appear owing to a succession of small doses. When the acidic aqueous extract from viscera is shaken with chloroform, the greater part of the extracted matter is digitoxin, which may be found not only in the stomach but also in the liver and kidneys.

Oleander Glycosides

The two most important toxic species of **oleander** are the white or sweet-scented oleander (*Nerium odorum*) and the yellow oleander (*Cerbera thevetia* or *Thevetia nerii folia*). Both belong to the natural order Apocyanaceae. The chief glycosidal constituents of the former are: neriodorein, neriodorin and karabin (from the Bengali name for the plant: Karabi).

Glycoside	Solvents			
	Water	Alcohol	Benzene	Ether
Neriodorein	Readily soluble	Slightly soluble	Insoluble	Insoluble
Neriodorin	Soluble at 100° C.	Soluble in absolute alcohol	Insoluble	Slightly soluble
Karabin	Insoluble, even in boiling water	Soluble in absolute alcohol	Soluble	Very soluble

White oleander is very poisonous, the usual symptoms being abdominal pain and vomiting; hurried respiration; slow pulse at first but afterwards rapid and weak. In the later stages there are muscular twitchings and tetanic spasms, followed by drowsiness, unconsciousness, coma and death from the paralysis of the heart. Tetany is common; diarrhoea is rare. The three glycosides are distinguished by their different solubilities in several solvents and by certain colour tests which will be described later.

In India white oleander poisoning is often due to the ingestion of the root as a remedy for venereal diseases; it also has a reputation as an abortifacient drug.

The active principle of the **yellow oleander** is the glycoside thevitin which is found in the milky juice which exudes from all parts of the plant. It is soluble in 124 parts of water at 14° C., freely soluble in alcohol and chloroform, but not in ether.

De and Chowdhury[1] describe the isolation of thevitin in a pure form, melting at 189°–190° C. This substance yielded, on hydrolysis, an amorphous product, to which they gave the name thevitidin; it is more toxic than thevitin. Thevitin is now believed to consist of a steroid aglycone, thevetigenin, condensed with two molecules of glucose and one of another sugar, possibly digitalose.

[1] " Calcutta University Thesis ", 1919.

Ghatak[1] claims to have isolated two glycosides from the kernels of the seeds of yellow oleander. The first, thevitin, was obtained in slender needles, melting at 192° C., by recrystallization from dilute alcohol. It is insoluble in water but dissolves in most of the organic solvents. When perfectly pure it is said to be tasteless; but, as usually obtained, it has a definite bitter taste. Ghatak's second glycoside, twice recrystallized from hot water, was obtained in needles, melting at 178° C. It is insoluble in *cold* water and has an intense bitter taste, even when pure. It is very soluble in alcohol but practically insoluble in most of the other organic solvents. Ghatak gave the name thevetoxin to this substance, but it is a misnomer, since, according to Bhatia and Lal,[2] it is less toxic than thevetin. Pharmacologically it resembles the glycosides of digitalis.

In India the yellow oleander is one of the commonest of cattle poisons.

In human beings the symptoms of yellow oleander poisoning are: burning pain in the mouth, dryness in the throat, tingling and numbness in the tongue, vomiting, sometimes diarrhoea, headache, giddiness, mydriasis, and unconsciousness. The pulse is slow at first, afterwards becoming more rapid, weak and irregular. The patients may then collapse and die from heart failure. Sometimes death is preceded by tetanic convulsions.

Yellow oleander poisoning is especially common in the Bombay and Madras Presidencies.

Glycosides of the Black Hellebore or Christmas Rose.

The rhizome of the **black hellebore** contains two glycosides, helleborin and helleborein, of which the former is a narcotic and the latter a cardiac poison and also a drastic purgative. The mixed glycosides are extracted in the usual way, and from the mixture helleborin can be extracted with boiling water and crystallized from this solvent. Its melting point is above 250° C. Helleborein remains in the mother-liquor. The products of hydrolysis are: from helleborin, glucose and helleboresin; from helleborein, glucose, acetic acid and a violet coloured compound called helleboretin.

Snake Root.

The dried and powdered root of *Polygala senega* irritates the mucous membrane of the nose, causing violent sneezing. It contains two glycosides, senegin and polygalic acid, of which the former is toxic and the latter sternutatory. A dried alcoholic extract is freed from fat with petroleum ether and taken up in water. From this solution crude polygalic acid separates out on standing and senegin can be extracted from the mother-liquor by the usual

---

[1] *Bull. Acad. Sci. Unit. Prov.*, **11**, No. 2.
[2] *Ind. J. of Med. Research*, 3.1.34, **21**.

methods. Senega root also contains oil of wintergreen (methyl salicylate) and the proportion of this constituent is said to increase on standing.

Saponins and Sapotoxins

Saponins are glycosides which form soapy solutions when shaken with water, and are commonly used as emulsifying agents and to produce foam in beverages. The more poisonous of them are called sapotoxins. Most saponins are amorphous, but a few, such as digitonin, gitonin and sarsaponin, can be obtained in crystalline form. Saponins are, in general, soluble in water and in hot alcohol, but are sparingly soluble in ether, benzene and chloroform.

A common source of sapotoxins is the corn cockle (*Lychnis githago*) which grows as a weed in cornfields. The crushed seeds of the plant may be mixed with the flour, and if such flour contains as much as 5 per cent. of corn cockle, dangerous poisoning symptoms are likely to occur.[1]

Sapotoxins are haemolytic poisons, i.e. they destroy the red corpuscles and this phenomenon can be observed in defibrinated blood.

This physiological action is said to be due to the extraction of the cholesterol from the blood corpuscles and the combination of the saponin with the cholesterol. This compound so formed is non-toxic and has no haemolytic effect, a fact which is utilized in the detection of saponins. A sample of defibrinated blood on a slide is focussed under the microscope; a drop of the suspected substance is mixed with it and the haemolytic effect is observed. A similar blood sample is then treated with a drop of the solution which has been deprived of its haemolytic activity by means of cholesterol. In this second sample the blood corpuscles should remain unaffected.

Saponins are extracted from plants with water, clarified with lead acetate, filtered and freed from lead in the usual way. The lead-free solution is evaporated to dryness and the residue is treated with alcohol to dissolve out the saponin which is then precipitated by mixing with ether.

Saponins can be hydrolyzed with dilute mineral acids and the sugar-free portions are called sapogenins; these are the physiologically active principles.

Very little is known about the fate of saponins in the body, but there is some evidence to show that hydrolysis occurs in the liver. In animal experiments sapogenins have been found in the faeces whereas the urine contains unchanged saponins.

Purgative Drugs

Many of the drastic organic purgatives, such as aloes, *cascara sagrada*, rhubarb and senna, are polyhydroxy or polymethoxy

[1] STOEKLIN. *Annal. Falsific.*, 1917, **10**, 561–72. *Analyst*, 1918, **43** 142.

derivatives of anthraquinone. Some of them are associated with glycosides, and it is a remarkable fact that the synthetic anthraquinone compounds have not the same purgative properties.

Aloes. The several varieties of this drug are obtained by the slow evaporation of the juice which exudes from the transversely cut leaves of the different species of the plant. The principal varieties are Curacao or Barbados aloes (from *Aloe Chinensis*), Socotrine aloes (from *A. perry*) and Cape aloes (from *A. ferox*). Natal aloes is no longer an article of commerce. When the juice is evaporated very slowly the product is opaque, whereas rapid evaporation yields vitreous products.

Cascara Sagrada. This drug is obtained from the bark of the North American tree *Rhamnus purshianus*. The fresh bark has emetic properties which it loses on keeping for a year. Cascara owes its purgative properties to a hydroxymethyl anthroquinone derivative.

Frangula Bark. This European variety of *Rhamnus*, the alder buckthorn, has very similar properties to cascara and contains the anthraquinone compound frangula emodin, which is also present in rhubarb.

Rhubarb. Several species of rhubarb, *Rheum palmatum*, *R. officinale* and *R. rhaponticum*, are in common use. The drug, which is extracted from the rhizome, contains several hydroxy anthraquinone compounds and their ethers, but the chief active principle is said to be a resinous constituent.

Senna. Two varieties of senna are used, *Cassia acutifolia* and *C. angustifolia*. The active principles, which consist of anthraquinone derivatives, are more abundant in the leaves than in the pods.

Elaterium. The dried sediment from the juice of the squirting cucumber, *Ecballium elaterium*, which grows wild in the Near East, is a very powerful purgative. It contains about 30 per cent. of a crystalline substance, elaterin, which can be prepared by pouring the alcoholic extract into water, filtering the product and washing with ether. It is recrystallized from absolute alcohol. Of this crystalline substance 60–80 per cent., α-elaterin, is inert; β-elaterin (20–40 per cent.) is the purgative. The medicinal dose is 3 mg., and death has been caused by 0·5 gm.

Jalap. The dried tubercles of *Ipomoea purga* contain 4 per cent. to 20 per cent. of a purgative resin which when dissolved in alcohol and diluted with water yields a precipitate which is partially soluble in ether. The ether-soluble portion is called scammonin and the remainder jalapin. Jalap resin on hydrolysis yields a mixture of aliphatic acids and glucose. Scammony, obtained from the root of

Convolvulus scammoniae, or Levant scammony, contains 3–13 per cent. of resin, which consists largely of glycosides.

Podophyllum, mandrake or may-apple, is an American perennial herb with a branching rhizome system. The fruit is a large oval berry which is lemon-yellow in colour when ripe and has round brown spots.

The dried rhizome yields not less than 3 per cent. of toxic resin. The leaves also are poisonous and sometimes contain as much of the active principles as the rhizome.

The most important of the active principles, podophyllotoxin, is a neutral, crystalline substance, melting, when pure, at 117° C., which is obtained by extracting the coarsely powdered rhizome with chloroform, after preliminary treatment with light petroleum to remove fat. The chloroform solution is evaporated on a tepid water-bath and the residue is taken up in benzene and filtered; the filtrate is allowed to stand three to eight hours. Brownish-yellow, strongly refracting prisms separate. These are washed with 50 per cent. alcohol, then with ether, and recrystallized, first from boiling benzene and then from 45 per cent. alcohol. The crystals, still impure, melt at 94° C.

Podophyllum is used as a cathartic. In overdoses it is an irritant poison. Five grains of the resin have caused the death of a sixty-year-old woman.

Colocynth is the dried pulp of the bitter apple, *Citrullus colocynthis*, freed from seed. The plant grows wild on the deserts of Egypt and elsewhere. The unripe fruit is about the size of a cricket ball and is green and spherical. When the fruit is ripe the rind becomes white and brittle.

The dried pulp is extracted with alcohol and precipitated with water; the precipitate is then washed with petroleum spirit which extracts about 3 per cent. of oil. The residue is made into a paste with lime, dried, powdered, and extracted twice with methyl alcohol. This extract gives a vivid carmine coloured ring in Keller's test for digitalis.

The residue is shaken up with water and precipitated with lead acetate; the filtrate is freed from lead and treated with tannin. The tannin-colocynthin compound so formed is decomposed by heating to dryness with lead carbonate and the colocynthin is dissolved out with boiling alcohol. When cold, ether is mixed with this solution to precipitate the colocynthin. This, according to some authorities, can be hydrolyzed to form colocynthein and glucose; others assert that it is unaffected by dilute acids.

The substance is partly soluble in water and from this portion a dihydric alcohol has been isolated which yields a diacetyl derivative. The mother-liquor contains traces of an alkaloid and a glycoside.

The insoluble portion is a resin from which β-elaterin has been isolated.

The purgative action is due to the alkaloid and the glycoside. The minimum lethal dose appears to be about 1 or 2 g. of the powder, but recovery after taking 11·7 g. has been recorded.

Cantharidin (Spanish flies).   Two species of insects yield cantharidin: *Cantharis vesicatoria* (0·4–1 per cent.) and *Mylabris phalerata* or *M. cichorii* (1–1·5 per cent.).

The powdered insects are extracted with chloroform or ethyl acetate in the presence of dilute sulphuric acid and the extract is filtered.   The filtrate is treated with barium carbonate, again filtered and evaporated to dryness.   Fat is removed from the residue with petroleum ether and the crude cantharidin is recrystallized from alcohol.   The crystals melt at 218° C., but they begin to sublime at about 80° C.   Cantharidin is volatile in steam, is soluble in alkalis, and, when heated with caustic soda on the water-bath, is converted into the sodium salt of cantharidic acid.   Heating on the water-bath may be continued until a dry residue is obtained, and from this the excess of soda can be washed out with alcohol.   From a soda-free aqueous solution of the cantharidate, crystals of the mercury salt can be obtained by adding mercuric chloride solution.

Cantharides has a certain reputation as an aphrodisiac and serious results have followed its administration for this purpose. The poisoning symptoms are inflammation and corrosion of the mucous membranes and of the genital organs.   There is usually a burning sensation in the mouth, nausea, vomiting of blood, severe thirst, difficulty in swallowing, pain in the loins, blood in the urine, diarrhoea, prostration and coma.   Twenty-four grains of the powder have been known to cause death and in another case 1 oz. of the tincture.

Cantharidin may be extracted from viscera by mixing with phosphoric acid and distilling in a rapid current of steam.   Two-thirds of the original volume is collected as distillate, and this is reduced in bulk by repeated re-distillation.   Finally, the concentrated distillate is made alkaline with caustic soda and evaporated almost to dryness.   Excess of phosphoric acid is again added and the mixture is heated for some time under a reflux condenser.   The inside of the condenser is then washed down with chloroform and the liquid is extracted with the same solvent, several times repeated. The chloroform is dried with anhydrous sodium sulphate and evaporated to dryness at a low temperature.

The crude cantharidin may be purified by sublimation, preferably under diminished pressure.

CHAPTER VIII

SYSTEMATIC TESTING FOR NON-BASIC POISONS

ORGANIC poisons other than alkaloids are extracted from the residue obtained by the evaporation of the alcohol in the Stas-Otto process. The residue is taken up in hot water, faintly acidified with sulphuric acid, and extracted successively with (a) light petroleum, (b) ether, (c) chloroform and (d) some specific solvent, other than these, which may be necessary, such as ethyl acetate or amyl alcohol.

The light petroleum extract may contain oils. Some of these have already been discussed among the poisons volatile in steam, and most of them are vesicants. A portion of the extract should be tested for vesicating action by mixing it with olive oil and rubbing it into the skin of the inner side of the forearm. The rubbed spot should be kept covered with a bandage for four hours. Slight irritation may be ignored, but if a definite blister is formed, special tests must be made for individual vesicants. One portion of the residue is submitted to steam-distillation (unless this process has already been used) and the distillate is shaken out with petroleum. After the evaporation of the latter, the tests for essential oils (savin, rue, pennyroyal, chenopodium, etc.) already described, are tried.

A second sample of the extract is soaked in cold caustic potash and allowed to stand for several hours, after which it is re-acidified with dilute hydrochloric acid and re-extracted with light petroleum. If this extract produces no vesicating action, marking-nut oil from one of the species of *Anacardium* is indicated, since the vesicating power of this oil is destroyed by treatment with cold potash.

The two kinds of marking-nut oil and also plumbagin (from lead-wort) can be distinguished by the colour-reactions shown in the Table on p. 191, although plumbagin should not be confused with marking-nut oils since it can be separated from them owing to its stability towards cold caustic potash.

If the activity of the extract is not destroyed by alkali, cantharidin may be present. The visual examination of the stomach-contents with the lens may have revealed iridescent fragments of Spanish flies. A special method for the isolation and purification of cantharidin has already been described (p. 189). It is usually asserted that no colour reactions for cantharidin are known, and that identification (in the absence of fragments of the flies) must depend on (a) vesication, (b) melting point and (c) the crystalline form of the salts of cantharidic acid such as the mercury, calcium and barium salts. There is, however, one highly characteristic colour reaction of cantharidin which must not be omitted. A few milligrammes of the purified substance are dissolved in about 1 ml. of Mecke's reagent. The liquid remains colourless in the cold, and even at 100° C., but if it is cautiously heated over a flame until the temperature approaches the boiling point of sulphuric acid, a wine-red colour develops which changes to deep violet.

Test	Oil from Semicarpus Anacardium	Oil from Anacardium Occidentale	Plumbagin
Dissolve in alcohol and add alcoholic potash	Bright green colour	Reddish yellow colour, turning violet	Crimson colour
Add basic lead acetate	Greenish-black precipitate	White precipitate turning red	Crimson precipitate

ETHER EXTRACT

The ether extract may contain **hypnotics** or soporifics. These are the derivatives of barbituric acid and hydantoin, the straight-chain ureides, adalin, bromural and sedormid, and the sulphonal group. These separate, usually as colourless crystals, when the ether is evaporated slowly. The reactions characteristic of the group (including the hydantoin derivative, nirvanol, but not the straight-chain ureides) are (1) the white gelatinous precipitate given by an aqueous solution with Millon's reagent, (2) the violet colour produced with an alcoholic solution of cobalt nitrate on the addition of ammonia and (3) the green colour given on heating with selenious acid and sulphuric acid. If positive reactions are obtained in these tests, the systematic scheme described below must be carried out for the identification of the individual drug.

If these tests give negative results, one of the straight-chain ureides may be present, although these are usually decomposed in the body and are only to be expected in the extracts from the alimentary organs. If bromine is present, **adalin, pernokton, dormalgin** or **bromural** may be suspected. If bromine is absent, the substance may be **sedormid**, which crystallizes in long slender needles from ether or on cooling a hot ammoniacal solution. This substance is only slightly soluble in ammonia even on boiling. With sedormid the sulphuric acid-*p*-dimethylaminobenzaldehyde reagent becomes faintly yellow in the cold and this colour deepens to orange when warmed on the water-bath. Mecke's reagent yields no colour in the cold, but becomes brown and afterwards grey on the water-bath.

Identification of the Barbituric Acid Derivatives

Earlier editions of this book included a scheme for the identification of barbiturates which the author evolved for dealing with the relatively small number of these substances available in Cairo in 1939. Other schemes, based on the formation of crystalline precipitates rather than on colour reactions had been produced by Rosenthaler[1] and by van Itallie and Steenhauer.[2] More recently Turfitt[3] has published a method, based primarily on colour reactions, and more comprehensive than that of Bamford, which it replaces in this edition.

Turfitt's Method. The crude ether extract (Stas-Otto) is purified as follows. The ether solution is thoroughly dried by first stirring with about 0·5 g. of anhydrous sodium sulphate and then pouring through an adsorption column containing a further 0·5 g. of anhydrous sodium sulphate. The solution is then stirred with 0·1 to 0·2 g. of activated charcoal (Norit) and poured through a column containing a 1 cm. layer of charcoal (the adsorption of barbiturates from a dried ether solution is negligible). The filtrate and washings are evaporated to dryness and the weight of the residue taken as an approximate measure of the amount of barbituric acid present. For further purification resublimation may be used, or the acid may be dissolved in a little alkali, reprecipitated by acid, and finally recrystallized from ether.

At this stage melting point may be determined, but further recrystallization may be needed to give a definitive result. It is useful also (if not already done) to make preliminary tests to confirm the presence of a member of the barbituric acid group and for this purpose the cobalt reaction and the selenious acid reaction may be used. For the former, Turfitt mixes two drops of an alcoholic solution of the test material with two drops of an alcoholic cobalt acetate solution such that the mixture has only a faint pink tinge ; on addition of one drop of 2N ammonia a purple-blue colour appears if barbiturates (or various interfering substances) are present. The selenious acid test is performed as described below.

The differentiation of the individual barbiturates depends primarily upon four colour reactions with an attempt to avoid rather nondescript yellows and browns. Identification should be checked by control tests with authentic samples. The results of these tests are shown in the Table on pp. 194-5.

(1) *Vanillin Reaction.* A small amount (about 0·1 mg.) of the material is mixed with an equal amount of vanillin in a white porcelain dish, a small drop (0·05 ml.) of concentrated sulphuric acid

[1] *Toxicologische Mikroanalyse.* Berlin, 1935.
[2] *Pharm. Weekbl.*, 1930, **67**, 977.
[3] *Quart. J. and Yearbook, Pharm.*, 1948, **21**, 1.

is added, and the dish is heated for two minutes on a boiling water-bath. Occasional tilting facilitates observation of the colour changes which may (e.g. hexobarbitone, pentothal, phanodorm) be very rapid. The dish is then cooled, and two drops (0·1 ml.) of alcohol are added. The deep blue end colours may be replaced by purples if only minute traces of barbiturate are present.

(2) *Selenious Acid Reaction.* A trace (0·01 mg.) of the test material and an equal quantity of solid selenious acid are mixed with one or two small drops (0·05-0·1 ml.) of concentrated sulphuric acid in a small (2 in. × ¼ in.) test-tube and slowly heated to boiling over a micro flame. A purple ring on the cooler part of the tube, appearing during the heating, is to be ignored. The initial colour changes to green. The final green colour disappears on continued heating, but if, while this colour is present, the mixture is poured into a porcelain basin and a few drops of alcohol are added, a red turbidity is produced.

(3) *p-Dimethylaminobenzaldehyde Reaction.* A small amount (0·01 to 0·1 mg.) of the test material is mixed with an equal amount of the solid aldehyde and one drop of concentrated sulphuric acid (0·05 ml.) in a porcelain dish which is then heated for one minute on the boiling waterbath. After cooling, two drops (0·1 ml.) of alcohol are added. Faint yellow-pink colours are to be ignored.

(4) *Resorcinol Reaction.* A little (about 0·1 mg.) of the material, mixed with an equal amount of resorcinol and about four drops of concentrated sulphuric acid in an ordinary (6 in. × ⅝ in.) test-tube is heated to 130° C. for five minutes. An oil-bath may conveniently be used, but in any case the temperature of 130° C. should not be exceeded appreciably ; at higher temperatures the resorcinol itself may produce interfering colours. After noting any colour, the contents of the tube are cooled, diluted with about 1 ml. of water, and examined under ultra-violet light. After the solution has been made alkaline by addition of 2N sodium hydroxide, the appearance is again noted in visible and ultra-violet light.

By these tests it is not possible to distinguish clearly :

(*a*) hebaral from sandoptal, amytal or barbitone ;

(*b*) hexobarbitone from phanodorm ;

(*c*) phemitone from phenobarbitone, rutonal.

Melting points (checked by mixed melting points with authentic samples) and crystalline form on crystallization from ether and on precipitation of the free acid from a solution in ammonium hydroxide (again checked by comparison with authentic samples) will then differentiate the members of these groups.

It must, however, be realized that absolute identification of an individual member of a group so similar in structure as the barbiturates is very difficult, and anything short of proof by mixed melting

	Vanillin Sulphuric Acid.	Alcohol.	Selenious Acid.	p-Dimethyl-aminobenzalde-hyde.
Reagent	Yellow	Colourless	Pale yellow→ colourless	Colourless
Allobarbitone ..	Yellow→pink and green streaks	Blue-green	Red-brown	Yellow→brown with pinkish streaks
Allonal (barbitur-ate)	—	—	Blood-red→ purple-green	Bright pinkish purple
Amytal	—	—	Yellow	—
Barbitone	—	—	Yellow	—
Barbituric Acid ..	Yellow→orange	Yellow	Turbid red-purple	—
Hebaral	—	—	Yellow	—
Hexobarbitone ..	Yellow→green →red-brown with purple streaks	Intense blue	Brown	Red-purple→ red-brown
Ipral	—	.	Red-purple	Bright pinkish-purple
Narconumal ..	Yellow,→yel-low-green	—	Red-brown→ red-purple	Bright pinkish-purple
Nembutal	Yellow→red purple	Intense blue	Brown	Red-brown with purple streaks
Pentothal	Yellow→ orange→ brown with purple streaks	Intense blue (Characteris-tic odour)	Brown	Red-brown with purple streaks
Pernocton	Yellow→ orange→dull green	Green	Brown	—
Phanodorm ..	Yellow→ green → red-brown with purple streaks	Intense blue	Red-brown	Red-purple→ red-brown
Phemitone	—	—	Purple	—
Phenobaritone ..	—	—	Purple	—
Rutonal	—	—	Purple	—
Sandoptal	—	—	Yellow	—
Seconal	Green, with purple streaks →dull green →purple	Blue	Red-brown	Brown with purple streaks
Soneryl	Yellow→ orange-brown	Dirty blue	Orange	

| Alcohol | Resorcinol | | | |
| | Acid | | Alkaline | |
	Visible	U.V.	Visible	U.V.
Pale yellow	Colourless	Colourless	Colourless	Colourless
Transient violet	Orange-red	Whitish-green	Yellow-green (fluorescence)	Blue green
Transient green	Orange-yellow	Very pale green	Pale green (fluorescence)	Pale blue
—	Orange	Very pale green	Colourless	Pale blue
—	Very pale yellow	Colourless	Colourless	Colourless
Bright yellow → pink on addition of water	Yellow	Very pale green	Colourless	Very pale blue
—	Orange-yellow	Very pale green	Pale green (fluorescence)	Pale blue
Violet	Blood-red	Grey green	Wine-red	Bright blue
Transient green	Yellow	Very pale green	Pale green (fluorescence)	Very pale blue
Transient green	Pink	Very pale green	Colourless	Colourless
Transient violet	Orange	Whitish green	Yellow	Pale blue
Transient violet (Characteristic odour)	Orange	Whitish green	Yellow green (fluorescence)	Blue-green
—	Purple-red	Dull green	Brown	Blue-grey
Violet	Blood-red	Grey-green	Wine-red	Bright blue
—	Yellow	Very pale green	Pale green (fluorescence)	Very pale blue
—	Very pale yellow	Colourless	Colourless	Colourless
—	Yellow	Very pale green	Pale green (fluorescence)	Very pale blue
—	Orange	Very pale green	Colourless	Very pale blue
Transient violet	Blood-red	Dull green	Brown	Dull green
—	Yellow	Colourless	Colourless	Very pale blue

point should be treated with some reserve. Fortunately it is often enough to prove the presence of a barbiturate in general.

Ultra-Violet Spectroscopy. Although the different barbiturates (sodium salts in 0·5N sodium hydroxide) have rather similar ultra-violet absorption spectra,[1] it is possible to identify some of them by measuring the ratios of the optical densities at selected wave-lengths. Thus the ratios at 235 mμ, 230 mμ and 225 mμ with reference to 255 mμ are 0·69, 0·97, 2·06 for phenobarbitone, and 0·59, 0·70, 1·55 for seconal.[2] At present, however, ultra violet spectrophotometry is more promising as a quantitative procedure of very considerable sensitivity. A method useful especially for blood analysis has been developed by Goldbaum.[2]

Quantitative Determination. The methods most commonly employed are founded upon the colour reaction with cobalt in alkaline solution as developed by Koppanyi.[3] The barbituric acid, extracted by one of the methods previously described (Chapter VI) is dissolved in *dry* chloroform. For each 2 ml. of solution, add 0·3 ml. of freshly-prepared 0·6 per cent. iso-propylamine in *dry* A.R. methanol and 0·1 ml. of 1% cobalt acetate in *dry* A.R. methanol. Compare the reddish-purple colour with that of a similarly treated standard solution of the barbituric acid in chloroform. If necessary the " test " solution may be diluted with chloroform or concentrated by evaporation to bring it within the range of comparison. The comparison should be made within an hour or so, as the colour gradually fades. The standard solution may conveniently contain 1·0 mg. of the barbituric acid per ml., or for direct visual comparison a series of standards may be used, covering the range 0·1 to 1·0 mg. per ml.

The Sulphonal Group

Chemical tests for the recognition of sulphonal and its homologues depend on the action of reducing agents. Finely divided iron, strongly heated, reduces them to mercaptans with characteristic foul odours, and iron sulphide is simultaneously produced. Addition of hydrochloric acid to the residual iron sulphide liberates hydrogen sulphide which blackens silver, precipitates lead sulphide from a solution of lead acetate, etc. If potassium cyanide is the reducing agent used, potassium thiocyanate is formed and this can be recognized by the usual tests.

Sulphonal, recrystallized from chloroform, melts at 125° C., trional at 76° C. and tetronal at 85° C.

[1] Eldridge. *Quart. J. Pharm. and Pharmacol.*, 1940, **13**, 219. Stuckey. *Ibid.*, 1941, **14**, 217 : 1942, **15**, 370.

[2] Goldbaum. *J. Pharm. Exp. Ther.*, 1948, **94**, 68.

[3] *J. Amer. Pharm. Assoc.*, 1934, **23**, 1,074.

Polyhydric Phenols

Among other ether-soluble poisons are the dihydric and trihydric phenols, which, like the urea derivatives, are colourless crystalline solids.

Catechol or pyrocatechin and **resorcinol** form definite colours with ferric chloride solution. The former gives a green colour which becomes violet and afterwards red on treatment with sodium bicarbonate, while the colour with resorcinol is immediately violet. The same reagent converts hydroquinone into quinone which may be recognized by its distinctive odour.

The most characteristic reaction of **resorcinol** is its conversion into fluorescein by fusion with phthalic anhydride and a little anhydrous zinc chloride as a condensing agent; the resulting melt dissolves in dilute alkali to form the well-known yellowish green fluorescent solution. The addition of bromine water converts fluorescein into the red dye-stuff, eosin, which is also fluorescent in dilute solution.

Pyrogallol in alkaline solution rapidly absorbs oxygen and darkens in colour, becoming almost black.

Phloroglucinol may be recognized by the red colour which it imparts to a pine-splinter moistened with concentrated hydrochloric acid.

All the **nitrophenols** are yellow in colour, the di-nitro and tri-nitro compounds being deeper in colour than the mono-. They all form deep yellow coloured solutions with alkalis and effervesce with alkaline carbonates. This distinguishes them from the di- and tri-nitrobenzenes.

Picric Acid. Picric acid can be sublimed under normal pressure without decomposition: it melts at 122·5° C. The silver salt crystallizes in bundles of needles or fine, curved, branching crystals. Picric acid also forms needles or prisms with a reagent consisting of equal volumes of 10 per cent. solutions of ammonia and copper sulphate. Alkaline reducing agents readily convert it into salts of picraminic acid, which may be recognized by their crystalline forms. A few particles of the substance in question are rubbed on a microscope slide with one or two drops of aqueous caustic soda and a drop of ammonium sulphide solution is added; the slide is then warmed gently without a cover-slip. Some of the picraminate crystals resemble snowflakes; others are circular in form.

The addition of a drop of concentrated potassium cyanide solution to an ammoniacal picrate solution produces a transient greenish blue colour, which changes quickly on warming, or more slowly if allowed to stand, to deep red: finally a red precipitate may be deposited.

The wool-dyeing property of picric acid may be used as a microtest. Two fibres, one of cotton and one of wool, are placed about 5 mm. apart in a drop of the solution on a microscope slide and covered with a slip until the liquid is soaked up, and after a few minutes the fibres are washed with water. The wool is dyed, but the cotton remains colourless. Treatment with potassium cyanide changes the yellow colour of the wool to reddish brown.

Salicylic acid is also among the substances which may be found in the ether extract from acidified aqueous solution after the ingestion of salicylates, acetyl-salicylic acid (aspirin) or phenyl-salicylic acid (salol). The well-known violet colour with ferric chloride is produced in neutral solution. If there is excess of acid present it must be neutralized with ammonia and any excess of the latter expelled by boiling before the test is made. Heated gently with methyl alcohol and a drop or two of concentrated sulphuric acid, salicylic acid gives the methyl ester (oil of wintergreen) recognizable by its odour. **Aspirin** is not usually excreted unchanged but may be found in vomits or stomach-contents mixed with the products of hydrolysis. The material should be acidified and submitted to steam-distillation, after which the distillate is made alkaline and evaporated to dryness. The residue is tested for acetates by the methods already described. The liquid in the flask is extracted with ether and the extract is tested with ferric chloride for free salicylic acid. This is usually detected easily. To detect unchanged aspirin the product must be hydrolyzed by boiling with dilute mineral acid, and treated as above described with ammonia, the excess of the latter being boiled off. The intensity of the violet colour is proportional to the amount of salicylic acid and therefore any increase in this intensity after hydrolysis is due to unchanged aspirin.

Phenacetin, if treatment is long continued, may cause symptoms of chronic poisoning, but it is justly regarded as one of the least harmful of antipyretics. If a small crystal of phenacetin is boiled with concentrated hydrochloric acid and, after dilution, a minute amount of phenol and a drop of sodium hypochlorite solution are added, a reddish violet colour develops. Another test which distinguishes between phenacetin and *p*-aminophenol is as follows: the solution in hydrochloric acid is prepared as before, boiled, cooled and filtered. A drop of chromic acid solution added to the filtrate produces a deep red colour. Under the same conditions *p*-aminophenol yields a negative result.

Extract of Felix-mas

Filicic acid from the extract of male fern is coloured red by ferric chloride solution. When this acid is hydrolyzed it decomposes into butyric acid which may be recognized by its odour, and phloroglucinol which imparts a red colour to a pine-wood splinter moistened with hydrochloric acid.

Frog Test

If the examination up to this stage has revealed no vesicating substance and no hypnotic drug, and if the medical reports, ante-mortem and post-mortem, have given no indications of definite poisons for which tests should be made, much fruitless work may be avoided by testing the extract for toxicity. The dry residue is thoroughly mixed with 1 or 2 ml. of water made faintly alkaline with sodium carbonate. A small portion of the liquid is taken up into a pipette through a small pad of cotton-wool which serves as a filter and this filtrate is exactly neutralized with dilute acid. It is then injected into the dorsal lymph-sac of a small lively frog and the frog is kept under observation in a cage or ventilated glass vessel for several hours. If no toxic symptoms have appeared within about four hours, and if the frog is alive and well on the following day, it can be taken as practically certain that the extract is free from poisonous substances.

If the frog exhibits any abnormal symptoms the search for poisons in the extract must be continued.

CHLOROFORM EXTRACT

Saponins

A portion of the extract is shaken vigorously with a few drops of neutral water. A permanent lather indicates the presence of a saponin which may be a sapotoxin, and this must be confirmed by the haemolytic test. A suspension of red blood cells is prepared as follows. Freshly-drawn ox-blood is shaken with fragments of broken glass until the fibrin separates. From this defibrinated liquid 25 ml. are measured out, and thoroughly mixed with 225 ml. of physiological saline (0·9 g. NaCl per 100 ml.). The mixture is centrifuged for forty-five minutes. The supernatant liquid is decanted and the residue, after again washing with saline, is mixed with 250 ml. of fresh saline to form a turbid suspension. A minute drop of the suspension is mixed with one or two ordinary drops of the solution of the supposed saponin, also in normal saline, and the mixed drops are observed under the microscope. If the turbid liquid becomes clear, haemolysis has taken place, but this is not necessarily due to a saponin; there are other haemolytic agents. To prove that a saponin is present the test must be repeated after mixing a fresh portion of the extract with a small quantity of cholesterol which inhibits the haemolysis, and this inhibition by cholesterol may be taken, with the lathering test, to be proof of the presence of a saponin. Some colour reactions are considered by Godamer[1] to be useful.

(a) Concentrated sulphuric acid dissolves saponins to form reddish yellow solutions, which become red, then reddish violet.

(b) With Fröhde's reagent the colour becomes bluish violet in fifteen minutes and, during the next fifteen minutes, changes to green.

The best-known of the saponins are: ordinary commercial saponin from *Quillaja* bark, a mixture of which one constituent is poisonous; senegin from *Polygala senega* and the glycoside of corn-cockle, *Lychnis githago*.

Some of the other glycosides have saponin-like properties, forming lathers with water, e.g. strophanthin and digitonin.

Glycosides

The methods of extraction of the following substances have already been described. Tests for their identification follow.

Digitoxin. Keller's reaction is probably the most usual test, and this is carried out in the same way as the test for ergotoxin; a trace of the substance is dissolved in glacial acetic acid containing a very small proportion of ferric chloride in a test-tube or a capillary tube; concentrated sulphuric acid is run in so as to form a separate layer and the following colour changes are observed: the zone of contact is brownish green; the acetic acid layer is at first greenish blue, changing in about half an hour to indigo-blue, but if the tube is allowed to stand for thirty-six hours the colour changes back again to green and finally to brown. The colour of the sulphuric acid layer is brownish red.

When a minute quantity of digitoxin is dissolved in a drop of concentrated hydrochloric acid by warming on the water-bath the initial colour is yellow; this changes to olive-green and, after evaporating to dryness, the residue is brown.

Warmed with dilute sulphuric acid in a porcelain capsule, digitoxin forms a brown solution of which the rim is bluish violet.

Treated with the bromine-sulphuric acid reagent,[2] digitoxin forms a greenish brown coloured solution which becomes purple on standing, even in the cold, and the purple colour is intensified by warming.

The *p*-dimethylaminobenzaldehyde reagent should be used in two forms: (A) a 1 per cent. solution in 95 per cent. alcohol containing 1 per cent. of concentrated sulphuric acid, and (B) a 1 per cent. solution of the aldehyde in concentrated sulphuric acid. The

[1] " Lehrbuch ", p. 440.
[2] One drop of saturated bromine-water in 20 ml. of concentrated sulphuric acid.

colours produced with these reagents are very intense, and only the minutest possible amount of digitoxin should be used.

With reagent (A) no colour is produced in the cold, but on warming three coloured zones develop: the outermost is violet; inside this is a blue ring, and innermost is blue-violet. If the liquid is evaporated to dryness and the residue is treated with a few drops of cold glacial acetic acid, part of it dissolves to form a green solution, leaving an insoluble portion which is green.

Reagent (B) yields a dirty brown solution in the cold, and purple tinges appear on warming.

With Sanchez's vanillin reagent[1] digitoxin yields no colour in the cold, but on warming the solution becomes olive-green and the rim of it blue.

Strophanthin-k (from the seeds of *Strophanthus kombé*) and **strophanthin-g**, or ouabain (from *Acocanthera ouabain*) can be differentiated by colour tests.

Reagent		Colours		
		Strophanthin-k		Ouabain
80 per cent sulphuric acid.		Green.		Red.
Bromine-sulphuric acid.[2]	Cold:	olive-green to brown.	Cold:	brick-red with purple tinges.
	Warm:	coffee-brown.	Warm:	coffee-brown; purple at the edges.
Sanchez's[1] vanillin reagent (evaporated to dryness on the water-bath).	Cold:	greenish yellow solution.	Cold:	colourless.
	Warm:	blue rim.	Warm:	brown solution with red rim.
	Residue:	dull blue.	Residue:	brown.
p-Dimethylamino-benzaldehyde (Acidified alcoholic solution) (evaporated).		Greenish yellow.		Yellow only (i.e. practically negative).
Concentrated hydrochloric acid with a trace of resorcinol.		Pink colour.		Colourless.
Mandelin's reagent.		Colourless.		Green.

To confirm the chemical tests for glycosides of the digitalis type in extracts from viscera a physiological test must be made on a frog. For this purpose three similar frogs are fixed on to a drawing-board with their abdominal surfaces facing upwards. Two neutral solutions are prepared, one containing a portion of the extract and the other a few milligrammes of digitoxin, each in about 1 ml. of water. The skin of the thorax is cut in such a way that it can be laid back to

---

[1] 0·3 g. pure vanillin in 100 ml. pure concentrated hydrochloric acid, free from iron.

[2] See p. 256.

expose the heart. The number of heart-beats in half a minute is counted, and it should be approximately the same for each of the frogs. The two solutions are injected into the thoracic cavities of the first and second of the frogs, care being taken not to touch the heart with the hypodermic needle. The heart-rates of all the three are counted at intervals of five minutes. After a short time it will be found that the rate in the frog which has received the digitoxin, and also of the second frog, if the extract contains a glycoside of the digitalis type, will become very much slower, while the heart of the third frog, used as a control, will continue to beat at the same rate as before.

Oleander Glycosides

Yellow Oleander. The seeds, either pericarps or kernels, boiled with dilute hydrochloric acid, impart a blue colour to the liquid. An alcoholic extract of the seeds dissolved in warm dilute hydrochloric acid forms a bluish green solution, the colour of which is discharged by the addition of permanganate.

The same extract dissolves in concentrated sulphuric acid with a cherry-red colour.

The so-called thevetoxin of Ghatak forms an orange-coloured solution with concentrated sulphuric acid, and this changes to deep red on standing for five minutes.

Sweet-scented Oleander (*Nerium odorum*). The following reactions are described by Rai Chooni Lal Bose Bahadur. (For the separation of the individual glycosides, see p. 184.)

Reagent	*Colours*		
	Neriodorein	**Neriodin**	**Karabin**
Concentrated sulphuric acid.	Maroon colour, changing to violet: unchanged by exposure to nitrous fumes or bromine vapour.	Yellowish brown; changed to mauve by nitrous fumes or bromine.	Light brown colour; changed to faint violet-brown by nitrous fumes or bromine.
Concentrated sulphuric acid plus potassium nitrate.	No change.	Reddish violet colour.	No reddish violet colour.
Concentrated hydrochloric acid: boiled.	No change.	Yellowish solution; no flocculation.	Greenish yellow solution; dark greenish blue flocks separate.
Fehling's solution.	No reduction until hydrolysis is effected by boiling 3 hours with 2 per cent. HCl and neutralizing with caustic potash.	Reduction without hydrolysis.	No reduction even after prolonged boiling with dilute hydrochloric acid.

Tests for Picrotoxin

It may be advisable before applying the following tests to purify the material by precipitating with lead acetate, removing the lead with H_2S, partially evaporating and re-extracting with chloroform.

Reagent	Colours
Concentrated sulphuric acid.	Deep orange-yellow, discharged by the addition of a drop of concentrated nitric acid.
Fuming nitric acid (one micro-drop).	Blue to green colour, discharged by excess.
Concentrated sulphuric acid plus benzaldehyde.	Blood-red colour, changing to rich purple on warming.
Concentrated sulphuric acid plus p-dimethylamino-benzaldehyde.	Brownish red, becoming blood-red on warming.
Concentrated sulphuric acid plus vanillin.	Lemon-yellow, becoming deep brown on warming.
Strong solution of vanillin in concentrated hydrochloric acid	No colour in the cold; after boiling for two or three minutes a green colour develops. This reaction is not very sensitive.

Reactions of Santonin and Santonic Acid

A small quantity of santonin and a particle of caustic potash, stirred with a few drops of alcohol, produce a very bright pink colour in the cold which becomes brown on warming. Santonic acid, treated in the same way, only yields the brown colour on warming.

Santonin remains colourless with concentrated sulphuric acid, nitric acid and Fröhde's reagent. Mandelin's reagent also does not change its yellow colour. Mecke's reagent slowly turns grey, the rim becoming brown; santonic acid yields a brick-red colour with this reagent.

A trace of santonin with 2–3 drops of a 2 per cent. alcoholic solution of re-distilled furfural and 2 ml. of concentrated sulphuric acid evaporated on the water-bath yields the following sequence of colours: reddish purple, carmine, blue.

Urine containing santonin becomes reddish violet when treated with Fehling's solution, and this becomes green with excess of acetic acid.

Reactions of Purgative Drugs

These include Aloes, Cascara Sagrada, Colocynthin, Jalap, Scammony, Podophyllin, Euphorbium, Elaterium, Croton oil and Castor oil.

Aloes. *The borax test.* An aqueous extract of aloes when shaken with a solution of borax, yields a green fluorescent solution. This reaction is common to all varieties of aloes.

Bornträger's reaction. A benzene extract of aloes is shaken vigorously with ammonia; when the two layers separate the ammoniacal layer is reddish violet. All varieties, except Natal aloes, produce this colour, which is due to the common constituent, barbaloin.

The cupraloin test. 10 ml. of a 1 per cent. aqueous solution of aloes are mixed with 5 ml. of 5 per cent. copper sulphate solution, 1 ml. of saturated sodium chloride solution, and a few drops of potassium cyanide solution. A deep claret colour, which is due to the presence of *iso*-barbaloin, indicates Curaçao aloes.

Colocynthin. The alcoholic extract yields the following colours with the common sulphuric acid reagents:

Concentrated sulphuric acid: brown.

Mandelin's reagent: brick-red.

Mecke's reagent: brighter red than with Mandelin's reagent; turning purple.

The alcoholic *p*-dimethylaminobenzaldehyde reagent (acidified with sulphuric acid) warmed on the water-bath with colocynthin shows the following play of colours: a red rim is first formed, which changes momentarily to orange, and this divides into two concentric rings, the inner one being bright red and the outer one yellowish brown. When the alcohol is completely evaporated the central spot is, for a moment, carmine-red, but this colour soon fades to brown.

Jalap, scammony and **podophyllin** are distinguished by the following colour tests:

Reagents		Colours	
	Jalapin	Scammony Resin	Podophyllin
Concentrated sulphuric acid.	Light brown. Bright red-violet rim formed slowly.	Dark brown, dirty purple rim.	Greenish yellow.
Fuming nitric acid.	No colour.	No colour.	Brick-red colour.
Mandelin's reagent.	Brown; bright red rim.	Dark brown; no red rim.	Dark brown.
Alcoholic potash.	No colour.	Bright yellow.	Yellow.

Mecke's reagent is very sensitive towards podophyllin, the colour produced being green.

Euphorbium Resin. The *p*-dimethylaminobenzaldehyde reagent in acidified alcoholic solution should be tried with (*a*) the resin, (*b*) an alcoholic extract of it, (*c*) an ethereal extract and (*d*) a boiling water extract. The following colours are seen during the evaporation of the solvent on the water-bath.

(*a*) The rim becomes bright green and this colour spreads inwards and finally an intensely green dry residue is left.

(*b*) The outer rim is purple at first, turning blue. When dry the innermost zone is blue with a green tinge.

(*c*) Greenish yellow colour.

(*d*) The rim is bright green at first, changing to olive-green.

Elaterin. The best colour tests for elaterin are with the sulphuric acid reagents.

Reagent	Colours
Concentrated sulphuric acid.	Brown.
Mandelin's reagent.	Almost immediately, blue and green streaks. Later, red streaks, turning brown.
Mecke's reagent.	Brownish red.
Fröhde's reagent.	Orange-red.

Croton Oil. A sample of croton oil is shaken vigorously with equal volume of absolute alcohol and the mixture is poured on to the surface of an equal quantity of saturated alcoholic potash in a test-tube. A reddish brown zone of contact develops slowly in the cold or more rapidly on warming. The colours produced by treating croton oil with an acidified alcoholic solution of *p*-dimethyl-aminobenzaldehyde depend on conditions. A transient red colour may be seen in the cold, and on adding 1 or 2 more drops of the reagent, a pale blue colour, which is also transient. On evaporating to dryness, the residue is brownish-purple and on adding more reagent to the residue the pale blue colour reappears.

Castor Oil. This oil, which is not usually considered to be toxic, does not give very satisfactory colour reactions. With concentrated sulphuric acid the colour is pale yellowish brown, and with nitric acid of sp. gr. $1 \cdot 42$ a darker brown colour is produced. The most characteristic test is with fuming nitric acid (sp. gr. $1 \cdot 5$) ; when one drop of the oil is mixed with a smaller drop of the acid there is effervescence and the liquid becomes pale green. With a greater proportion of acid the colour is less intense.

CHAPTER IX

NON-VOLATILE BASIC ORGANIC POISONS

ALKALOIDS

THE poisonous substances which are readily volatile in steam have already been discussed. There remains an enormous number of non-volatile substances, usually of relatively high molecular weight and complex structure, to which steam-distillation as a process of isolation is not applicable.

Many of these substances are derived from plants, but the number of synthetic drugs which come into the same category is large and is constantly increasing.

For the purposes of analysis the non-volatile poisons are divided into two main groups, basic and non-basic ; of the latter group some have acidic or phenolic properties, while others are neutral. The basic group includes all the vegetable alkaloids and the synthetic drugs which have come into use as substitute for natural alkaloids, e.g. the cocaine substitutes. The non-basic group includes glycosides, synthetic ureides, which are either simple or complex derivatives of urea, purgative drugs, many of which are natural hydroxy- or methoxy-derivatives of anthraquinone, sometimes also glycosidal in character ; hypnotics like sulphonal, substances like picrotoxin which do not fit into any larger group, poisons of animal origin like cantharides, some anthelmintics like santonin, and many plant products of unknown constitution, common especially in India and farther east, such as the active principle of madar juice, marking nuts, etc.

The vegetables alkaloids are basic substances which are very widely distributed in nature. Most of them have high molecular weight and complicated structures ; in many cases the structure is still not completely known. A few are soluble in water, forming solutions which are alkaline to litmus, but the majority are only slightly soluble in water and only feebly basic. The salts of the more feebly basic alkaloids are readily hydrolyzed by water : and this, of course, is more especially true of salts of weak acids. A few, of which morphine is the most conspicuous example, contain phenolic groups in the molecules which cause them to be soluble in caustic alkalis, and even in lime water.

A few of the alkaloids, like nicotine, are volatile in steam, a fact which simplifies the extraction of them from their sources and from mixtures.

With a few exceptions the free bases can be isolated from alkaline aqueous solutions by shaking with such solvents as chloroform, ether, benzene, amyl alcohol and ethyl acetate. Chloroform is almost a universal solvent for alkaloids, although morphine is again exceptional; it is practically insoluble in pure chloroform but readily soluble in a mixture of chloroform and alcohol.

Nearly all the alkaloids are powerful drugs, many of them being very poisonous indeed. The toxicity varies over a very wide range from aconitine, one of the most deadly poisons known, to quinine, which is only poisonous in very large doses, and caffeine, which is practically non-toxic.

As a class, alkaloids are characterized by the formation of almost insoluble compounds with many reagents, such as phosphomolybdic acid, phosphotungstic acid, gold chloride, platinic chloride, tannic acid, picric acid, and some double iodides prepared by dissolving the iodide of a heavy metal in excess of potassium iodide solution. Not all the compounds formed with such reagents are equally insoluble and these differences in solubility are of some assistance in the identification of alkaloids. Differences in crystalline form of the derivatives are more valuable than differences in solubility; but the most useful characteristics for the purposes of identification are colour reactions and pharmacological properties which will be described later.

For descriptive purposes the alkaloids will be classified according to their botanical sources, but for identification a totally different classification will be necessary, based mainly on colour reactions.

The Opium Group

Opium is the dried juice of the capsules of the oriental poppy (*Papaver somniferum*) which is cultivated in many Eastern countries, China, India, Persia, Asia Minor, Turkey and Egypt. The cultivation is nominally controlled by Government licence in all these countries except Egypt, where it is forbidden by law; nevertheless poppies are illicitly grown in fields in Upper Egypt, the plants being concealed behind tall growths of maize or sugar-cane.

After the flowers have fallen and the capsules are almost fully ripe, the pericarp is slit with a sharp knife while the capsules are still on the plant and the white latex which exudes is collected. This quickly sets to a brown semi-solid mass. Opium for the market is dried to an extent which varies in different countries. The form in which the dried opium is prepared for the market also varies. Descriptions of the common types of packing are to be found in Squire's " Companion to the British Pharmacopoeia ".

When completely dried opium becomes brittle, and finally falls into a powder.

About twenty-five different bases have been isolated from opium but only about seven need to be considered: morphine, codeine, narcotine, papaverine, narceine, thebaine and pseudo-morphine.
The most abundant, the most important medicinally, and the most toxic of the opium alkaloids is morphine, of which the proportion present commonly varies between 7 and 15 per cent., although quantities as low as 3 per cent. have been found in some samples.

FIG. 20. *Papaver somniferum.*

Opium for therapeutic use should, according to the British and American pharmacopoeias, contain not less than 9·5 per cent. of morphine; the B.P. specifies between 9·5 and 10·5 per cent. The method of assay is described in detail in the official publications, and, in order to get concordant results, the conditions laid down for the analysis should be rigidly adhered to.

Morphine differs from the other important alkaloids of opium in the fact that it is readily soluble in dilute caustic alkalis and in lime water. From such a solution it can be separated by adding an ammonium salt or by first neutralizing with dilute mineral acid and then adding ammonia until alkaline. From a concentrated solution morphine separates out in crystals and this process can be accelerated by adding ether and shaking.

The use of morphine for the relief of pain and the induction of sleep is well known. The usual therapeutic dose is from 8 to 16 mg. With larger doses morphine produces both a depressing and a stimulating effect on the central nervous system, the former effect being mainly on the brain and the latter on the spinal cord. Breathing becomes slower and in the higher animals death may result from the cessation of respiration. The effect of morphine on the pupils of the eyes is peculiar: until just before asphyxia supervenes they are contracted almost to pin-points, after which they are dilated. The minimum lethal dose of morphine is not definitely known. According to Goodman and Gilman[1] the toxic dose for an adult not in pain is about 60 mg., serious symptoms are usually produced by the ingestion of 100 mg., and 250 mg. are usually fatal. Children are particularly susceptible and fatal results have followed the administration of very small doses even of tincture of opium and other preparations containing relatively little morphine.[2] On the other hand, morphine exhibits to a most marked degree the properties of a drug of addiction and people who are accustomed to it take astonishingly large doses daily.

The molecular structure of morphine has been studied by many workers, and full discussions of the merits of the various formulae proposed will be found in text-books such as Evers' " Chemistry of Drugs ", Henry's " The Plant Alkaloids ", or in the monograph of Small (*Pub. Health Report*, 1932, Supplement 103). The essential points are that the molecule is a phenanthrene derivative with two hydroxy groups of which one is a secondary alcoholic group and the other is phenolic.

Codeine, or methylmorphine, is the ether obtained by methylation of the phenolic hydroxy-group in morphine and can be prepared synthetically in this way, but it is usually obtained from the mother-liquor after the separation of morphine by shaking out with chloroform or toluene. The potency of codeine as an analgesic is less than one-sixth that of morphine. The average dose for adults is 16–60 mg. orally or hypodermically. The minimal lethal dose for man is unknown, and it is doubtful whether death caused directly by codeine has been reported. Codeine is not, like morphine, a drug of addiction; there is no evidence of patients acquiring tolerance of it.[3] On the contrary, according to Cushny, they may become more susceptible to its effects after long-continued administration, and such symptoms as vomiting may follow doses which produced no effect when the treatment was first begun. Codeine undergoes decomposition in the body to a much smaller extent than morphine does, about 80 per cent. being excreted in the urine.

Narcotine, like papaverine and narceine, is a benzyl isoquinoline derivative and, like them, has only a weak physiological activity and toxicity. These three have little or no narcotic effect and are not much used therapeutically, though papaverine has some antispasmodic activity. Next to morphine this is the most abundant alkaloid in opium. In some samples, indeed, the amount of narcotine may exceed that of morphine. It is precipitated from

---

[1] " Pharmacological Basis of Therapeutics ", 1941, p. 209.
[2] For a case in which a child aged twelve days died after the administration of a very small quantity of morphine, see Lancashire County Analyst's Annual Report, 1934, p. 134.
[3] Lewin appears to be the only toxicologist of outstanding authority who disputes this statement, see p. 292.

the mother-liquors, together with papaverine, after the separation of morphine and codeine, by the addition of sodium acetate.

A mixture of narcotine and morphine has been claimed to be more toxic than morphine alone. Nicholls[1] states that 3·3 mg. of a mixture of equal parts of morphine and narcotine has a narcotic effect equal to that of 10 mg. of pure morphine.

Its chief use is in the manufacture of hydrastinine, which is much used in gynaecology. Cotarnine is an intermediate product.

Papaverine is separated from the narcotine with which it is precipitated by dissolving in alcohol and adding oxalic acid, the acid oxalate of papaverine being less soluble than that of narcotine.

Narceine occurs only in small quantities in opium and is, physiologically, practically inert.

Thebaine (dimethyl-morphine) is present in opium in varying amounts (from 0·1 to 1 per cent.) and can be isolated as the acid tartrate after the removal of morphine, codeine, narcotine and papaverine. It is a convulsant poison and produces strychnine-like effects rather than narcosis.

Pseudo-morphine or oxydimorphine has been found in opium in small quantities. It can be prepared by the cautious oxidation of morphine with such mild oxidizing agents as potassium ferricyanide. It is of interest to the toxicologist chiefly because it is sometimes formed in the organism after the administration of morphine and in such cases it may be extracted along with the morphine itself.

Artificial Derivatives of Morphine

Apomorphine. This is prepared from morphine by heating with concentrated hydrochloric acid in a sealed tube to 140°–150° C. It has lost the narcotic properties of morphine, but the excitant effect on the central nervous system has been increased to such an extent that apomorphine is a powerful emetic. A dose of 5–10 mg. given hypodermically usually causes vomiting in an adult within fifteen minutes: sleep sometimes follows.

Other artificial derivatives are in use; these include (a) ethers analogous to codeine in which the hydrogen of the phenolic group is replaced by an alkyl or aryl radical; (b) esters in which the hydrogen of both the hydroxy-groups is replaced by an acidic group; and (c) less closely related substances, some entirely synthetic products, e.g. dicodide (dihydrocodeinone), eucodal (dihydrohydroxycodeinone) and dilaudid (dihydromorphenone), metopon (methyldihydromorphinone), pethidine, etc.

The ethers which are on the market are ethylmorphine (**dionine**) and benzylmorphine (**peronine**). Physiologically they are similar to codeine and apparently present no advantages over it.

[1] Streatfield Memorial Lecture, 1938. Institute of Chemistry Publication.

Heroin. Of the esters the only important one is diacetylmorphine (heroin) which is recommended as a cure for coughs. Since its introduction it has become more and more the favourite drug of addiction and it is said that after continued use its narcotic action diminishes and the symptoms are those of excitement. It is more toxic than morphine owing to its more powerful action on the respiratory organs.

Dilaudid, Dicodide and Eucodal. These are artificial derivatives of the opium alkaloids which have come into use since about the year 1925.

Dilaudid[1] is derived from morphine by oxidizing the secondary alcohol to a ketone group and hydrogenating the adjacent double bond. It has about 10 times the analgesic effect of morphine, and the effective dose is 2–4 mg. Doses of 5 mg. have been shown to have undesired depressant effects on the respiratory centre. In a case of cerebral tumour, 5 mg. produced narcosis. Headache, vomiting and giddiness have been observed. Dilaudid is habit-forming.

Dicodide bears the same structural relationship to codeine as dilaudid does to morphine. Toxic symptoms have been reported after doses of 10 mg.[2] These were vertigo, cold sweat, lassitude, nausea and vomiting, and in one case, severe collapse. Nevertheless, such doses are usually well tolerated.

Eucodal[3] is also a derivative of codeine. It is said to be more easily tolerated than other opium alkaloids, the analgesic effect more profound, and it is recommended as a general substitute for morphine. The claim is also made that withdrawal symptoms after a course of treatment are less severe.

Physical and Chemical Properties of the Chief Opium Alkaloids

Morphine forms colourless crystals with one molecule of water of crystallization, which is lost on heating to 120° C. The anhydrous morphine can be converted into a crystalline sublimate by heating under reduced pressure. It is usually stated that morphine melts with decomposition at 230° C., but Kofler has found that it behaves differently when cautiously heated on the electrically heated microscope stage: he obtained a stable and a metastable sublimate, both belonging to the rhombic system. The former, when the temperature is raised regularly by 2° per minute, melts at 240° C., the latter, if it does not first change into the stable form, melts at 197° C. Morphine hydrochloride crystallizes in needles with three molecules

[1] " Merck's Annual Report ", 1928, pp. 175–7.
[2] Ibid., 1929, p. 94.
[3] Ibid., 1929, p. 118.

of water of crystallization. By sublimation it can be obtained in anhydrous rhombic crystals.

Morphine forms characteristic crystals with Marmé's reagent (potassium-cadmium iodide solution), with Wagner's reagent (iodine in potassium iodide solution) and with zinc chlor-iodide solution. These crystals are easily prepared and the chemist should make himself familiar with their appearance. Another reagent which yields crystals with morphine is an alcoholic solution of 1 : 3 : 4-dinitrochlorbenzene. This reaction, which was first described by Mannich and afterwards modified by Nicholls, can be used for the gravimetric determination of morphine. The procedure recommended by Nicholls[1] is to dissolve the morphine, which should be less than 0·1 g., in N/10 acid and, after diluting with water, to add alcohol in the proportion of 25 ml. to 60 ml. of water; to this are added 10 ml. of strong ammonia and 5 ml. of a 2 per cent. alcoholic solution of dinitrochlorbenzene. After standing for eighteen hours the crystals are collected on asbestos in a Gooch crucible, washed with 30 per cent. alcohol and then with a little ether and dried at 100° C. The weight of the crystals multiplied by 0·632 gives the weight of anhydrous morphine.

Codeine forms colourless crystals with one molecule of water of crystallization which become anhydrous when heated to between 64° and 67° C., and at this temperature there may be an appearance of melting; the M.P. of the anhydrous substance is 155° C. Like morphine, codeine can be converted into a crystalline sublimate by heating under reduced pressure. The most characteristic crystalline derivatives of codeine are obtained with (a) Wagner's reagent, (b) picrolonic acid in alcoholic solution, and (c) mercuric chloride solution: according to Wagenaar a minute crystal of sodium bromide should be added to the drop of mercuric chloride solution.

Narcotine forms prismatic crystals which melt at 176° C. It is a feeble base and is precipitated from solutions of its salts by sodium acetate solution. The precipitate slowly crystallizes in small prisms, a change which can be accelerated by the addition of a drop of alcohol. Crystalline sublimates have been obtained by heating, both under normal and under diminished pressure.

Narceine forms fine needles or prisms which lose water of crystallization at 100° C., and the anhydrous substance melts at 170° C. The sublimate formed by heating under normal pressure is amorphous but may be made to crystallize by moistening with water.

Papaverine melts at 147° C. It forms an amorphous sublimate which can be crystallized from acetone.

Thebaine forms rhombic plates or prisms melting at 193° C. The

[1] *Analyst*, 1937, **62**, 440–2.

amorphous sublimate formed by heating under normal pressure can be crystallized by dissolving in acetone, adding water until turbid and evaporating the acetone. Under diminished pressure a crystalline sublimate is formed directly.

Apomorphine, when pure and freshly prepared, forms colourless prisms which become greenish on exposure to air. A solution of an apomorphine salt, made alkaline with ammonia and shaken with chloroform, imparts a violet colour to this solvent.

Heroin. The free base melts at 171° C. to 173° C. and the hydrochloride at about 230° C. **Dicodide, eucodal** and **dilaudid** have the following melting points respectively: 193°–194° C., 220° C., and 259°–260° C.

Meconic Acid

The most important non-alkaloidal constituent of opium is, to the analyst, meconic acid, with which part of the alkaloids is combined.

It is a hydroxy-dicarboxylic acid derived from γ-pyrone. The only known source of it in nature is opium, and, therefore, its detection is an important part of the proof of the presence of opium. It can be precipitated from aqueous solution by the addition of lead acetate, and regenerated from this precipitate by means of hydrogen sulphide. Its most characteristic reaction is the production of a red, or reddish-purple, colour with ferric chloride. This colour is not discharged by boiling the solution with hydrochloric acid or by the addition of mercuric chloride, and so is distinguished from the colours due to acetates and thiocyanates.

Identification of Opium

For the identification of opium the following are the important points:

(1) The colour of the substance in the moist state is dark brown, but after drying and grinding the colour is much lighter.

(2) The odour is characteristic. In small samples of old opium this odour may be faint, but it can be usually detected after grinding the sample.

(3) The test for meconic acid can be made on a white tile. A particle of opium is put into a drop of water, acidified with dilute sulphuric or nitric acid and a drop of very dilute ferric chloride solution or ferric alum solution is added. Red streaks spread through the liquid.

(4) The Marquis reagent (formalin-sulphuric acid) gives a definite violet colour with a good sample of opium. If this test is not decisive with the solid opium, an aqueous extract should be made

and a drop of this evaporated to dryness on a water-bath; the dry residue seldom fails to yield a characteristic colour. ' In the rare cases in which these simple tests fail to give a satisfactory colour, the morphine must be extracted from an ammoniacal aqueous solution by shaking with a mixture of chloroform and alcohol, evaporating the extract to dryness and applying the Marquis test to the residue. It may be advisable, but it is not usually necessary, to make a preliminary extract with ether in presence of caustic soda to remove substances other than morphine; if this is done, the aqueous solution must be neutralized with mineral acid and made again alkaline with ammonia before shaking out with chloroform and alcohol.

Indian Opium

It is stated in many text-books that Indian opium contains a substance, porphyroxine, which is not found in opium from other countries, and that the detection of this is a proof that the sample is of Indian origin.[1],[2] The test recommended by Lal Dey is to shake the aqueous extract of the opium with ether after adding sodium carbonate or ammonia. The residue left on evaporating the ethereal solution is moistened with hydrochloric acid, when a reddish-purple colour is produced.

Our experience does not confirm the statement that this test is specific for Indian opium.[3] We have obtained this colour from samples seized as contraband in Turkey and from samples guaranteed by Messrs. British Drug Houses Ltd. to be Persian and Smyrna opium respectively. Moreover, we have observed several times in the extraction of viscera for opium that the ether extract from alkaline solution has given a red colour with hydrochloric acid when there was no reason to suspect the presence of Indian opium.

The Strychnos Alkaloids

Since strychnine and brucine are found together in nature they are usually considered together although they differ greatly in their behaviour towards chemical reagents; and physiologically strychnine is thirty to forty times more active than brucine. The chief sources of the alkaloids are the seeds of various species of strychnos of which S. nux vomica and S. Ignatii (Ignatius beans) are the most important. The former contains a larger proportion of brucine and the latter of strychnine. Some species of strychnos are known which contain no strychnine.

Strychnine is chiefly used (undeservedly) as a tonic; its bitter taste causes increased salivation and improved appetite. The

[1] Allen's " Commercial Organic Analysis ", 5th ed., **7**, 714.
[2] SYDNEY SMITH. " Forensic Medicine ", 5th ed., p. 595.
[3] BAMFORD. *Analyst*, 1930, **55**, 445.

therapeutic dose of the hydrochloride is from 1 to 4 mg. and the minimum lethal dose is usually stated to be from 120 to 180 mg. Poisonous doses produce muscular tremors and convulsions which last about a minute and follow one another at intervals of 10–15 minutes. Death usually follows the second to fifth convulsion but may occur immediately after the first. Death results from medullary paralysis. In frogs convulsions may continue with quiescent intervals for hours: and when a frog is used for the purpose of identification it is usually sufficient to observe two or three characteristic tetanic spasms, after which the frog can be killed by means of chloroform. In making the physiological tests on a frog it is convenient to have it held by an assistant, the body being lightly but firmly held on the bench and the back legs gently but firmly stretched away from the edge of the bench and at right angles to it; the skin a little to one side of the spine is then pinched and raised and the needle inserted parallel to the spine and pointing towards the head, i.e. into the dorsal lymph sac. While waiting for symptoms to begin the frog is covered with a bell-jar slightly raised from the bench at one side. Both in mammals and in frogs the convulsions occur more frequently if there is some external stimulus such as vibration of the bench caused by striking it with the fist.

Strychnine forms colourless prisms melting at 265°–266° C. Its solubility in ether is only three times its solubility in water (0·043 and 0·014 per cent. respectively) but a saturated solution in chloroform contains 16·6 per cent. of the base. Chloroform even extracts strychnine from an aqueous solution of the hydrochloride and therefore chloroform should not be used for the removal of fat or non-basic poisons from aqueous solutions.

Strychnine sublimes in crystals when heated either under normal or diminished pressure.

In addition to the usual tests for strychnine (p. 259-60) the following crystalline derivatives may be prepared on microscope slides and used for identification[1]: the picrate, the ferrocyanide, the chromate, the aurichloride and the thiocyanate.

Brucine. The minimum lethal dose of brucine is relatively large and poisoning with the pure alkaloid is rare, but in poisoning by nux vomica or Ignatius beans brucine may be extracted along with strychnine from the viscera. A partial separation may be made by washing with acetone or 25 per cent. alcohol, in which solvents brucine is more soluble than strychnine; or the mixed alkaloids may be dissolved in absolute alcohol and treated with an alcoholic solution of oxalic acid: brucine oxalate is insoluble.

In spite of the similarity between brucine and strychnine, brucine

---

[1] By comparison with similar preparations from an authentic sample of strychnine.

being dimethoxy-strychnine, the colour reactions of the two alkaloids are very different (see pp. 259 and 258).

Pure brucine is obtained in colourless crystals which lose water of crystallization on heating and when anhydrous melt at 178° C. It forms crystalline derivatives with platinic chloride, mercuric chloride, potassium ferricyanide, sodium nitroprusside and potassium antimoniodide.

Curare, used as an arrow poison in South America, is extracted from various species of strychnos (e.g. *S. toxifera*). The terms " tubo- ", " gourd -" and " pot- " curare refer to the containers used by the natives in storing and transporting the crude material. Curare is poisonous only when injected. Several alkaloids have been isolated. Of these, *d-tubocurarine* is widely used (as are various derivatives) in surgery, in shock therapy and in spastic conditions because of its effect in blocking nerve impulses at the myoneural junctions and so preventing contraction of voluntary muscles. Overdosage causes progressive paresis of the skeletal musculature with respiratory embarassment and, in extreme cases, produces death by respiratory paralysis. The colour reactions of curare are vaguely similar to those of strychnine, but the dichromate test does not show such clear colours.

Alkaloids of the Yellow Jasmine and *Corynanthe johimbe*

The alkaloids from these two sources are sometimes said to resemble strychnine in their colour reactions, hence their inclusion at this point, but actually the resemblance is not sufficient to prevent easy differentiation (see pp. 259-60).

Yellow jasmine (*Gelsemium sempervirens*) contains the alkaloid **gelsemine,** which has been isolated in crystals which melt at 178° C. and which forms a hydrochloride melting at 300° C. According to Cushny, gelsemine has no physiological effect on mammals. However, another alkaloidal product has been isolated to which the name gelseminine has been given; this is probably a mixture of alkaloids. It is toxic, the symptoms resembling those of coniine (q.v.): applied externally to the eye gelseminine dilates the pupil.

A variety of jasmine, *G. elegans*, was the cause of three deaths in Hong Kong.[1]

Yohimbine is the chief active principle in the bark of the tree *Corynanthe johimbe* which is used in veterinary medicine as an aphrodisiac. According to Fourneau and Page it is identical with quebrachine which occurs in the bark of the tree *Quebracho blanco*, also known as *Aspidosperma quebracho*. In large doses it causes nausea, and very large doses produce marked stimulation of the central nervous system, which may lead to convulsions. The melting point of yohimbine is 247°–248° C.

[1] *Analyst*, 1938, **63**, 603.

Alkaloids of the Atropine Group

This very important group of alkaloids includes about eight or nine natural substances of which the important ones are atropine, hyoscyamine and hyoscine, which is also called scopolamine. They are obtained from some, but not all, of the solanaceous plants. Alkaloids from other solanaceae such as solanine from the potato show no resemblance to this group, and are considered elsewhere. The chief sources of the alkaloids are:

Atropa belladonna or deadly nightshade.
Datura stramonium or thorn apple, stinkweed, Jimson weed, etc.
Datura metel.
Datura fastuosa.
Hyoscyamus albus.
Hyoscyamus muticus or Egyptian henbane.

The plant richest in alkaloids is the Egyptian henbane which grows wild in many parts of the desert. It has also been cultivated and, according to Ibrahim R. Fahmy,[1] the crop may be harvested at

intervals of three months for three successive years after which a fresh cultivation is necessary. This worker found that the percentage of alkaloids varies from less than 0·1 per cent. in wild seedlings to 1·1 per cent. in plants cultivated in dry sandy areas at the extreme south of Egypt. Apparently the wild plant and the cultivated plant contain similar quantities of alkaloid if grown in similar soil and under similar climatic conditions.

Atropine is probably not present as such in any of the living plants. It is the optically inactive (racemic) form of **hyoscyamine** and the latter is apparently converted more or less completely into atropine during the process of extraction.

Hyoscine (Scopolamine) is not isomeric with the other two: the molecule contains two atoms of hydrogen less and one atom of oxygen more than that of atropine. Hyoscine is obtained

FIG. 21. *Hyoscyamus muticus.*

from *D. metel* and *D. fastuosa*. Both atropine and hyoscine are esters of which the acid component is tropic acid, which may be regarded as a homologue of mandelic acid, the hydroxy group of the latter

[1] Reports of the Pharmaceutical Soc. of Egypt, 1936, p. 25.

being replaced by a —CH_2OH group.   The acid is represented by the formula:

$$\underset{\text{Tropic acid.}}{\overset{C_6H_5}{\underset{HOCH_2}{\diagup}}C\overset{H}{\underset{COOH}{\diagdown}}} \qquad \underset{\text{Mandelic acid.}}{\overset{C_6H_5}{\underset{HO}{\diagup}}C\overset{H}{\underset{COOH}{\diagdown}}}$$

The other components are cyclic secondary alcohols containing a tertiary amino group.   The base from atropine is called tropine and that from hyoscine is called scopine.   Many analogues of atropine have been prepared synthetically, some with other acids (e.g. mandelic) substituted for tropic acid, some with other bases replacing tropine, and some with both parts different from those of atropine.   Several are in use, but **homatropine** (tropine mandelate) is the commonest.   They are termed **tropëines.**

The most striking, and one of the most important characteristics of the atropaceous alkaloids is their mydriatic activity or power of causing dilatation of the pupil, whether they are taken internally or applied externally.   Although other drugs have this property, the term " the mydriatic group " is usually reserved for the atropine series.   In toxicological examinations the mydriatic test is one of the essential steps in the process of identification.   It is carried out by dissolving the alkaloidal extract from the viscera or excreta in a very small quantity of acidified water and making exactly neutral with sodium bicarbonate; 2 or 3 drops of this liquid are put into the eye of a cat, which should be wrapped in a towel and held by an assistant.   The eyelid is turned back and the drops instilled underneath it, after which the eye should be opened and shut several times to make sure that the drops are retained.   The animal is then kept in a dark room or cupboard and brought out into the light at intervals of fifteen minutes.   If no enlargement of the pupil is seen within an hour the liquid may be considered free from mydriatic alkaloids.   Although this test is very sensitive it is advisable not to make the solution of the alkaloidal extract unnecessarily dilute.

Taken internally, minute doses such as 0·6 mg. of atropine[1] produce perceptible dryness of the throat; larger doses cause hoarseness and difficulty in swallowing followed by severe palpitation and then by delirium.   The hysterical symptoms are often very severe, amounting to mania.   Another strongly marked symptom is the suppression of secretions such as sweat, saliva, gastric juices and mucus.   In fatal cases convulsions may precede death.   The minimum lethal dose of atropine or hyoscyamine appears to be 130 mg., but hyoscine is even more toxic, 30 mg. having caused

[1] The usual adult dose of atropine is 0·3—1·0 mg. : of hyoscine, 0·5 mg.

death, though a case of recovery after 500 mg. of hyoscine has been recorded.

Hyoscine is used with morphine to produce the state of semi-anaesthesia known as " twilight sleep ", for which the standard injection is 10 mg. of morphine tartrate and 0·5 mg. of hyoscine hydrobromide, but the dose of hyoscine is sometimes repeated. A more modern therapy recommends that a quickly acting hypnotic like amytal should be given in addition.

Poisoning by datura and hyoscyamus seeds is common in the East but fatal results are much less common, as a large proportion of the seeds passes into the faeces unbroken. In the examination of vomited matter, stomach-washings or faeces in such cases a careful search must be made for seeds and fragments of seeds. For this purpose the material is put into a large conical urine-glass, diluted with water if necessary, stirred and allowed to stand. The seeds, being heavy, sink to the bottom and the supernatant fluid with as much of the food matter as possible is decanted off. The vessel is then filled up again with water, again stirred and allowed to stand, and the water containing light suspended matter decanted off. This process of washing is repeated until nothing remains but the seeds which are at the bottom of the glass. They are washed out into a basin from which they can be picked out with forceps and dried on blotting paper. The seeds are examined with a lens or, better, with a binocular magnifier. Datura seeds are kidney-shaped and measure about 2 mm. along the major axis. The surface is covered with minute pits: the seeds of *D. stramonium* are black or nearly so; those of *D. metel* and *D. fastuosa* are light-brown. Any seeds found must be compared with known samples and carefully distinguished from seeds of tomatoes and egg-plant which are similar in size and shape, but not otherwise. Sections should be cut parallel to the flatter surface and compared with a known sample under the low power of the microscope.

Hyoscyamus seeds are usually similar in shape to datura seeds, but the kidney form is not so universal; they are brown in colour and have pitted surfaces. The length is about one-third of that of datura seeds.

Henbane poisoning is sometimes the result of drinking a decoction of the leaves. The identification of fragments of leaves in stomach contents is much more difficult than the identification of seeds and should only be attempted by a person thoroughly trained and experienced in botanical pharmacognosy.

Atropine is a white substance crystallizing in needles or prisms which melt between 115° and 118° C. When atropine is heated to 200° C. or above, the sublimate consists of tropine: but by maintaining the temperature at 95°–96° C. for thirty to forty-five minutes under diminished pressure, Kelin and Sonnleitner obtained a sublimate of atropine in the form of oily drops which crystallized on standing overnight in fan-like bundles of needles.

The following crystalline derivatives may be used for identification in addition to those mentioned on pp. 257-8.

(a) Wormley's reagent (bromine in hydrobromic acid) produces a turbidity and after a short time crystals in various forms, including spindles, crosses and stars, are formed.

(b) A solution of the sodium salt of alizarin sulphonic acid forms bundles of fine crystals which are bent into an almost circular form, but the crystallization process is very slow.

The products of hydrolysis of atropine have the following properties:

(1) Tropic acid crystallizes from water in small plates melting at 117°–118° C. and subliming at 150° C. to form fan-like bundles. It forms crystals with lead acetate solution.

(2) Tropine crystallizes in shining needles melting at 63° C. and subliming at 150° C. It forms crystals of very varied shapes with hydriodic acid and with (a) gold chloride, and (b) a mixture of 5 per cent. gold chloride and 10 per cent. sodium bromide in aqueous solution.

Hyoscyamine forms shining needles or prisms melting at 108·5° C.; sublimation under reduced pressure yields crystals; under normal pressure an amorphous sublimate is produced which crystallizes on moistening with water.

Hyoscine does not crystallize very readily. The salt generally used in medicine is the hydrobromide, which melts at 193°–194° C. when anhydrous. The picrate melts at 193° C. and the aurichloride at 208° C.

The natural alkaloids of the atropine group all give strong violet colours in the Vitali test (p. 257), but the artificial tropëine, homatropine, does not respond to this test as usually carried out. However, Droop Richmond has stated that the sulphate of homatropine behaves like the other mydriatics. The base, the hydrochloride and the hydrobromide which do not give the colour may be made to do so by first treating with sufficient sulphuric acid to form the sulphate, replacing the halogen acid if necessary. In our laboratory we have failed to confirm this.

The Alkaloids of Coca

The plants from which **cocaine** and alkaloids of the same group are obtained are various species of *Erythroxylon* of which the chief are *E. coca* and *E. Truxillense*. They are cultivated in South America, Java and Ceylon.

All the natural cocaine alkaloids are derivatives of the parent base ecgonine, which is a carboxylic acid of tropine, one of the products of hydrolysis of atropine. The two bases are represented by the following graphic formulae:

$$
\begin{array}{ccc}
CH_2 \!\!-\!\!-\!\!-\!\! CH \!\!-\!\!-\!\!-\!\! CH_2 \\
| \qquad\quad | \qquad\quad | \\
| \qquad\quad NCH_3 \quad CH.OH \\
| \qquad\quad | \qquad\quad | \\
CH_2 \!\!-\!\!-\!\!-\!\! CH \!\!-\!\!-\!\!-\!\! CH_2
\end{array}
\qquad
\begin{array}{ccc}
CH_2 \!\!-\!\!-\!\!-\!\! CH \!\!-\!\!-\!\!-\!\! CH.COOH \\
| \qquad\quad | \qquad\quad | \\
| \qquad\quad NCH_3 \quad CH.OH \\
| \qquad\quad | \qquad\quad | \\
CH_2 \!\!-\!\!-\!\!-\!\! CH \!\!-\!\!-\!\!-\!\! CH_2
\end{array}
$$

Tropine.   Ecgonine.

Ecgonine is both an alcohol and an acid and can therefore be esterified by combination with acids and alcohols. Thus, by treatment with benzoic anhydride the alcoholic group is esterified with the formation of benzoyl-ecgonine and when this is methylated the hydrogen of the carboxyl group is replaced, yielding methyl-benzoyl-ecgonine, which is cocaine.

The leaves contain some cocaine together with benzoyl-ecgonine and other esters in which the acid component may be cinnamic acid or truxillic acid. Cocaine is in much greater demand than the other alkaloids and, therefore, it is usual to convert the latter into cocaine. The method is to digest the leaves in alkaline water and to extract the alkaloids from the aqueous liquid with light petroleum. The petroleum is agitated with dilute hydrochloric acid to extract all the alkaloidal salts and this aqueous solution is evaporated to a small bulk. Cocaine, if present in sufficiently large quantity, separates as an impure hydrochloride. The alkaloids in the mother liquor are then hydrolyzed to form ecgonine, which is afterwards benzoylated and methylated.[1]

One of the alkaloids of coca which is not a derivative of ecgonine is tropacocaine, which is variously stated to be benzoyl-*pseudo*-tropine or benzoyl-*pseudo*-tropëine.

The chief legitimate use of cocaine is to produce local anaesthesia, but it has gained an unpleasant reputation as a drug of addiction, taken in the form of snuff.

For the identification of cocaine in extracts from viscera and urine it is essential to isolate the drug in a state of absolute purity.[2] This can be done by precipitating the alkaloid, after purifying as far as possible by the general methods described in the section on the extraction of alkaloids, as the double potassium-mercuric iodide, by adding Mayer's reagent, and after collecting the precipitate on an asbestos filter and washing, decomposing it with hydrogen sulphide. The mercuric sulphide is filtered off and the alkaloid is re-extracted with ether or chloroform from the filtrate after making it alkaline with sodium carbonate. This procedure often yields a

[1] EVERS. "The Chemistry of Drugs", p. 102.
[2] BAMFORD. *Analyst*, 1938, **63**, 648.

pure base, but if not, micro-sublimation (preferably under reduced pressure) must be tried.

Cocaine crystallizes in prisms melting at 98° C. and its hydrochloride, which also forms in prisms, melts at 191° C.

When a crystal of cocaine or a drop of the aqueous solution is applied to the tip of the tongue a feeling of numbness is produced, but this effect is common to the whole group of local anaesthetics. Cocaine has also feeble mydriatic properties.

Cocaine Substitutes

Cocaine has been synthesized in the laboratory, but the process has not been made a commercial success. On the other hand an enormous number of synthetic substitutes have been marketed. Some of these have atomic groupings which are also present in the cocaine molecule. For example, α-**eucaine** contains a methylated carboxyl group, a benzoylated hydroxyl group and a tertiary amino group. It is derived from triacetonamine.

β-**eucaine** is a structurally simpler compound containing a benzoyl group but no methylated carboxyl group; also the amino group is secondary, not tertiary. Both the eucaines contain piperidine nuclei.

Stovaine differs from cocaine in having no cyclic nucleus except that of the benzoyl radical. It is a benzoylated tertiary alcohol containing also a tertiary amino group.

Alypin is similar but contains two tertiary amino groups.

It has been found that much simpler compounds have local anaesthetic properties. These are the esters of p-amino-benzoic acid. The ethyl ester is **anaesthesine,** while in **procaine** (=*novocaine*) the alcoholic component is dimethylaminoethyl alcohol, and in **tutocaine,** α-dimethylamino-β. γ-dimethylpropyl alcohol.

Pantocaine[1] is a derivative of p-aminobenzoic acid in which the carboxy group is esterified with γ-dimethylaminoethyl alcohol and the p-amino group is replaced by a n-butylamino group.[1]

It is claimed that pantocaine is the perfect cocaine substitute.

Percaine[2] differs very considerably from other local anaesthetics in constitution. It is derived from α-hydroxy cinchoninic acid. The hydrogen of the hydroxy group is replaced by the butyl radical, and the carboxyl group is converted into a substituted acid-amide group. The structure is:

$$CO.NH.CH_2.CH_2.N(C_2H_5)_2.$$

$-OC_4H_9$

---

[1] " From Cocaine to Pantocaine." Medicine in its Chemical Aspects. Bayer, 1934.
[2] Merck's Annual Reports, 1930, p. 294.

Psicaine[1] is unique among the artificial cocaine substitutes, being actually a stereoisomer of cocaine, dextro-*pseudo*-cocaine. The salt on the market is the acid tartrate of this base. It is claimed that the anaesthetic action, as determined by experiments on frogs, is twice as great as that of cocaine; but its toxicity is actually less.

R. Fischer[2] has published a scheme for the identification of thirteen local anaesthetics, based on the crystalline forms and melting-points of derivatives obtained with the following reagents: (*a*) trinitroresorcin, (*b*) trinitrobenzoic acid, (*c*) picric acid, and (*d*) platinic chloride. Not all the alkaloids give precipitates with all the reagents, but when precipitates are formed they are allowed to crystallize and the crystals are washed repeatedly, using drop after drop of water, each drop being taken up with filter-paper before the next one is added. The washing may be done under the microscope and controlled so that the crystals are not washed away. The crystals are then dried at a low temperature and the melting point is observed on the heated microscope stage. Another system of identification is described in Chapter X.

The Aconitine Group

At least seventy species of aconite are known. The one most familiar in Europe is *Aconitum Napellus*, or Monkshood. Formerly, *A. Ferox* was referred to as a second important species, but Stapf has shown that two different species were known by this name, and these are now differentiated as *A. Deinorrhizum* and *A. Spicatum*; they contain the alkaloids pseudaconitine and bikhaconitine respectively. Two important species grow in Japan; one, from the Hondo district, is called *A. Fischeri* var. *Hondo* and the other is *A. Japonicum*. An Indian species, *A. Chasmanthum*, is also important.

Not all the aconites are poisonous, but among the poisonous species are some of the most toxic of all known substances. All parts of the plant are poisonous but most especially the tuberous roots. The root is sometimes found in two parts, an older or parent tuber and a newer or daughter tuber attached to it. The newer part usually contains a greater proportion of alkaloid.

Poisoning has sometimes occurred owing to aconite being eaten in mistake for horse-radish. Actually there is considerable difference in form and in other respects, the aconite tubers being tapering or carrot-shaped. On scraping the surface of a fresh aconite tuber the portion exposed soon becomes reddish. If a piece of the tuber is chewed a sensation of tingling is felt from the lips to the back of the mouth and this effect may persist for some hours. This

---

[1] *Ibid.*, 1926, p. 315.
[2] ROSENTHALER. " Toxikologische Mikroanalyse ", p. 340.

sensation is characteristic of aconite and is one of the best available means of identifying fragments of the plant and also its active principles, although similar but milder effects are produced by delphinine and veratrine.

Relatively few aconite species have been submitted to thorough chemical study, and our knowledge even of these is little more than rudimentary. The pure alkaloids are not easily extracted, partly because they are readily hydrolyzed during the extraction process; the ether soluble extract contains a mixture of alkaloids and their decomposition products which are difficult to separate. Nevertheless at least six distinct alkaloids have been extracted from different species. They are:

Aconitine from *A. Napellus.* Melting point 197° C.
Japaconitine from *A. Fischeri* var. *Hondo.* M.P. 204° C.
Indaconitine from *A. Chasmanthum.* M.P. 202°–203° C.
Pseudaconitine from *A. Deinorrhizum.* M.P. 211°–212° C.
Bikhaconitine from *A. Spicatum.* M.P. 113°–116° C.
Jesaconitine from *A. Japonicum.* M.P. 128°–130° C.

All these substances are very poisonous, pseudaconitine being the most toxic of all though, because of the greater amount present, it is aconitine which mainly accounts for the toxicity of aconite. The minimum lethal doses are not known with certainty but that of aconitine has been put as low as 6 mg. and that of pseudaconitine 2·5–3 mg.

Chemically they resemble one another in that they are all double esters, each containing two acid radicals, of which one is the acetyl group and the other is either the benzoyl group or one of its derivatives. The acetyl group is more readily removed by hydrolysis than the radical of the aromatic acid. After the elimination of the acetyl group the toxicity is very much reduced and after complete hydrolysis the residues are not poisonous. The basic products of hydrolysis are called aconine, japaconine, etc. Their constitutions are not known, but aconine has been shown to contain four methoxy groups, three hydroxy groups and a methyl group attached to the nitrogen atom.

Aconite in the form of tincture was formerly administered internally to reduce temperature and pulse rate, but it has been found that its effect in the small doses which can be safely used are very uncertain and it is now very little used.

In aconite poisoning the first symptoms are usually the sensation of warmth and tingling in the mouth and throat. Secretions, especially that of saliva, are increased; there may be nausea and even vomiting. The pulse is irregular and becomes weaker. Death, which may be preceded by convulsions, is sometimes due to failure of respiration but sometimes the heart fails first.

Aconitine is difficult to identify in small quantities as it yields no characteristic colour reactions. The product obtained by micro-sublimation is amorphous and attempts to make it crystalline have been unsuccessful.

The best-known crystallization test is that with permanganate; excellent crystals are easily obtained with the pure alkaloid, but we have not succeeded in producing them with all samples purchased as "pure aconitine". Wagenaar describes crystals obtained with potassium iodide, potassium chloride, potassium bromide, ammonium thiocyanate, sodium nitrate, sodium perchlorate and potassium dichromate. Of these reagents the dichromate is the most sensitive.

The ordinary method of extraction from viscera is used, but if the quantity ingested is little more than the minimum lethal dose the hope of detection is small. Special precautions must be taken to avoid hydrolysis by keeping the solutions as nearly neutral as possible and by keeping the temperature low. A special reason for avoiding hydrolysis is that the products thereof are non-poisonous and therefore the physiological tests upon which one has to rely to a large extent are useless.

When injected into a frog aconitine sometimes, but not always, produces a peculiar symptom, the frog making movements as if it were about to vomit. Sometimes, but not always, convulsions are produced. The only invariable physiological reaction is the tingling of the mouth: this test, of course, must be applied with the utmost caution, using 1 or 2 drops of a neutral or faintly acid solution of the salt and applying it to the tip of the tongue with a glass rod. In the famous Lamson murder case Sir Thomas Stevenson succeeded in extracting aconitine and demonstrating its toxic effect on a mouse as well as experiencing the tingling sensation.

Alkaloids of Stavesacre

Stavesacre is obtained from the dried ripe seeds of *Delphinium Staphisagria*, a plant bearing blue flowers which is indigenous in southern Europe. The seeds are irregular, being usually roughly triangular but occasionally quadrilateral; when fresh they are dark brown but become greyish on keeping. They contain a fixed oil and have a nauseous acrid taste. The chief active principle is delphinine, a crystalline alkaloid melting at 192° C. Its reactions with the usual reagents are not very distinctive (see p. 250 *et seq.*).

Delphinine is poisonous, producing symptoms similar to aconitine, but much larger doses are required to produce similar effects. It is not much used in England but is more common in France. An ointment containing it is used to kill parasites; this should never be applied to broken or abraded skin.

From the mother liquors after the separation of delphinine one crystalline and two amorphous alkaloids can be obtained. These are **delphisine** (M.P. 189° C.), **delphinoidine** (M.P. 150°–152° C.), and **staphisagrine,** which melts a little above 90° C. Larkspur seeds of the same genus are definitely triangular or tetrahedral; they contain somewhat similar, but not identical, active principles. Two species, *D. Ajacis* and *D. Consolida,* have been used in the U.S.A. in the treatment of asthma and similar diseases.

The Veratrine Group

Among the sources of this group of alkaloids are the rhizomes of the white and green helusing hellebores, *Veratrum album* and *Veratrum viride.* The active principles of the black hellebore or Christmas rose (*Helleborus niger*) are the glycosides **helleborin** and **helleborein.** According to Husemann and Marmé, the green hellebore also contains traces of the glycosides but the main distinction is as stated: the white and green hellebores are sources of alkaloids, and the black of glycosides. A third important source of alkaloids of this group is *Schoenocaulon officinale,* or sabadilla, the seeds being richer in alkaloids than the other parts of the plants.

There has been some confusion in the nomenclature of this group of alkaloids which has now been cleared up by the adoption of new names, cevadine for the old " crystallized veratrine " and veratridine for " amorphous veratrine ".

Veratrum album contains the alkaloids **jervine, pseudojervine, rubijervine, protoveratrine** and **protoveratridine.**

Veratrum viride contains **cevadine, jervine, pseudojervine** and possibly traces of **veratridine.**

Sabadilla seeds contain **cevadine** and **veratridine.**

The substance usually sold as **veratrine** is an intimate mixture of cevadine and veratridine, which are difficult to separate by treatment with water in spite of the fact that the former is practically insoluble and the latter is soluble; they can be separated and obtained pure by fractional crystallization from alcohol.

All the above bases, with the exception of veratridine, have been obtained in crystalline form. The melting points are as follows: jervine, 238° C.; pseudojervine, 299° C.; rubijervine, 240°–246° C.; protoveratrine, 245°–250° C.; protoveratridine, 265° C.; cevadine, 205° C.; and veratridine, 150°–155° C.

The most toxic of these compounds is protoveratrine; cevadine is also very poisonous, and jervine is a little less so. Pseudojervine, rubijervine and protoveratridine are non-toxic. Little appears to be known of the physiological action of veratridine.

The toxic alkaloids of this group produce symptoms similar to, but milder than, those produced by aconitine. A similar tingling sensation is one of the characteristics of the veratrine alkaloids, and the powdered drugs cause violent sneezing.

A further resemblance between the veratrine and aconitine groups is that the alkaloids of both become less toxic on the elimination of acid radicals from the molecule. The effect of injecting the alkaloids into frogs is to produce characteristically prolonged muscle contractions which result in clumsy movements. Larger doses cause paralysis and death. Therapeutically, veratrine has been used in the form of an ointment for external application to relieve neuralgia.

Alkaloids of Ipecacuanha

Ipecacuanha and its constituent alkaloids are poisonous, but serious symptoms are very rarely produced when the drug is taken by the mouth even in comparatively large doses, owing to its powerful emetic action. Formerly it was used to produce vomiting in cases of poisoning, but it has been superseded by apomorphine and the stomach-tube.

Syrup of ipecacuanha, which contains about 0·12 per cent. of total alkaloids, is used as a remedy for croup in children and for other conditions in which the respiratory passages are obstructed or inflamed. Ipecacuanha is one of the constituents of Dover's powder

An impure base was extracted from the root of the plant as early as 1817, and this was long known as **emetine.** Later it was found to contain at least three alkaloids which have been named **emetine, cephaeline,** and **psychotrine.** The first two are similar in physiological action; the last is said to be inactive. At the present time the chief use of emetine is in the treatment of amoebic dysentery; it is usual to administer 10 grains in a series of injections spread over a period of ten days or more. In chronic amoebic dysentery the compound emetine-bismuth iodide is given by the mouth.

Experiments on animals have shown that large doses injected hypodermically cause, in addition to emesis, violent purging with bloody stools, and death may occur within a few hours from exhaustion or heart failure. None of the ipecacuanha alkaloids form satisfactory crystalline precipitates with the usual reagents.

Alkaloids of the Meadow Saffron

The meadow saffron or autumn crocus contains, chiefly in the seeds and corms of the plant, the alkaloid **colchicine.** A second alkaloid, **colchiceine,** is found in the extract when the ordinary processes of extraction are used, but since the latter is formed very readily from the former by the elimination of methyl alcohol from the molecule, it is not certain that it is originally present in the plant.

Colchicine is remarkable among alkaloids in several respects.

It is not white even when quite pure, but yellow, and the colour darkens on heating. The base, as well as the salts, is soluble in water. Mayer's reagent only precipitates it from very concentrated solution although most of the other alkaloidal precipitants, including tannic acid, yield precipitates from comparatively dilute solutions. In this respect it resembles caffeine.

When a chloroformic solution of colchicine is evaporated just to dryness the residue consists of a compound of the alkaloid with chloroform. This compound is unstable and can be decomposed by suspending it in water and passing a current of steam through the liquid.

Colchicine is usually amorphous, but it can be obtained in rhombic crystals by dissolving in 3 parts of water at 15° C. and allowing the solution to evaporate slowly.

The alkaloid is very feebly basic, aqueous solutions of it being neutral to litmus; it can be extracted with chloroform from neutral or even acidic aqueous solution. A solution containing colchicine can be freed from fat if necessary by shaking with light petroleum in the presence of mineral acid. Colchiceine, unlike colchicine, is colourless, but it dissolves in dilute acids to form yellow solutions.

Tincture of colchicum (B.P.) or tablets of colchicine are given by mouth to relieve acute gout, and the alkaloid is present in some proprietary remedies for gout. The therapeutic dose is $0 \cdot 5$–$1 \cdot 0$ mg. of the alkaloid. Larger doses (often after an interval of several hours) cause severe gastro-intestinal disturbance with pain, vomiting and diarrhoea (often with bloody stools), haematuria and oliguria. There may be marked muscular depression and death may result, after a day or two, from respiratory arrest. As little as 6 mg. of the alkaloid (in 15 c.cm. of tincture) has caused death, but much larger doses have been survived.

In the examination of viscera for colchicine, as for aconitine, particular care must be taken to avoid hydrolysis. Purification of the final extract can often be effected by precipitation with tannic acid; the precipitate is collected on a filter and washed, after which it is decomposed by grinding with freshly precipitated lead hydroxide. Another method is to precipitate the alkaloid with phosphomolybdic acid; in this case the colchicine is extracted by shaking the precipitate with ammonia and chloroform. Micro-sublimation as a method of purification has not been found successful.

The Calabar Bean and its Alkaloids

Calabar beans (*Physostigma venenosum*) are obtained from West Africa. They are oval in shape, dark in colour, and about an inch in length. The West African natives sometimes employ them in trials by ordeal for witchcraft.

The only important alkaloidal constituent is **physostigmine,** or eserine, which is extracted by the usual method, the extraction from alkaline aqueous solution being made with ether. The ethereal solution is concentrated to a small volume and agitated with successive small portions of dilute sulphuric acid. The acid extract is neutralized and from the neutral solution the alkaloid can be precipitated, in the form of a slightly soluble salicylate. The salicylate is one of the official preparations and is used in doses of 2 mg. orally or $0 \cdot 5$–$1 \cdot 0$ mg. hypodermically for the average adult.

The base is crystalline and it exists in two forms, one of which is stable and the other unstable: the unstable variety melts at 86°–87° C. and the stable at 105°–106° C. The crystals when pure and freshly prepared are colourless, but they frequently have a pale pink colour. Physostigmine, especially in the presence of alkalis, is readily oxidized on exposure to air with the production of rubreserine, which is red in colour. Oxidation with hydrogen peroxide yields geneserine which can be reconverted into physostigmine by reduction with zinc dust and acetic acid. Geneserine, on heating with acetic anhydride, yields a red product which is turned green by the addition of a drop of concentrated sulphuric acid.

Solutions of physostigmine salts become reddish-brown on heating.

The most important physiological property of physostigmine is its power to cause contraction of the pupil of the eye, in which respect it resembles arecoline and pilocarpine. Its action is opposed to that of atropine, not only in its effect on the eye but on the secretions, which are suppressed by atropine but increased by physostigmine.

Among the symptoms of physostigmine poisoning are colic, vomiting and diarrhoea, perspiration, muscular twitching, especially in the limbs, slow and weak pulse, difficulty in breathing, pupils of pin-point size and blurring of vision. Cessation of breathing is the immediate cause of death in fatal cases. The alkaloid is to some extent decomposed in the body, but part of it is excreted through the kidneys.

It can be extracted by the ordinary Stas-Otto process, chloroform being used as the immiscible solvent. If ammonia is used to render the aqueous solution alkaline, the chloroformic extract is usually reddish in colour.

Crystals of physostigmine salicylate are rhombic or hexagonal in form and melt at 180° C. With sodium alizarin sulphonate physostigmine yields a precipitate which is at first amorphous but which becomes crystalline on standing, the crystals being thin needles arranged fanwise.

The synthetic base *prostigmine* resembles physostigmine in its pharmacological action (as an inhibitor of choline esterase), therapeutic use, and toxic effects. It is a white crystalline powder melting at 143°–144° C. and forming characteristic crystals with picric acid, mercuric chloride and potassium ferrocyanide.

Pilocarpine

Pilocarpine is the chief alkaloid of *Pilocarpus jaborandi, P. microphyllus* and other species of the same genus, being present chiefly in the leaves. In most of its physiological effects it resembles physostigmine though by a totally different mechanism, and is antagonistic to atropine. It stimulates secretions, especially that of saliva, causes contraction of the pupils of the eyes, slows down the pulse rate and produces nausea, vomiting, and diarrhoea. In large doses it first accelerates and afterwards retards respiration, finally causing cessation of breathing.

Once used to stimulate sweating in the treatment of oedema, pilocarpine is still employed for its miotic effect, to induce salivation or as an expectorant.

As usually obtained pilocarpine base is an oily liquid, but it can with difficulty be converted into a crystalline form which melts at 34° C. Characteristic crystals are formed with Kraut's reagent (potassium-bismuth iodide) and with copper-lead nitrite solution, which is prepared by dissolving 0·5 g. of cupric acetate and the same amount of lead acetate in 10 ml. of water and mixing with 10 ml. of a 25 per cent. solution of sodium nitrite. The highly characteristic colour reaction with potassium chromate and hydrogen peroxide is described on p. 263.

Muscarine

Muscarine, the alkaloidal constituent of the poisonous fungus *Amanita muscaria,* or fly agaric, produces poisoning symptoms which are very similar to those of pilocarpine. These symptoms, excessive salivation, perspiration, lachrymation, contraction of the pupils and vomiting, usually appear one or two hours after the ingestion of the poison. The rate of mortality in muscarine poisoning is relatively low compared with that in poisoning by the other common poisonous fungus *Amanita phalloides*; usually sleep follows the vomiting and the patient recovers. In fatal cases there is haemorrhage into the stomach, and ulcers may be found on the mucous membranes.

Muscarine is obtained from the fungus as a tasteless, colourless and odourless syrup with a strongly alkaline reaction. It is soluble in water, insoluble in ether and only slightly soluble in chloroform.

For these reasons the isolation of muscarine is difficult and complicated. Aqueous solutions of the base should first be purified by
treatment with basic lead acetate and, after the removal of the
excess of lead, concentrated *in vacuo* to a small volume. The
liquid is then acidified with dilute sulphuric acid and treated with
Mayer's reagent, which should be free from excess of potassium
iodide. The precipitate is isolated and made alkaline with baryta
water, after which the compound is decomposed with hydrogen
sulphide. The mercuric sulphide is filtered off and the filtrate
treated with dilute sulphuric acid to remove barium which is also
removed by filtration. To the filtrate, freshly precipitated silver
chloride is added to eliminate traces of iodine. The liquid is again
filtered and the filtrate, concentrated to a small bulk if necessary,
is treated with platinic chloride solution to precipitate the alkaloid.
If choline is present this is precipitated first and removed by filtration
before the precipitation of the muscarine. Muscarine hydrochloride
is separated from the platinum compound by evaporating to dryness
with excess of potassium chloride solution and extracting the residue
with absolute alcohol, and from the hydrochloride the free base can
be isolated by treating with moist silver oxide, filtering and evaporating the filtrate *in vacuo*.

The gold and platinum compounds of muscarine are crystalline.

The Betel or Areca Nut

The betel nut, which is the fruit if the areca palm (*Areca catechu*),
contains a physiologically active alkaloid **arecoline** and smaller
quantities of inert alkaloids. The palm is cultivated in eastern Asia
where the nuts, mixed with lime, are habitually chewed by the
natives. The alkaloid is used in veterinary medicine as a remedy
for tape-worm. It is toxic, causing slowing of the pulse, and, in
large doses, tetanic cramps and paralysis. It contracts the pupil
of the eye, being more active in this respect than pilocarpine and
less so than physostigmine.

Arecoline is an oily liquid which boils at 220° C. and is volatile
in steam. It is very soluble in water and in most of the organic
solvents. Many of the salts are crystalline. It yields precipitates
with most of the alkaloidal precipitants and can be separated from
solution as the potassium-bismuth iodide compound which forms
rhombic crystals. The crystals are best obtained for identification
purposes by adding a drop of Kraut's reagent to a drop of the
alkaloidal solution on a microscope slide, warming slightly and
stirring while the liquid is still warm. Mercuric chloride solution,
added to a neutral solution of the alkaloid, forms crystals, many of
which are octahedral: they are soluble in excess of the reagent.

Hemlock and its Alkaloids

The common or spotted hemlock, *Conium maculatum*, has been known as a poisonous plant for certainly more than 2,000 years.[1] The active principles exist in all parts of the plant, but the fruits, especially when not quite ripe, are the most toxic. Hemlock is said to be harmless when fully ripe, dried, and mixed with hay. A Scottish variety exists which is non-poisonous.

The most actively poisonous constituent of common hemlock is **coniine,** the other alkaloids present being physiologically much less active.

It is necessary to distinguish between common hemlock and water hemlock (*Cicuta virosa*), a common wild plant which is also very poisonous but which owes its toxicity chiefly to a bitter non-alkaloidal substance, **cicutoxin,** which is present chiefly in the root.

The alkaloids of conium are volatile in steam and are isolated by passing steam through a mixture of the crushed fruits and sodium carbonate. The distillate is neutralized with hydrochloric acid and evaporated to dryness. The mixed hydrochlorides are extracted with absolute alcohol. The residue from evaporation of the filtered extract is dissolved in water and made alkaline with soda. From this solution the free bases are extracted with ether. The extract, dried over anhydrous sodium sulphate, is evaporated, and the residual liquid is fractionally distilled in a current of hydrogen. The fraction distilling below 190° C. contains coniine mixed with γ-coniceine and is converted into the hydrochlorides which are dried by evaporation. Extraction with acetone removes the γ-coniceine and the residual coniine hydrochloride is converted to the *d*-tartrate for final purification by recrystallization.

The odour of coniine, which is noticeable in the bruised plant and in dilute aqueous solution, resembles that of the urine of mice, while the anhydrous base has a more nicotine-like odour.

The common symptoms of coniine poisoning are weakness, drowsiness, nausea and vomiting. Respiration is difficult and sometimes ceases before the heart is seriously affected. The poison is rapidly excreted in the urine and in non-fatal cases the symptoms often pass away in a relatively short time. The alkaloid can be extracted from viscera by the Stas-Otto process, particular care being taken to keep the solutions acidic until just before the last stage when they are made alkaline and shaken with the immiscible solvent. Ether is a better solvent for coniine than chloroform. An alternative method is to take the residue which is left after the evaporation of the alcohol, mix it with sodium carbonate and distil in a current of steam; the alkaloid can then be extracted with ether from the distillate.

[1] Socrates died of hemlock poisoning in 399 B.C.

Nicotine

Nicotine, the chief alkaloidal constituent of tobacco, exists in the leaves in the form of salts such as the citrate and the malate. The amount of nicotine in various kinds of tobacco varies considerably; pipe tobacco usually contains from $0 \cdot 5$ to $0 \cdot 8$ per cent. of the base while some kinds of cigars contain as much as $2 \cdot 8$ per cent.

The usual method of isolating nicotine is to extract the powdered tobacco with acidified water and to concentrate the extract at a low temperature; the concentrated liquid is then made alkaline and submitted to the steam distillation process. The free alkaloid is extracted from the distillate with ether. When pure and freshly prepared, nicotine is a colourless and almost odourless liquid which can be distilled in a current of hydrogen, the boiling point being from 240° to 242° C. On exposure to air it becomes brown in colour and acquires a characteristic odour.

Nicotine is highly toxic and acts extremely rapidly, affecting both the central and the peripheral nerves, increasing secretions and causing constriction of the blood vessels. It also produces nausea and vomiting. Breathing is at first rapid and shallow, then deeper; and death may result from paralysis of the respiratory organs. Convulsions sometimes precede death. The fatal dose is probably about 60 mg.

Nicotine can be extracted from viscera in the same way as coniine. If steam distillation is the method adopted, the alkaloid is extracted from the distillate with ether. This extract is dried over anhydrous potassium carbonate, filtered and concentrated to a small volume; an ethereal solution of picric acid is then added in excess. Nicotine dipicrate separates out and, according to Wenusch, the separation is quantitative. The precipitate is filtered off, washed with ether and afterwards recrystallized from hot water. The crystals melt at 218° C. and the identity of the alkaloid can be established by taking a mixed melting point with pure nicotine dipicrate.

Nicotine may also be recognized by its odour, its strongly alkaline reaction and by the tests described on p. 262.

Sparteine (Lupinidine)

The flowering tops of the common broom (*Spartium* or *Cytisus scoparius*) contain the alkaloid **sparteine** as well as minute quantities of other bases. It is identical with **lupinidine,** which is one of the alkaloids present in the seeds of the yellow lupin.

The broom plant also contains a resinous substance, scoparin, which is a diuretic, but sparteine has no action on the kidneys. Sparteine is a strongly alkaline liquid which, as it is volatile in steam and soluble in ether, can be extracted by methods similar to those used for nicotine and coniine. After extraction the alkaloid can be distilled in a current of hydrogen; it boils at 326° C. under normal pressure. The liquid, which has an odour resembling that of aniline, becomes dark brown in colour and finally resinous on exposure to air. Many of the salts are crystalline. The physiological effects of sparteine are similar to those of coniine, but it is less toxic. At the present time sparteine is not used in medicine, but a decoction of broom tops is sometimes used as a household remedy.

Alkaloids of Lupins

The most abundant of the alkaloids of the yellow lupin is **lupinine,** which can be extracted together with sparteine from the seeds. Lupinine can be obtained free from sparteine (lupinidine) by dissolving the mixture in acidified water, rendering the solution alkaline, and extracting with light petroleum, sparteine being insoluble in this solvent.

According to Couch,[1] the most toxic of the lupin alkaloids is *d*-**lupinidine,** the minimum lethal dose of which, found by experiments on guinea-pigs, is 22 mg. per kilogramme of body weight.

One variety of lupin is a common article of food in Egypt, but before being used the seeds are submitted to a thorough process of washing to remove the alkaloidal constituents. Symptoms of poisoning occasionally arise when unwashed seeds are eaten.

Lupinine forms crystals melting at 68°–69° C. The aurichloride and the platinic chloride are also crystalline.

Alkaloids of the Golden Seal

The rhizome of the golden seal (*Hydrastis canadensis*) contains two chief alkaloids, **berberine** and **hydrastine,** and smaller quantities of a third, **canadine.** Berberine is non-toxic and of small importance medicinally. The alkaloids are extracted together and berberine is precipitated from aqueous solution as the sulphate; hydrastine is obtained from the mother-liquor by the addition of ammonia.

When hydrastine is oxidized it yields **hydrastinine,** together with opianic acid. Hydrastinine is also manufactured from berberine and from narcotine, which are more plentiful and less useful in themselves than hydrastine. In another process for the manufacture of hydrastine the raw material is piperonal. Both hydrastine and hydrastinine are used in gynaecology, especially in cases of uterine haemorrhage.

Hydrastine is poisonous in large doses, acting on the central nervous system, the heart, and the respiratory organs. Still larger doses give rise to convulsions and paralysis. Hydrastinine is probably less toxic than hydrastine, but very large doses may cause death by paralysis of the respiratory system. Hydrastine crystallizes

---

[1] *J. Agric. Res.*, 1926, **32**, 51–67. *Analyst*, 1926, **51**, 361.

in four-sided prisms which melt at 132° C. It is very soluble in chloroform, much less so in ether, and almost insoluble in water. It is a feeble base and can be extracted from aqueous solution by shaking with chloroform even in presence of hydrochloric acid.

Hydrastinine base can also be obtained in crystals, which melt at 116°–117° C. Unlike hydrastine it is strongly basic and dissolves in water to form an alkaline solution.

Cytisine, the Alkaloid of Laburnum

The seeds of laburnum (*Cytisus laburnum*) and certain other leguminous plants, including furze, contain the poisonous alkaloid **cytisine**. It can be extracted by any of the ordinary methods and it forms large, colourless, rhombic crystals which melt at 153° C., and can be sublimed by heating under normal pressure, the sublimate being also crystalline. The base is soluble in water, alcohol and chloroform and is almost insoluble in ether and in light petroleum.

Poisoning with laburnum is in most cases accidental, as when the seeds are swallowed by children. The symptoms have been compared with those of nicotine poisoning. There is usually nausea, and there may be convulsions; death is due to asphyxiation.

Taxine, the Alkaloid of the Yew Tree

The poisonous alkaloid **taxine** is found in the leaves and the seeds of the yew tree (*Taxus baccata*), but the fleshy part of the berries is harmless. The leaves contain from 0·6 to 1·3 per cent. of the base. Taxine is not known in the crystalline form. It is insoluble in water and in light petroleum, but soluble in most of the other organic solvents.

Taxine is a cardiac depressant; it interferes with respiration and may cause death by suffocation. Other common symptoms are abdominal pains, vomiting and diarrhoea; sometimes there is delirium, and death may be preceded by convulsions. The following colour reactions characterize taxine and its salts:

(1) With concentrated sulphuric acid a reddish-violet colour is produced, which disappears on adding water.

(2) The addition of a drop of nitric acid to the sulphuric acid solution changes the colour to rose-red.

(3) Fröhde's reagent produces a deep violet colour.

(4) An alcoholic solution of hydrochloric acid gives a green colour.

Ephedrine

Ephedrine and its optical isomer **pseudo-ephedrine** were originally obtained from the Chinese drug " Ma Huang " (*Ephedra vulgaris*). They have since been obtained from European varieties of the same genus. Ephedrine can be obtained from the powdered plant by extracting with alcohol, evaporating the solution to dryness, taking up the residue in acidified water, filtering and rendering the filtrate alkaline. The base can be extracted with chloroform from the alkaline liquid.

Ephedrine has come into use in recent years as a substitute for adrenaline in the treatment of asthma, urticaria, hay-fever, migraine and other allergic diseases. It has the advantage that it can be taken by the mouth, whereas adrenaline must be injected. Ephedrine is a mydriatic alkaloid and in large doses is poisonous. The maximum therapeutic dose of ephedrine is 0·1 g. Among the symptoms of an overdose are palpitation, insomnia, nervous excitement and depression of the cardiac muscle.

Ephedrine melts at 38°–40° C. and pseudo-ephedrine at 117°–118° C. The aurichloride of ephedrine forms yellow needles and characteristic crystals are also formed with potassium thiocyanate.

Alkaloids of Mescal Buttons

The flowering tops of the plant *Anhalonium Lewinii*, which is indigenous to Central America, are known as mescal buttons and are used by the natives to make an intoxicating drink which causes hallucinations and frequently produces vivid-coloured visions and dreams in which imaginary music is heard. Large doses produce poisoning symptoms which may end in paralysis. The plants and their active principles have been studied by Lewin and others and the subject is discussed in great detail in a monograph by Lewin called " Phantastica ".[1]

The following alkaloids have been extracted from mescal buttons: **mescaline, anhalonine, anhalonidine** and **lophophorine.** Of these, mescaline is the most abundant and lophophorine is the most toxic.

Ergot

Ergot is obtained from the fungus (*Claviceps purpurea*) which grows on many varieties of cereals but is most common on rye. The fungus is dark purple in colour and has the same shape as the cereal grains themselves. When powdered, ergot is coffee-coloured.

In the past, epidemics of poisoning which were due to the eating of bread made with ergotized rye flour were common in Central Europe.[2] The symptoms were of two kinds, epileptic and gangrenous. In epileptic ergotism the characteristic features were blindness, deafness, delirium, convulsions and sometimes insanity; frequently death followed the convulsive attacks. In gangrenous ergotism the afflicted persons suffered from burning pains in the extremities

---

[1] Re-issued under the title " Drugs and their Abuse ". Kegan Paul.
[2] BARGER. *Analyst*, 1937, **62**, 340. " Ergot and Ergotism ", 1931. Gurney and Jackson.

which in severe cases were followed by atrophy of the fingers and toes, and sometimes whole limbs became mummified and dropped off. The disease used to be known as " St. Anthony's Fire " because St. Anthony was a victim of it. According to Barger, historical records show that in regions where the staple diet was rich in vitamin A the epidemics of gangrenous ergotism were much less severe than in places where there was scarcity of dairy products.

Ergot and liquid extracts of the drug have been long used in midwifery to bring about contractions of the uterus. Preparations containing ergot have also been employed illegally for the purpose of procuring abortion, and in medico-legal work it is sometimes necessary to examine viscera for the constituents of ergot when death has followed the illicit administration of the drug.

Much recent research has been done on the alkaloidal constituents of ergot, which are now known to comprise four pairs of inter-convertible isomers, as well as some other bases of less importance. One alkaloid in each pair is physiologically active and the other more or less inert. These alkaloids are **ergotoxine** and **ergotinine, ergotamine** and **ergotaminine, ergosine** and **ergosisine, ergometrine** (or **ergonovine**) and **ergometrinine.** The most abundant of these alkaloids and the most poisonous is ergotoxine. The specific action of ergot and its preparations on the gravid uterus is attributed to ergometrine.

Other constituents of ergot which have some physiological importance are histamine and acetyl choline.

In the preliminary purification of visceral residues before the extraction of ergot alkaloids, chloroform should not be used since the alkaloids are to some extent extracted from a solution by this solvent. Moreover, the use of mineral acids is to be avoided as far as possible as there is a tendency for ergotoxine to be precipitated by strong electrolytes; citric acid is recommended instead.

Fat may be removed from ergot in an acid medium by means of light petroleum. Shaking with ether, also in presence of acid, extracts a colouring matter, **sclererythrin** (*vide infra*). From the residual liquor the mixed alkaloids are extracted with ether or ethyl acetate after making the solution alkaline. Ergometrine, which is only toxic in large doses, can be removed from the ethereal solution by shaking with successive small portions of water. The organic solvent is then driven off; the residue is taken up in water acidified with citric acid, filtered and made alkaline with caustic soda; shaking with ether extracts ergotinine from this liquid, and this can be purified by recrystallization from alcohol. The aqueous mother-liquor is then acidified, made alkaline with sodium carbonate and again repeatedly shaken with ether to extract ergotoxine. The residue left after the evaporation of the ether may be dissolved in

80 per cent. alcohol and neutralized with an alcoholic solution of phosphoric acid. Ergotoxine phosphate slowly crystallizes out, several days being necessary for its complete separation. This salt may be obtained in a crystalline form, melting at 186°–187° C., by recrystallization from boiling 90 per cent. alcohol.

Ergotoxine can be converted into ergotinine by boiling with methyl alcohol, and conversely, dilute acetic acid converts ergotinine into ergotoxine. This latter change can be brought about by dissolving ergotinine in three parts of glacial acetic acid, diluting with water to 100 parts and allowing to stand for ten days. From the solution, neutralized with sodium carbonate, ergotoxine can be extracted with ether. The conversion of ergotinine into ergotoxine can be accelerated by warming.

The examination of viscera for ergot should be undertaken as soon as possible after death. A successful issue is unlikely unless the samples examined contain at least the equivalent of 1 g. of the crude drug. The ergotoxine present is liable to be converted into ergotinine during the process of extraction and therefore the extract should be treated with dilute acetic acid as above described to reconvert it onto ergotoxine.

All the principal alkaloids of ergot are derivatives of lysergic acid, which is itself derived from indol. The colour reactions of ergotoxine (described on pp. 250–2) are, in reality, reactions of indol. They can, therefore, not be regarded as conclusive proofs of the presence of ergot, which can only be satisfactorily demonstrated by a physiological test. A minute dose of the pure alkaloid, injected intramuscularly into a young cock, causes the comb and wattles to become blue, the colour remaining for several hours. A solution injected into a frog sometimes gives rise to a gangrenous condition in which the skin of the extremities of the limbs cracks.

The ether extract from the acidic aqueous solution, referred to above, is orange coloured if ergot itself, or a liquid extract of it, is present. The colouring matter, sclererythrin, can be removed from the ether by repeated shaking with small quantities of sodium bicarbonate solution. This alkaline solution is coloured pale to deep violet, according to the amount of colouring matter present. The colouring matter is obtained in a purer condition by acidifying the aqueous liquid with hydrochloric acid and re-extracting with ether. Both the ethereal solution and the alkaline aqueous solution of sclererythin should be examined spectroscopically. The former shows two absorption bands ($\lambda 538$ and $\lambda 499$ respectively), one in the green portion of the spectrum and the other in the blue: the latter shows a strong band in the yellow and two faint bands in the green. This examination is a most important part of the process of identifying ergot in extracts from viscera. According to

Marino-Xuco and Duccini[1] the detection of sclererythrin is not possible if putrefaction is far advanced. They failed to detect it seven days after the death of the patient.

Solanine and Solanidine

Many species of the solanum group, including *S. nigrum* (the woody nightshade), *S. tuberosum* (the potato), *S. lycopersicum* (the tomato), *S. dulcanara* (bittersweet), and *S. chenopodinum*, contain a glycosidal alkaloid, **solanine,** which is insoluble in water, ether, chloroform and light petroleum; it is soluble in hot ethyl alcohol and in amyl alcohol. From concentrated solution in amyl alcohol it separates as a gelatinous mass. It can be obtained in colourless needle-like crystals which melt at 280° C. after shrinking at 235° C.

When solanine is heated with dilute mineral acid it is split up into the basic aglycone **solanidine** and a mixture of three sugars, glucose, rhamnose and galactose. In spite of its sugar content solanine does not reduce Fehling's solution, but it does reduce an ammoniacal solution of silver nitrate. Solanidine is a much stronger base than solanine and is soluble in alcohol and ether. From these solvents it can be obtained in crystals which melt at 210° C. The colour reactions of solanine and solanidine are similar to one another. Solanine is found in unripe potatoes, in the young shoots and the green parts of the plant. Many outbreaks of potato poisoning have been described and the whole matter is very fully discussed in a paper by Willimott[2] describing such an outbreak in Cyprus and in another by Harris and Cockburn.[3] The symptoms are, in the main, those of an irritant poison. The victims suffer from abdominal pains, vomiting, diarrhoea, shivering and acceleration of the pulse and respiration. Solanine is also said to cause haemolysis of the blood corpuscles. When an outbreak occurs there are usually one or two deaths, but most of the patients recover. When the Stas-Otto process is used for the extraction of solanine the immiscible solvent used should be amyl alcohol.

Harris and Cockburn give the following description of Meyer's method of extracting solanine from potatoes. The tubers are pared and grated and the liquid is pressed out. The residue is well washed with distilled water and the washings are added to the expressed juice, which is then allowed to stand until the starchy matter settles. The supernatant liquid is decanted and the residue washed, the washings being added to the decanted liquid, which is then made alkaline with ammonia and evaporated to dryness. The residue is extracted twice with hot alcohol and the filtered extracts are evaporated to dryness. The original pressed residue from the tubers is also

[1] *Gazz. Chim. Ital.*, 1914, **44**, 437. *Analyst*, 1915, **40**, 16.
[2] *Analyst*, 1933, **58**, 431.
[3] *Analyst*, 1918, **43**, 133.

extracted twice with alcohol, and these extracts are added to the one already obtained. The united extracts are digested overnight with water acidified with sulphuric acid and the liquid is filtered. Ammonia is added to precipitate the solanine, and after warming to 50° C., the latter is filtered off. It is then washed through the paper with hot alcohol into a tared dish and the liquid is again evaporated to dryness. The residue is washed with a little ether and weighed.

Lampitt and his collaborators[1] purify crude solanine by repeated precipitation with ammonia from acetic acid solution, then isolation from solution in hot amyl alcohol by addition of ammonia, and final recrystallization from ethyl alcohol. They use the purplish-red colour with concentrated sulphuric acid and formaldehyde for quantitative estimation.

The usual quantity of solanine contained in wholesome potatoes is 0·09 parts per 1,000. Potatoes which have been found to contain about 0·4 parts per 1,000 have been responsible for outbreaks of poisoning.

Lobeline

Lobelia inflata, the American " Indian wild tobacco ", is so named because of its distended or inflated fruits. It contains a number of alkaloids, which have been studied in detail by Wieland and his collaborators.[2] They isolated **lobeline, lobelidine, lobelanine, lobelanidine** and **iso-lobelanine.** Lobeline was obtained in crystals melting at 130°–131° C. Moreover, its structure was established and the synthetic product is on the market. It is a derivative of N-methylpiperidine:[3]

$$CH_2$$

$$H_2C \quad\quad CH_2$$

$$C_6H_5.CO.H_2C\text{-}CH \quad\quad HC.CH_2.CH.(OH.)C_6H_5.$$

$$N$$

$$CH_3.$$

It has been recommended for the stimulation of respiration in the treatment of phenol poisoning, the dose being 0·02 g. intramuscularly and 0·01 g. intravenously. Another of its pharmacological properties is to paralyse the vagus endings and for this reason it has been used in treating certain diseases due to X-rays.

[1] *J. Soc. Chem. Ind.*, 1943, **62**, 20, 48.
[2] KRAMER. " Scientific and Applied Pharmacology ", 3rd ed., p. 780.
[3] Merck's " Annual Report ", 1930, p. 242.

Like adrenaline and ephedrine it relieves the symptoms of urticaria. Poisoning symptoms produced by overdoses of extracts from the leaves and fruit are: nausea, vomiting, copious sweating, burning pain in the fauces and the oesophagus; failure of voluntary motion; rapid feeble pulse; fall in temperature; collapse with stupor or coma. Sometimes convulsions precede death.[1]

Quinine

Quinine can be administered in large doses or in successive normal doses (1 g. daily in malaria) without producing toxic symptoms. It is, nevertheless, poisonous. Large doses sometimes cause loss of sight and hearing. Occasionally convulsions have been reported, but these may have been due to other cinchona alkaloids present as impurities. Death is usually attributed to failure of respiration, and the heart may be found to be beating after the patient has ceased to breathe. Children have been fatally poisoned by swallowing quinine tablets. Dr. Sydney Smith[2] quotes cases of fatal poisoning of adults by 2 and 4 g. of quinine sulphate, respectively. On the other hand, Cushny mentions a case in which 30 g. of the same salt were swallowed without serious consequences.

Quinine is extracted by the usual Stas-Otto method, but it is important to remember that both the tartrate and the normal sulphate are almost insoluble in water. The alkaloid may therefore be precipitated by the use of tartaric acid, or if an aqueous solution is exactly neutralized with sulphuric acid. The thalleioquin reaction (*q.v.*) may be used as a spot test for quinine. One drop of a solution of a quinine salt is spotted on filter-paper and thereafter treated with bromine vapour and ammonia fumes. The spot shows a green fluorescence when examined in ultra-violet light.

Summary of Physiological Effects of Alkaloids

The following résumé of the physiological effects of alkaloids may be found useful as an indication of the substances which should be sought for:

Alkaloids causing marked nausea, vomiting, abdominal pains or diarrhoea
> Coniine: vomiting in early stages.
> Nicotine.
> Cytisine: nausea, vomiting and diarrhoea.
> Muscarine.

---

[1] " The United States Dispensatory ", 21st ed., p. 664.
[2] " Forensic Medicine ", 5th ed., p. 540.

Aconitine: sometimes vomiting and rarely diarrhoea.
Apomorphine: vomiting.
Narcissine: from the wild daffodil.
Emetine: nausea and vomiting, abdominal pains.
Lobeline (powerful emetic action on cats and dogs).
Colchicine: severe colic and diarrhoea.
Pilocarpine: sometimes nausea and vomiting.
Physostigmine: griping pains, vomiting, sometimes diarrhoea.
Ergot: vomiting, abdominal pains, diarrhoea.
Gelsemine: sometimes nausea, vomiting.
Veratrine alkaloids: persistent vomiting, colic and diarrhoea.

Alkaloids increasing secretions (salivation, etc.)
Pilocarpine.
Muscarine.
Coniine.
Nicotine.
Aconitine.
Emetine.
Physostigmine.
Veratrine alkaloids (cevadine and protoveratrine).

Alkaloids decreasing secretions
Atropine and other atropaceous alkaloids.

Cardiac stimulants
Aspidospermine.
Caffeine.

Cardiac depressants
Sparteine.
Lupinine.
Taxine.

Powerful mydriatics
Atropaceous alkaloids.
Gelsemine: dilatation, sometimes blindness.

Mild mydriatics
Cocaine.
Ephedrine.
Coniine.
Solanine.

Alkaloids producing contraction of the pupils
Pilocarpine.
Physostigmine.
Muscarine.

Synthetic substances contracting pupils

    Prostigmine (related to physostigmine).
    Doryl.
    Mecholine (related to acetyl choline).

Alkaloids producing mydriasis and contraction at different stages of poisoning

    Morphine.
    Codeine.
    Aconitine.
    Cocaine (rarely causes contraction).
    Nicotine.
    Physostigmine (dilatation has been reported).
    Strychnine.

Alkaloids causing convulsions

    Strychnine.
    Thebaine.
    Sanguinarine.
    Cytisine.
    Aconitine (not always).
    Atropine (rarely).
    Cocaine (sometimes).
    Ergot.
    Nicotine.

Practically all toxic alkaloids cause disturbances of the respiratory system and also affect the central nervous system.

Approximate Times of Onset of Symptoms and Death after Ingestion of Fatal Doses of Alkaloids

	Time of onset	Time of death	Approximate M.L.D.
Aconitine ·	Almost immediately after absorption.	Average, 3–4 hours. Minimum, 8 minutes. Maximum, 4 days.	3–6 mg.
Atropine ·	Usually almost immediately after absorption. Within 1 hour after ingestion into stomach.	Average, within 24 hours.	Minimum, 2–3 mg. Average much higher.
Cocaine ·	Almost immediately after absorption.	Often in less than ½ hour. If patient survives ½ hour he usually recovers.	Varies enormously. Probably about 1 g., less if injected.
Colchicine ·	Within 3–4 hours.	Sometimes within 24 hours, sometimes delayed for days, even weeks.	Great uncertainty. Probably about 60 mg.
Coniine ·	Very rapid.	Not often more than 3 hours.	Uncertain. Probably 3–16 mg.
Ipecacuanha (Emetine)		Shortest recorded 1½ hours, usually several days.	Rabbits and dogs, Intravenous, 3 mg. per kg. Subcutaneous, rabbit, 25–30 mg. Calculated for man, 120–200 mg.
Gelsemine ·	Immediately after absorption.	Minimum recorded, 1 hour. Average, 1–8 hours.	60 minims fluid extract ($\frac{1}{10}$ fl. oz.).
Morphine ·		Average, 9–10 hours. Minimum, 45 minutes. Maximum, 4 days. If patient survives 48 hours, prognosis is favourable.	Average, about 65 mg. 32 mg. dangerous.
Heroin ·			10 mg. is dangerous in non-addicts. Death has resulted from 600 mg.
Nicotine ·	Immediately poison reaches circulation.	Large doses a few seconds. Many reported deaths within 5 minutes.	Probably about 60 mg.
Strychnine ·	Almost immediately.	Minimum, 10 minutes. Average, 1–3 hours.	32 mg. often fatal.

ANTIPYRINE AND PYRAMIDONE

These are two closely related antipyretic drugs which are basic and can be extracted with the true alkaloids in the Stas-Otto process. They are both derivatives of iso-pyrazolone. (I)

$$\text{I} \qquad\qquad \text{II} \qquad\qquad\qquad \text{III}$$

Antipyrine or phenazone is prepared by condensing phenyl-hydrazine with ethyl acetoacetate to form phenylmethylpyrazolone. When a second methyl group is introduced the product is phenyl-dimethylpyrazolone or antipyrine (II).

Antipyrine readily yields a nitroso compound on treatment with nitrous acid and this can be reduced to an amino-compound and afterwards methylated. The new product is 1-phenyl 2 : 3-dimethyl-4-dimethylaminopyrazolone, which is sold under the name amidopyrine or pyramidone (III).

Antipyrine does not usually produce undesired effects in doses less than 2 g. although people who are idiosyncratic to the drug sometimes suffer from troublesome inflammation of the skin, especially the skin of the face and the genital organs. In larger doses it acts as an irritant, causing the usual symptoms.

Pyramidone is said to be less toxic than antipyrine and it is much more effective as an antipyretic.

Antipyrine and pyramidone are both crystalline substances, the former melting at 113° C. and the latter at 108° C. Both products form crystalline sublimates when heated under normal pressure. Both yield precipitates with Mayer's reagent and some other precipitants. Pyramidone forms excellent crystals with a solution of mercuric chloride. A series of colour reactions which serve to distinguish between these two drugs is given on page 258.

Antipyrine can be distinguished from pyramidone by the action of nitrous acid. The former yields a green coloured solution of the nitroso-compound which separates in crystals from concentrated solution.

With pyramidone, nitrous acid like other oxidizing agents, such as ferric chloride, produces a blue to violet colour.

Pyramidone is not found unchanged in the urine. The replace-ment of the dimethylamino group by urea yields antipyryl-urea. A more complicated change results in the formation of rubazonic acid.

These substances can be extracted from the urine by a method devised by Jaffé.[1]

Rubazonic Acid. The urine, acidified with hydrochloric acid, is allowed to stand until the impure, red, rubazonic acid has completely separated. This is filtered off, mixed with ammonia and repeatedly extracted with ethyl acetate. When the solvent is distilled off the residue consists of needle-like crystals of rubazonic acid. Recrystallized from hot ethyl acetate it is obtained pure, melting at 184° C.

The substance behaves like many dye-stuffs ; it can be reduced to a colourless leuco-compound which reoxidizes in the air, reproducing the original colour.

Antipyryl-urea. The acid filtrate from the crude rubazonic acid is neutralized with sodium carbonate and evaporated to a thin syrupy consistency. The viscous liquid is decanted while warm into four times its volume of a mixture of equal volumes of alcohol and ether. This is allowed to stand for several days with frequent shaking. The liquid is poured off and the residue is again treated with the alcohol-ether mixture. The alcohol-ether solution is again decanted off and evaporated to dryness. The residue, containing much urea, is neutralized with 5 per cent. sulphuric acid and a small excess of the acid is added. Phosphotungstic acid is added until precipitation is complete. The precipitate is filtered off and washed with 5 per cent. sulphuric acid and decomposed by warming with baryta water. Carbon dioxide is passed through the liquid to precipitate excess of barium. The precipitate is removed by filtration and the filtrate is evaporated *in vacuo* until a crystalline residue is obtained. This is treated with acetone to dissolve out antipyryl-urea. After evaporating the acetone the residue is dissolved in water and tested with ferric chloride, which gives a violet colour. The substance, when warmed with Millon's reagent, becomes yellow, then red, and finally a red precipitate is produced.

[1] *Ber. d. Deutsch. Chem. Ges.*, 1901, **34**, 2,737.   *Ibid.*, 1902, **35**, 2,891.

CHAPTER X

A SYSTEMATIC SCHEME FOR THE IDENTIFICATION OF ALKALOIDS

In the following tables an attempt is made to classify the more common alkaloids according to the reactions which may be used for their identification. The alkaloids in the list include the chief opium constituents and their artificial derivatives, cocaine and the more common substitutes for it, the other common toxic alkaloids and one or two which are not toxic, but which may be present in viscera or excreta and which must therefore be identified.

The reagents required are:—

Precipitants

1. *Ammonia solution.* 10 ml. 0·880 ammonia per 100 ml.
2. *Gold chloride solution.* 3 g. per 100 ml.
3. *Marmé's reagent,* potassium cadmium iodide solution. Dissolve 10 g. CdI_2 in 60 ml. of warm 30 per cent. (w/v) KI solution and add an equal volume of cold saturated KI solution.
4. *Mayer's reagent,* potassium mercuric iodide solution. 13·55 g. $HgCl_2$ and 50 g. KI in 1,000 ml. water.
5. *Mercuric chloride solution.* 5 g. per 100 ml.
6. *Picric acid solution.* Dilute a saturated aqueous solution of picric acid with an equal volume of water.
7. *Potassium chromate solution.* 5 g. per 100 ml.
8. *Potassium ferrocyanide solution.* 5 g. per 100 ml.
9. *Sonnenschein's reagent,* phosphomolybdic acid solution. Precipitate ammonium phosphomolybdate by adding ammonium molybdate to sodium phosphate solution, wash the precipitate, dissolve in sodium carbonate solution, evaporate to dryness, moisten the residue with nitric acid and ignite. Dissolve 10 g. of the residue in 100 ml. of 30 per cent. nitric acid.
10. *Wagner's (Bouchardet's) reagent,* iodine (1 g.) and potassium iodide (2 g.) in 50 ml. water.

Colour Reagents

1. *Alcoholic potash.* 5 g. KOH per 100 ml.
2. *Ammonia solution* dilute.
3. *Chloranil.* 1 g. in 100 ml. benzene.
4. *Copper sulphate solution.* 1 g. per 100 ml.

5. *p-dimethylaminobenzaldehyde.* (1) 1 g. in 100 ml. alcohol with 20 drops of concentrated sulphuric acid; (2) 1 g. in 100 ml. of dilute sulphuric acid containing 40 ml. of the concentrated acid.

6. *Fröhde's reagent.* 1 g. ammonium molybdate in 10 ml. concentrated sulphuric acid.

7. *Hydrogen peroxide.* " 10 vols."

8. *Mandelin's reagent.* 1 g. sodium vanadate in 100 ml. concentrated sulphuric acid.

9. *Marquis' reagent.* Add two drops of formalin to 3 ml. concentrated sulphuric acid. Prepare immediately before use.

10. *Mecke's reagent.* 1 g. selenous acid in 200 ml. concentrated sulphuric acid.

11. *β-naphthol.* Suspend 1 g. in about 50. ml. water, add enough sodium hydroxide to dissolve and dilute to 100 ml. with water.

12. *Nitric acid* (fuming). S.G. 1.50.

13. *Potassium dichromate.* Solid, finely powdered.

14. *Potassium permanganate.* $0 \cdot 1$ g. $KMnO_4$ in 100 ml. N/10 H_2SO_4.

15. *Sodium nitrite solution.* $0 \cdot 5$ g. per 100 ml. Prepare fresh.

16. *Sulphuric acid* (pure, concentrated).

Preliminary Observations

The majority of the alkaloids are white solids and form white, usually crystalline salt with mineral acids. One or two are yellow (colchicine, cotarine). A few are liquid at ordinary temperatures, usually colourless when pure and freshly prepared, but become dark on exposure to air (nicotine, coniine, sparteine) ; these may be recognized by their odours. Others are solids of low melting point which are usually in the liquid state when extracted from their salts, but become solid on cooling or long standing. A few of the bases are easily soluble in water, forming alkaline solutions. Nearly all solutions of alkaloidal salts, even when very dilute, yield precipitates with the precipitating reagents, the first three of these being especially sensitive: exceptions which only yield precipitates with Mayer's reagent in very concentrated solutions are caffeine, ephedrine and colchicine. Many of these precipitates are crystalline or become crystalline on standing.

If the bases have to be extracted by means of immiscible solvents in presence of alkali before testing, some useful indications may be observed during this process: e.g. if an ammoniacal solution of an alkaloid is shaken with chloroform and the latter becomes violet-coloured, apomorphine may be suspected; if it becomes pink, it probably contains physostigmine.

Before tests for identification are applied to an alkaloid it must be made as pure as it is possible to make it.   The tests in the tables can only be regarded as specific when non-alkaloidal impurities have been eliminated.   It is better to examine 1 mg. of a pure alkaloid than 10 mg. of a residue containing decomposition products of proteins, traces of fat and other animal matter.

The first step in the identification process is to make sure that the substance is alkaloidal, by testing a faintly acid aqueous solution with the precipitating reagents; after which colour-tests and other means of identification should be applied.   When the quantity of substance is small the greatest economy must be exercised in the use of it.   A solution of the alkaloidal base in alcohol should be made and small drops of this evaporated to dryness for individual tests.   The tests should be applied in a definite order, as in the " group-analysis " of metals.   Most of the alkaloids are characterized by colour reactions, but a small number, found in the last group, give no colours with any of the reagents and can only be identified by physiological tests, the crystalline forms of derivatives, and by melting-point determinations.

Most of the colour tests are made in small porcelain basins, but the azo-dye tests in Group V are most conveniently carried out in ordinary capillary tubes.

For crystallization tests, with the exception of the reactions with potassium permanganate in Group VII, capillary tubes of a special form are recommended.   They are elliptical in section and as flat as possible.   They are made by heating a clean test tube in a blow-pipe flame, keeping the tube still, until the side sinks in towards the centre.   The tube is then rotated through 180° and the other side is made to sink in similarly.   When the tube is pulled out the capillary portion should be almost ribbon-like, the width being from 1·5 to 3 mm., and the thickness less than 0·5 mm.   The method of using the tubes is to take up a quantity of the alkaloidal solution, sufficient to occupy about 1 cm. of the length of the tube, and then a similar quantity of the reagent.   The latter may be taken from a drop hanging from a glass rod.   The two liquids must, of course, make contact, i.e. there must be no air between them.   The mixture is allowed to run up and down once or twice, after which the two ends of the capillary are sealed in a flame.   Such tubes, containing the specimens, may be preserved almost indefinitely by passing them through pairs of holes punched into a sheet of rice-paper which also serves as a label.   The advantages of such tubes over cylindrical tubes is that their contents can be easily seen in sharp focus under a microscope.   Their advantages over microscope slides are:—

(1) They are more economical of material. The quantity of alkaloidal solution used need not be more than about 7 c.mm., so that one drop (50 c.mm.) is sufficient for seven tests.

(2) There is no risk of evaporation. One of the difficulties in using microscope slides, when crystallization is not immediate, is that the constituents of the reagent sometimes crystallize out.

(3) Time is saved in the microscopic examination, since the area to be searched for crystals is very small.

If photographs of crystals are needed, they can be obtained just as easily from flat tubes as from slides.

For the systematic identification the tests should be made in the following order, the first to give a definite colour being followed by the tests as described for the appropriate group.

(1) Concentrated sulphuric acid.
(2) Marquis reagent.
(3) Vitali's reagent.
(4) Sulphuric acid and solid potassium dichromate.
(5) p-dimethylaminobenzaldehyde in alcohol and sulphuric acid.
(6) potassium chlorate.

GROUP I

Group Reagent: Pure Concentrated Sulphuric Acid

The following alkaloids yield definite colours. (Some others give faint transient colours, but these show better reactions in the later group.)

(1) *Thebaine* :   colour immediately blood-red, slowly turning orange.

(2) *Narcotine* :   colour immediately lemon-yellow.

(3) *Narceine* :   colour immediately greenish brown turning orange-yellow.

(4) *Hydrastine* :   green and brown patches ;   the whole slowly turning pink.

(5) *Solanine* :   yellow to yellowish brown.

(6) *Cytisine* :   orange, faint at first, becoming much deeper.

(7) *Piperine* :   reddish orange, turning brown.

(8) *Veratrine* :   yellow to orange-red, turning violet at the edges.

(9) *Delphinine* :   brown.

(10) *Colchicine* :   yellow.

(11) *Ergotoxine* :   yellow, becoming olive-green at the edges and finally entirely dark green.

The Marquis Reagent

A portion of the sample is next tested with the Marquis reagent.

Group Ia. Contains the alkaloids which give the same colour, or nearly the same colour, as with sulphuric acid alone : *thebaine, cytisine, piperine, delphinine, colchicine* (more orange coloured).

Group Ib. Contains the alkaloids which give different colours with the Marquis reagent : *narcotine, narceine, hydrastine, solanine, veratrine, ergotoxine.*

Narcotine : blue-violet colour, quickly becoming darker ; yellowish green rim develops at the edges ; the middle becomes olive-green and the edges yellow ; the whole becomes yellowish green and finally brown.

Narceine : brown colour becoming reddish in the middle and green at the edges.

Hydrastine : pink with violet tinges, becoming a pinkish shade of violet throughout.

Solanine : bluish violet, quickly turning brown and slowly olive-green.

Veratrine : yellow, changing to orange and afterwards brown.

Ergotoxine : almost black, with a violet tinge.

Mecke's Reagent

Group Ia.

Thebaine : like sulphuric acid alone.

Delphinine : like sulphuric acid alone.

Cytisine : orange, becoming deeper in colour.

Piperine : dark brown, turning greenish, with red streaks.

Colchicine : greenish yellow.

Group Ib.

Narcotine : grass-green, becoming olive-green, then yellow, orange-brown and finally orange-red.

Narceine : brown, changing to violet and then orange.

Hydrastine : pale yellowish green, changing to brown.

Solanine : grass-green, pale blue at the edges ; changing to dull grey with a violet tinge.

Veratrine : yellow, quickly becoming brownish and green in patches ; reddish violet at the edges ; the whole finally turning violet.

Ergotoxine : yellow, quickly changing to light green, and then slowly to dark green with red edges.

Fröhde's Reagent

Group Ia.

Thebaine : brown.

Delphinine : brown.

Cytisine : strong reddish orange.

Piperine : brown, with red and violet streaks.

Piperine : brown, with red and violet streaks.
Colchicine : strong yellow.
Group Ib.
    Narcotine : pale green.
    Narceine : yellowish brown.
    Hydrastine : pale yellow, slowly turning green.
    Solanine : dirty green, becoming reddish, then lilac.
    Veratrine : red-violet.
    Ergotoxine : bluish violet, changing to green.

Mandelin's Reagent
Group Ia.
    Thebaine : brown, changing to blood red.
    Delphinine : brown, changing to violet.
    Cytisine : orange.
    Piperine : dark brown, changing to violet.
    Colchicine : momentary bright green, quickly turning brown.
Group Ib.
    Narcotine : pink, changing to bright red.
    Narceine : dark brown, changing to red.
    Hydrastine : intense red-brown.
    Solanine : bright pinkish violet.
    Veratrine : red-violet.
    Ergotoxine : violet with green tinge.

p-Dimethylamino-benzaldehyde (alcoholic reagent)
Group Ia.
    Thebaine : no colour in the cold ; orange-brown with green rim on warming.
    Delphinine : no colour in the cold ; olive-green, changing to brown on warming.
    Cytisine : no colour in the cold ; bright yellow on warming.
    Piperine : pale yellow in the cold ; bright yellow on warming.
    Colchicine : pale yellow in the cold ; bright yellow on warming.
Group Ib.
    Narcotine : no colour in the cold ; yellow when heated, with red-brown edges.
    Narceine : no colour in the cold ; orange-brown on warming.
    Hydrastine : no colour in the cold ; yellow on warming.
    Solanine : no colour in the cold : red (purple shade) on warming, turning brown.
    Veratrine : no colour in the cold ; yellowish green, changing to olive-green and then dirty violet on warming.
    Ergotoxine : bright blue-violet rim on standing in the cold ; the whole becomes bright violet on warming.

Gallic Acid Test

The alkaloid is dissolved in concentrated sulphuric acid, a small quantity of gallic acid is added, and the mixture is warmed.

Group Ia.

Thebaine : red colour disappears and becomes dirty brown with violet tinge.

Delphinine : dirty brown.

Cytisine : brown.

Colchicine : brown, becoming reddish violet.

Group Ib.

Narcotine : brown, becoming green, then bright blue.

Narceine : brown, becoming green, but not blue.

Hydrastine : like narcotine.

Solanine : like narcotine.

Veratrine : red-brown in the cold with a strong green fluorescence, becoming violet-red on heating.

Ergotoxine : olive-green, then brown.

Concentrated Hydrochloric Acid Test

Group Ia.

Thebaine : no colour in the cold ; pale yellow on boiling.

Delphinine :   ,,   ,,   ,,   or on boiling.

Cytisine :   ,,   ,,   ,,   ,,   ,,

Colchicine : intense yellow in the cold ; no change on boiling.

Group Ib.

Narcotine : no colour in the cold or on boiling.

Narceine :   ,,   ,,   ,,   ,,   ,,

Hydrastine :   ,,   ,,   ,,   ,,   ,,

Solanine :   ,,   ,,   ,,   ,,   ,,

Veratrine :   ,,   ,,   ,, ; reddish violet on boiling

Ergotoxine :   ,,   ,,   ,, or on boiling.

Vitali's Test (cf. p. 257).

Colours in the Cold with Fuming Nitric Acid		Colour of Residue	Colour with Alcoholic Potash
Cytisine:	Bright orange-red	Orange	Green, changing to dull violet
Veratrine:	Yellow, becoming colourless	Pale brown	Red-violet
Colchicine:	Dark violet, becoming paler	Brown	Red-violet
Ergotoxine:	Brown	Brown	Brown with violet tinge
All others:	Brown	Brown	Brown

Ferric Chloride Test

Cytisine :   red colour, discharged by hydrogen peroxide.
All other alkaloids : no colour.

Dilute Sulphuric Acid and Potassium Permanganate

The permanganate is added until the colour no longer disappears immediately, and the mixture is allowed to stand until the red colour entirely disappears.

Hydrastine only yields a fine blue fluorescent solution.

Sulphuric Acid—Potassium Nitrate Test

The alkaloid is dissolved in concentrated sulphuric acid and, as quickly as possible, a little finely powdered potassium nitrate is drawn through the liquid with a glass rod.

Colchicine yields vivid and characteristic colours ; the initial yellow becomes bright green, then blue, violet, brown and finally colourless.   With veratrine and delphinine the initial colour fades almost completely.

The red colour of *thebaine* fades to reddish orange.

Ergotoxine yields a pale greenish yellow colour.

All the other alkaloids in the group yield various shades of brown.

GROUP II

Group Reagent: Marquis

This group contains alkaloids which give little or no colour with sulphuric acid alone, but give colours with the Marquis reagent:—

Violet colours (various shades from bluish to reddish) are given by *morphine, apomorphine, heroin, dilaudid, codeine, dionine, eucodal, dicodide.*

Cherry-red to reddish violet : *lobeline.*

These alkaloids are sub-divided into Groups IIa and IIb according to their behaviour in Oliver's test (*vide infra*).

Group IIc consists of alkaloids which give colours with the Marquis reagent not closely resembling that given by morphine.

Violet with tinges of green : *pseudo-morphine.*

Yellowish, becoming pale red-violet (not sensitive) : *papaverine.*

Light brown, becoming darker : *ephedrine.*

If a strong violet colour is produced, **Oliver's test** should be applied.   To a faintly acid solution of the alkaloid, a drop of hydrogen peroxide is added and a drop of dilute copper sulphate solution; the liquid is then made alkaline with ammonia.

Red to brown colours are produced with : *morphine, apomorphine, heroin* and *dilaudid* (Group IIa).   No colour is obtained with : *codeine, dionine, dicodide, eucodal* or *lobeline* (Group IIb).

Group IIa.

Colours with Oliver's reagents :—

$\left.\begin{array}{l}\text{Morphine}\\\text{Apomorphine}\end{array}\right\}$ red, quickly fading to brown.

Dilaudid : yellow to brown.

Heroin : bright red which persists for about half an hour.

Ferric Chloride Test

To a neutral solution, or a particle of dry substance, a drop of dilute ferric chloride solution is added. *Morphine* gives a green colour ; *dilaudid,* blue ; *apomorphine,* reddish brown.

No colour is produced by *heroin.*

Mecke's Reagent

This reagent yields colours which serve to distinguish between the alkaloids in Groups IIa and IIb.

Group IIa.

Morphine : olive-green, changing to bluish violet and then again to olive-green with red edges.

Apomorphine : bluish violet, changing to dark green with red edges.

Dilaudid : yellow, changing to olive-green and finally to dull bluish violet.

Heroin : bright pure blue ; a green rim slowly develops and finally the whole is olive-green.

Group IIb.

This reagent distinguishes between codeine and dionine, and dicodide and eucodal.

Codeine : greenish blue, changing to bright pale blue and finally to bright green.

Dionine : green, changing to olive-green with blue edges and the whole becomes olive-green.

Dicodide : bright yellow, changing to grass-green, then bluish green.

Eucodal : yellow, changing slowly to orange-green at the edges.

Lobeline : faint, dirty grey, almost negative.

p-Dimethylaminobenzaldehyde Reagent (alcoholic)

All the alkaloids in Groups IIa and IIb give bright colours on evaporating to dryness with this reagent.

Nearly all become bright purple : the shades with *eucodal* and *dicodide* being redder. *Lobeline* gives no characteristic colour, the residue being little different from that given by the reagent alone.

Papaverine and *pseudo-morphine* give only faint colours which are not very characteristic.

Fröhde's Reagent

Morphine : red-violet changing to light green.
Apomorphine : immediately green, changing to blue.
Dilaudid : pale mauve, fading to colourless.
Heroin : like morphine.
Codeine : yellow, turning green and finally blue.
Dionine : yellow, turning green and finally blue.
Dicodide : no colour.
Eucodal : no colour.
Lobeline : practically negative.

Pellagri's Test

This test is carried out by dissolving a particle of the substance in about 1 ml. of concentrated hydrochloric acid with one drop of concentrated sulphuric acid. The solution is evaporated to dryness on the water-bath and the colour of the residue is noted. The residue is dissolved in water and the solution is just neutralized with sodium carbonate; or excess of chalk is added. One or two drops of iodine solution (Wagner's reagent) are then added and the mixture is allowed to stand for ten to fifteen minutes. Any excess of iodine is then removed with sodium thiosulphate solution, and the solution is shaken with ether. The colours of the aqueous and ethereal layers are noted. *Morphine, heroin, codeine, dionine* and *apomorphine* leave a violet residue on drying. After adding thiosulphate the colour is green and the colour of the ether extract is purple.

The other opium alkaloids give no definite colours. *Ephedrine* yields a yellowish brown residue, not decolorized by thiosulphate, insoluble in ether, dissolving in concentrated sulphuric acid with a violet colour, quickly turning brown.

Group IIc. Pseudo-morphine, papaverine and *ephedrine.*

Papaverine is distinguished by **Warren's test.** The Marquis reagent is applied first. The pink to pale reddish violet colour is noted. Then a minute crystal of potassium permanganate is put into the drop. A deep blue colour develops. In this test *pseudo-morphine* yields a bluish green colour and *ephedrine* brown.

(The Marquis reagent alone with potassium permanganate turns violet.)

Mecke's reagent produces the following colours:

Papaverine : green, turning dark green, then blue ; finally a reddish rim forms. (A very sensitive test.)
Pseudo-morphine : reddish violet, becoming dark brown.
Ephedrine : no colour.

Mandelin's reagent also shows distinctions :
Papaverine : dull green, finally lighter green.
Pseudo-morphine : violet, becoming very dark, with green tinges.
Ephedrine : faint brick red (fading).

With **Fröhde's reagent** *papaverine* and *ephedrine* give no colours ;
pseudo-morphine, pale brown only.

The most characteristic reaction of *ephedrine* is the purple colour
formed on treating the *free* alkaloid with copper sulphate solution.
The alkaloid must be in excess, and therefore the copper sulphate
solution must be dilute. On shaking the solution with chloroform,
the purple colour passes into this solvent.

GROUP III

This group contains the alkaloids which respond to **Vitali's Test,**
or give colours with nitric acid, and are not included in Groups I
and II. The atropaceous alkaloids, *atropine, hyoscyamine* and
scopolamine, constitute Group IIIa, and the others, *physostigmine,
brucine, antipyrine* and *pyramidone*, not responding to Vitali's test,
Group IIIb.

In **Vitali's test** the alkaloid is evaporated to dryness on a water-
bath with a drop of fuming nitric acid. The brownish residue is
treated, when cold, with a drop of alcoholic potash. The alkaloids
of the atropine group, *atropine, hyoscyamine* and *scopolamine*
(hyoscine), yield a strong bluish violet colour.
Group IIIa.

These three alkaloids are strongly mydriatic and their presence
must be confirmed by instilling a drop of a neutral solution into a
cat's eye. The cat is kept in a dark cupboard for half an hour and
then brought out into the sunlight. Marked dilation of the pupil
is produced by very minute traces of these alkaloids. Other
alkaloids which are less strongly mydriatic do not respond to
Vitali's test.

To distinguish between the three atropaceous alkaloids the
crystalline form of three derivatives of each should be observed.
The reagents recommended are: Wagner's reagent, picric acid and
gold chloride, and the reactions are as follows:

	Wagner's Reagent	Picric Acid	Gold Chloride
Atropine · · ·	Crystals	Crystals	Oily drops
Hyoscyamine · ·	Crystals	Crystals	Crystals
Scopolamine · ·	Oily drops	Oily drops	Crystals

The crystals formed with *atropine* and Wagner's reagent are mostly short tapering needles, some of which are arranged in star-like clusters. Another characteristic form is ribbon-like, the ends being bifurcated into a fish-tail form. *Hyoscyamine* with the same reagent forms long rhomboids.

The picrates of all the three alkaloids separate first as oily drops, but whereas the *scopolamine* compound remains amorphous for at least three days in a sealed tube, the picrates of *atropine* and *hyoscyamine* become crystalline within forty-five minutes. The individual crystals of atropine picrates are of many forms, but they are all arranged in fern-like growths. Hyoscyamine picrate consists chiefly of very fine needles, arranged in bunches; a few short rectangular prisms may also be seen.

Group IIIb.

Physostigmine (eserine) dissolves in concentrated nitric acid to form a reddish orange solution which, on evaporating to dryness, begins to turn green, and after prolonged heating on the water-bath the whole of the residue is green.

The best test for physostigmine consists in evaporating the solution with a large excess of ammonia, on the water-bath. A blue residue remains. If the whole does not become blue, more ammonia should be added and the evaporation repeated. Before the final blue colour is attained the following sequence of colour changes may be observed: pink, red, orange, yellow and green. The blue compound finally obtained is soluble in alcohol.

Another reaction characteristic of physostigmine is the pink colour produced when an ammoniacal solution is shaken in air: if the pink liquid is shaken with chloroform the colour passes into the latter solvent.

Brucine yields the well-known red colour with nitric acid. This is more characteristic if the alkaloid is dissolved in concentrated sulphuric acid and a very minute trace of nitric acid is added. The red colour is discharged by the addition of stannous chloride, but not by sodium sulphite. The further addition of nitric acid restores the colour.

The antipyretics, *antipyrine* (phenazone) and *amidopyrine* (pyramidone), which behave like alkaloids in being precipitated by the ordinary alkaloidal precipitants, also belong to this group.

The following are the characteristic reactions: with a drop of fuming nitric cid, antipyrine gives a blood-red to reddish purple colour; pyramidone, greenish yellow. On evaporating to dryness the residue from antipyrine is nearly black; that from pyramidone is yellowish brown. The addition of a drop of alcoholic potash turns the residue from antipyrine brown, and the residue from pyramidone a redder shade of brown.

Much more characteristic reactions are produced by nitrous acid. The substance is dissolved in dilute sulphuric acid and a trace of sodium or potassium nitrite is added. Antipyrine gives an intense green colour; pyramidone, bluish violet which quickly fades.

Ferric chloride also produces colours which differentiate the two, viz. antipyrine, blood-red; pyramidone, blue with a violet tinge.

Silver nitrate solution yields a purple colour with pyramidone, while antipyrine remains almost colourless.

Fröhde's, Mandelin's and Mecke's reagents are of little value as tests for these antipyretics, but Mandelin's reagent gives a faint green colour turning pale blue with pyramidone; with antipyrine a pale blue colour is very slowly developed.

With an acidified alcoholic solution of p-dimethylaminobenzaldehyde, antipyrine yields a bright red colour in the cold; no colour is produced with pyramidone.

GROUP IV

This group consists of the alkaloids which yield characteristic colours when dissolved in sulphuric acid, and a minute crystal of potassium dichromate is drawn through the liquid, viz. strychnine, yohimbine, gelsemine, curare, cotarnine and hydrastinine. Most of the colours are quite distinctive, thus:

Strychnine: blue-violet, changing to red-violet, then to red and finally to orange.

Yohimbine : blue, changing to blue-violet and then to green.

Gelsemine : bright red, changing to brown.

Curare : red-violet.

Cotarnine : pink, changing to green.

Hydrastinine: salmon-pink, changing to brown.

The group can be sub-divided by the use of **Fröhde's reagent.**

Group IVa. *Strychnine* and *gelsemine* remain colourless.

Group IVb. The other alkaloids yield colours :

Yohimbine : blue.

Curare : brown. (This may be due to impurities since pure curare alkaloids are difficult to obtain.)

Cotarnine : reddish, quickly changing to bright green.

Hydrastinine : yellow, changing to bright green, which colour soon fades.

Group IVa.

No colour is produced when *strychnine* or *gelsemine* is treated with **Mecke's reagent.**

With **Mandelin's reagent** *strychnine* yields a blue-violet colour, becoming red-violet and then bright vermilion.

With *gelsemine* the initial colour is red, changing to reddish violet and slowly fading.

With potassium permanganate in concentrated sulphuric acid *strychnine* gives the same sequence of colours as with potassium dichromate.

With *gelsemine* the colour is red at first, fading to pale violet.

Group IVb.

Mandelin's reagent produces the following colours :

Yohimbine :   bright blue.

Cotarnine :   bright orange, changing to brown which becomes violet at the edges and the final colour is bluish violet.

Hydrastinine :   bright orange, fading to green.

Curare :   violet.

Mecke's reagent also yields distinctive colours:

Yohimbine :   greenish blue, changing to green.

Cotarnine :   yellow, changing to brown.

Hydrastinine :   greenish yellow.

Curare :   brown.

Hydrastinine and *cotarnine* may be further distinguished as follows:

In dilute sulphuric acid solution hydrastinine shows a brilliant blue fluorescence.   The solution of cotarnine is pale yellow without fluorescence.

In the gallic acid-sulphuric acid test (see Group I), cotarnine yields a solution which is first green, then blue, then purple.   With hydrastinine the colour is also green, changing to blue, but it remains blue.

GROUP V

The group-reagent is *p*-**dimethylaminobenzaldehyde** in alcoholic solution acidified with concentrated sulphuric acid.   The only natural alkaloids included are *nicotine*, *mescaline* and *pilocarpine*, the other substances being the artificial cocaine-substitutes, *novocaine*, *anaesthesine*, *tutocaine*, *pantocaine* and *stovaine*.

All the substances in Group V are local anaesthetics.   They produce numbness when applied to the tip of the tongue.

The group is subdivided into the substances which yield colours in the cold, and those of which the colours develop on evaporating just to dryness on the water-bath.

Group Va.   (Colours produced in the cold):

Strong yellow colour :   *novocaine, anaesthesine, tutocaine.*

Pale yellow colour :   *pantocaine* and *stovaine.*

Effect of evaporating to dryness on the water-bath :

Novocaine, anaesthesine and *tutocaine* become bright reddish orange.

Pantocaine : the colour becomes strong lemon-yellow.

Stovaine : the colour becomes fainter, almost colourless.

Group Vb. (Colours developed only on warming) :

Blue-violet at the edges, red-violet in the middle : *nicotine.*

Orange to red, rapidly fading on cooling : *mescaline.*

Strong yellow, pink at the edges: *pilocarpine.*

Group Va. (Confirmatory tests) :

The first three, *novocaine, anaesthesine* and *tutocaine,* contain arylamino-groups in the molecules. They can be diazotized and coupled with β-naphthol to produce bright red azo-dyes. The test is carried out in capillary tubes, the solutions being taken up into the tubes in the following order: test-solution, dilute hydrochloric acid solution, nitrite solution, alkaline β-naphthol solution.

To distinguish between the three, microcrystalline tests are applied. The following are the results obtained with seven reagents:

Reagent	Substance	Form of Precipitate	
		After 15 minutes	*After 24 hours*
Mayer's reagent	*Novocaine*	Oily drops	Few prisms : still mostly oil
	Anaesthesine	Practically negative	No change
	Tutocaine	Oily drops	No change
Wagner's reagent	*Novocaine*	Oily drops	No change
	Anaesthesine	Mostly oily drops. Few rhombic crystals	All crystallized in overlapping rhomboids
	Tutocaine	Oily drops	Unchanged
Kraut's reagent	*Novocaine*	Oily drops	Unchanged
	Anaesthesine	Oily drops	Thick branching needles; some rhomboids
	Tutocaine	Oily drops	Unchanged
Marme's reagent	*Novocaine*	Oily drops	Still mostly oil : some prisms
	Anaesthesine	Negative	Very small crystals ; not characteristic
	Tutocaine	Oily drops	Unchanged
Picric acid	*Novocaine*	Oily drops	Still mostly oil : few crystals
	Anaesthesine	Long needles formed immediately	Unchanged
	Tutocaine	Oily drops	Rosettes
Mercuric chloride	*Novocaine*	Some overlapping prisms : remainder amorphous	All prismatic crystals
	Anaesthesine	Practically negative	Still negative
	Tutocaine	Oily drops	Unchanged
Gold chloride	*Novocaine*	Amorphous	Unchanged
	Anaesthesine	Oily drops	Prisms, arranged in stars
	Tutocaine	Amorphous	Unchanged

The best crystalline tests are:

For *novocaine,* mercuric chloride solution.

For *anaesthesine,* picric acid solution.

For *tutocaine,* picric acid solution.

Of the three, anaesthesine forms crystals most readily and tutocaine least readily.

Stovaine and *pantocaine* are well differentiated by means of **Mecke's reagent,** *stovaine* only yielding a sequence of colours, viz. yellow, becoming red, first at the edges, and finally reddish violet.

The microcrystalline tests given above may also be applied to stovaine and pantocaine.

Stovaine yields only oily drops with Mayer's, Wagner's, Kraut's and Marmé's reagent, and mercuric chloride; and these do not crystallize in forty-eight hours. With picric acid and gold chloride, crystals are formed almost immediately, the former being large needles and the latter flat crystals with serrated edges.

With *pantocaine*, Kraut's reagent and Marmé's reagent yield oily drops only, which do not crystallize in forty-eight hours. With Mayer's reagent, Wagner's reagent, picric acid and mercuric chloride, the precipitates are also in the form of oily drops, but partial or complete crystallization occurs on standing, thus:

With Mayer's and Wagner's reagents some long needles are formed and with mercuric chloride some small crystals of indistinct forms.

Pantocaine picrate crystallizes completely on standing in curved, branching needles.

Gold chloride yields small dark green crystals which do not change on standing.

Group Vb.

The most characteristic colour-test found for *nicotine* is with the *p*-dimethylaminobenzaldehyde reagent in sulphuric acid (40 volumes made up to 100 volumes with water). With this reagent nicotine yields a bright pink colour in the cold. The colour disappears on adding water or concentrated sulphuric acid. Therefore it is essential to use sulphuric acid of this definite concentration. No other alkaloid in this scheme behaves in this way.

With the seven microcrystal reagents mentioned above, only picric acid and gold chloride yield crystalline precipitates with nicotine.

The following colour reactions may be used as confirmatory tests for *mescaline* :

Fröhde's reagent: brown, fading to almost colourless.

Mandelin's reagent: green, quickly changing to violet, then fading to grey.

Mecke's reagent: intense greenish brown changing to brown.

When extracted from alkaline solution by means of chloroform, mescaline is obtained in a liquid state. It becomes solid on exposure to air owing to absorption of carbon dioxide.

Characteristic microcrystalline reactions can only be obtained from mescaline in concentrated solutions. The following reagents then yield well-defined crystals within fifteen minutes:

Wagner's reagent: long, curved, branching needles.

Picric acid: very long rods.

Mercuric chloride: bunches of long needles.

Gold chloride: rhombic prisms.

The precipitates with Mayer's, Kraut's and Marmé's reagents consist of oily drops. Of these only the precipitate with Kraut's reagent crystallizes on standing, forming very characteristic curved needles in star formations and some thick prisms.

Pilocarpine gives no colour with any of the sulphuric acid reagents.

The best colour test is with potassium chromate in neutral solution. A small crystal of potassium chromate and one of pilocarpine are put into 1 ml. of chloroform; a similar volume of hydrogen peroxide is added and the two liquids are well shaken together. The aqueous layer becomes dark purple in colour and the chloroform blue. The presence of free acid or alkali prevents this reaction. The test must be carefully distinguished from the ordinary perchromic acid test for chromates which is carried out in presence of sulphuric acid, with ether as the immiscible solvent.

All the above reagents yield amorphous precipitates with pilocarpine. Two of them crystallize on standing:

Mercuric chloride: closely packed rosettes of spatulate crystals.

Gold chloride: flat prisms and branching needles.

GROUP VI

This is a miscellaneous group of alkaloids all of which react with nascent chlorine to form products which are either coloured themselves or become coloured on treatment with ammonia. The test is made by dissolving a few particles of the solid substance in a drop of concentrated hydrochloric acid, adding a minute quantity of potassium chlorate and evaporating to dryness on the water-bath. The colour, if any, is noted, and then the residue is exposed to ammonia fumes or touched with a glass rod moistened with ammonia; excess of ammonia should be avoided. The following results are obtained with the alkaloids in the group :

Alkaloid	Colour of Dry Residue	Colour with Ammonia
Caffeine	Red at the edges	Purple
Quinine	Yellow at the edges	Green
Quinidine	Yellow	Green or brown
Sparteine	Colourless	Reddish purple
Emetin	Pink (red before it is completely dry)	Brown
Percaine	Yellow	Olive green

Quinine and quinidine salts of oxy-acids are strongly fluorescent in dilute solution.

The Thalleioquin Test.   This is not a specific test for *quinine* ; *quinidine* reacts in the same way, and so do certain less common cinchona derivatives, but the other alkaloids in this group do not react.   The alkaloid is dissolved in water acidified with sulphuric acid in a test-tube.   The well-known blue fluorescence is seen. Bromine water is added drop by drop until the fluorescence disappears and there is a faint odour of bromine.   Ammonia is added so as to form a separate layer on the top of the acid solution. A green zone of contact is formed in presence of quinine or quinidine. On mixing the two liquids the whole may become pink if the acid is not completely neutralized by the ammonia.   If ammonia is in excess the mixed liquid is green.   With large quantities of alkaloid, the green compound is precipitated.   The test may be modified by dividing the liquid into two equal parts after adding the bromine. To one of these a drop of potassium ferrocyanide solution is added, and then both are treated with ammonia.   The solution containing the ferrocyanide becomes pink and remains pink even with excess of ammonia.

Emetin gives the following additional colour reactions :

Fröhde's reagent: yellow, changing to green.

Mandelin's reagent: green.

Mecke's reagent: green, changing to brown; the edges slowly become red, and finally the whole liquid becomes reddish violet.

This very characteristic reaction between emetin and Mecke's reagent is only obtained with pure emetin, free from cephaelin.

The other alkaloids in this group give little or no colour with these reagents; except that quinine slowly yields faint colours with Mandelin's and Mecke's reagents, green and yellow respectively.

Sparteine is the only liquid alkaloid in the group.   The base is a colourless liquid, soluble in water; it can be extracted with ether. On exposure to air for several days the liquid base becomes brown. Its most characteristic reaction is the immediate production of almost black crystals when an ethereal solution of the base is mixed with an ethereal solution of iodine.   If excess of iodine is avoided crystals rapidly settle, leaving a colourless supernatant liquid. These crystals dissolve readily in chloroform, but are re-precipitated on adding ether to the solution.   The crystals are sometimes fern-like, and sometimes delicate curved needles in star-formations. The crystals dissolve in concentrated sulphuric acid to form a violet-coloured solution.

Emetin also yields a compound with iodine under the same conditions, but it is amorphous.   It dissolves in acetone, from which it separates in minute square crystals.   It also dissolves in concentrated sulphuric acid to form a green solution which becomes yellowish green on standing, changing sometimes to pink.

(*Nicotine*, under the same conditions, yields a resinous precipitate from which crystals may be obtained by careful treatment with alcohol. These are called Roussin's crystals: they are not easily obtained.)

Percaine is the only anaesthetic in this group ; applied to the tip of the tongue it causes numbness.

Micro-crystalline Tests

Caffeine. Except in very strong solutions caffeine forms no precipitates with Mayer's reagent, Marmé's reagent, picric acid or mercuric chloride solution. Minute crystals are obtained with Wagner's and Kraut's reagents, and masses of very fine needles with gold chloride solution.

Quinine does not easily give crystalline derivatives with these reagents.

The most striking difference between quinine and quinidine is in their reactions with gold chloride. The precipitate with quinidine crystallizes in needles, almost immediately; that with quinine remains amorphous for at least three days.

Sparteine

Reagent	After fifteen minutes	After two days
Mayer's reagent	Small crystals, not characteristic	Unchanged
Wagner's ,,	Oily drops, beginning to crystallize	Thin needles
Kraut's ,,	Practically amorphous	Unchanged
Marmé's ,,	Needles	Unchanged
Picric acid	Small crystals	Unchanged
Mercuric chloride	No visible precipitate	Very small crystals arranged in circles
Gold chloride	Clusters of small prisms	Unchanged

Emetin gives only amorphous precipitates with all the above reagents. Even after three days no characteristic crystals appear.

Percaine yields oily drops with six of the seven reagents; mercuric chloride produces very small needles closely packed together. Within two days the Kraut precipitate crystallizes in needles, and a few stars appear in the auric chloride. The other precipitates remain amorphous.

GROUP VII

This group contains the alkaloids for which, with one exception, no satisfactory colour reactions are known. It includes *cocaine*, *tropacocaine, psicaine, alypin, cinnamyl cocaine, α-eucaine, β-eucaine, aconitine, coniine, lupinine* and *arecoline*. The first seven are local anaesthetics and produce the characteristic feeling of numbness when applied to the tip of the tongue.

Aconitine causes a tingling sensation. *Arecoline* hydrochloride has merely a saline taste.

The group can be subdivided according to whether or not crystals are formed with potassium permanganate. This test is conveniently carried out by Hankin's method, in which a thin film of crystals is spread over a microscope slide by evaporating a moderately dilute solution of the permanganate on the slide with the aid of gentle heat, the solution being stroked up and down the slide meanwhile with a glass rod. A drop of half-saturated alum solution is put in the middle of the slide, and a few crystals of the alkaloid are put into the drop. The wet spot is then covered with a cover-slip.

Group VIIa.

This consists of the substances which yield crystals of characteristic form :

Cocaine : rectangular crystals, often overlapping and joined in tree-like formations.

Tropacocaine : small branching needles.

Psicaine : crystals of various forms, some being hexagonal. These are very rapidly oxidized.

Alypin : the crystals are mostly quadrilateral ; a few are hexagonal ; some ribbon-like with fish-tail ends. These are oxidized fairly quickly, but may retain their characteristic shapes.

Aconitine : short rods many of which are arranged in stars ; not rapidly oxidized.

The substances in Group VIIa can be further differentiated by their reactions with the seven precipitating reagents used in previous groups, although the permanganate crystals are the most diverse in form and therefore the most useful.

Cocaine

Reagent	After fifteen minutes	After twenty-four hours
Mayer's reagent	Very small crystals	Unchanged
Wagner's ,,	Oily drops	Mostly oily drops; some large rectangular prisms
Kraut's ,,	Oily drops and some small crystals	Unchanged
Marmé's ,,	Very small crystals	Unchanged
Picric acid	Oily drops	Completely crystallized in very long, branching needles

Reagent	After fifteen minutes	After twenty-four hours
Mercuric chloride	Oily drops	Unchanged
Gold chloride	Small branching crystals	Some needles, some octahedra and some tetrahedra (very characteristic)

Tropacocaine

Mayer's reagent	Small crystals	Needles and large rectangular prisms
Wagner's ,,	Oily drops	Completely crystallized in fine branching needles
Kraut's ,,	Oily drops and some small crystals	Plates, and small, curved, branching needles
Marmé's ,,	Small crystals	Very fine needles
Picric acid	Mostly amorphous solid precipitate	Completely crystallized in fine branching needles
Mercuric chloride	No visible precipitate	Long crystals with serrated edges
Gold chloride	Needles in star-like formations; some branching	Unchanged

Psicaine

Mayer's reagent	Practically amorphous	Mostly oil; few crystals, not well formed
Wagner's ,,	Practically amorphous	Oily drops
Kraut's ,,	Oily drops	Unchanged
Marmé's ,,	Small crystals	Prisms or rods arranged in bunches
Picric acid	Amorphous	Oily drops
Mercuric chloride	No visible precipitate	A few needles
Gold chloride	Small crystals	Unchanged

Alypin

Mayer's reagent	Small crystals	Unchanged
Wagner's ,,	Oily drops	Mostly unchanged; some long rods
Kraut's ,,	Mostly oily drops; some long needles	Mostly unchanged; some long rods
Marmé's ,,	Mostly amorphous; some long needles	Masses of fine needles
Picric acid	Oily drops beginning to crystallize	Prisms and leaf-like crystals with serrated edges

Reagent	After fifteen minutes	After twenty-four hours
Mercuric chloride	Oily drops beginning to crystallize	Prisms
Gold chloride	Oily drops; some stars	Prisms and needles, mostly in star formations

Of the four local anaesthetics in Group VIIa, only tropacocaine forms well-defined crystals with all the reagents and psicaine is the only one of which the picrate fails to crystallize on standing; while the best distinguishing tests for cocaine and alypin are with mercuric chloride, picric acid and potassium permanganate.

Aconitine

None of the above seven reagents yield characteristic crystals even on standing for twenty-four hours.

Potassium chromate solution quickly produces very fine needles in star formation.

Potassium dichromate also forms good crystals on standing, consisting of fan-like bundles of needles.

Potassium iodide, on standing, deposits long prisms with small stars (composed of short rods) attached to the prisms.

If the quantity is sufficiently large, which is not likely in poisoning cases, a portion may be distilled with concentrated sulphuric acid in a micro-apparatus and the distillate tested for acetic acid by the lanthanum test.

Since aconitine is seldom obtained pure (many of the commercial samples being very impure), identification usually depends on the physiological test, the tingling sensation produced on the tongue. The symptoms produced by injecting aconitine into frogs vary very greatly. Sometimes convulsions, quite different from those caused by strychnine, occur. In the spasms the frog may throw itself into the air, shoot out one leg at a time and bend the back legs towards the head. Another symptom which is sometimes observed is the dropping of the lower jaw, accompanied by movements as though the frog were about to vomit.[1] With other (less pure) samples of aconitine, the frog may become comatose almost at once and die without moving.

Group VIIb.

This includes the local anaesthetics not in Groups V, VI and VIIa, viz. cinnamyl cocaine, α-eucaine and β-eucaine, all of which quickly reduce permanganate. They are differentiated by their reactions with precipitating reagents which are tabulated below.

---

[1] In experiments made in our laboratory, this symptom was observed in three frogs out of six. The M.L.D. for a frog is very minute: $\frac{1}{16}$ mg. kills in less than ten minutes.

Cinnamyl Cocaine

Reagent	After fifteen minutes	After twenty-four hours
Mayer's reagent	Small crystals	Unchanged
Wagner's ,,	Amorphous solid	Still amorphous
Kraut's ,,	Amorphous solid	Still amorphous
Marmé's ,,	Amorphous solid	Still amorphous
Picric acid	Beginning to crystallize	Long needles, arranged in tufts
Mercuric chloride	Amorphous	Unchanged
Gold chloride	Amorphous	Flat prisms

α-Eucaine

Mayer's reagent	Amorphous solid or minute crystals	Short rods
Wagner's ,,	Oily drops; branching crystals beginning to form	Many fine branching crystals
Kraut's ,,	Masses of minute crystals	Partly in needles and partly in crystals shaped like fish-bones
Marmé's ,,	Masses of minute crystals	Unchanged
Picric acid	Masses of minute crystals	Mostly minute crystals ; some rhombs and long needles with serrated edges
Mercuric chloride	Small prisms	Unchanged or short rods
Gold chloride	Some branching crystals	Crystals of several forms, all branching

β-Eucaine

Mayer's reagent	Oily drops	Some long crystals with tapering ends and serrated edges. Also some small crystals
Wagner's ,,	Oily drops	Unchanged
Kraut's ,,	Oily drops	Unchanged
Marmé's ,,	Oily drops	Unchanged
Picric acid	Curved needles arranged in stars (Excellent)	Unchanged
Mercuric chloride	No precipitate	
Gold chloride	Rods and needles	Overlapping prisms and thin needles

Group VIIc.

This sub-group consists of the alkaloids *coniine, lupinine* and *arecoline.* They are all volatile in steam. Coniine when heated with water has a distinct odour, resembling that of the urine of mice. Lupinine under the same conditions is said to have a fruity odour, but this is almost imperceptible. Arecoline is odourless.

All the bases are liquid when first extracted, but lupinine quickly solidifies. The solid can be recrystallized from ether to form feathery crystals melting at 67°–68° C.

The best test for *coniine* is that of Klein and Herndlhofer. The reagent is a 1 per cent. solution of chloranil[1] in benzene. A small quantity of coniine base is dissolved in a few drops of benzene and mixed with an equal volume of the reagent. The liquid becomes green and on evaporation green crystals separate. These become blue on exposure to air for a few minutes. If a few drops of ether are added to the blue substance, part of it dissolves to form a violet solution leaving a bright green residue.

Lupinine with the same reagent forms an olive-green solution. The residue after evaporation (whether this be rapid or slow) is amorphous and the colour is olive-green to brown.

Chloranil is not a sensitive reagent for *arecoline :* no change in colour is observed on mixing benzene solutions of the base and the reagent; but on evaporating to dryness a reddish brown rim is seen on the edge of the residue.

These three alkaloids do not form many crystalline precipitates with the usual reagents.

Coniine forms oily drops with Mayer's reagent, Wagner's reagent and Kraut's reagent, which do not crystallize within two days. The picrate, the aurichloride and the mercurichloride are only precipitated from strong solutions (compare nicotine, which is precipitated quantitatively by picric acid). Marmé's reagent yields characteristic clusters of flat crystals with rounded edges.

Lupinine differs from coniine in forming crystals with Kraut's reagent on standing (flat crystals with serrated edges, and some square plates); with Marmé's reagent it forms oily drops which do not crystallize, and with gold chloride, cubes and rectangular prisms.

Arecoline forms only amorphous precipitates in capillary tubes, except that the aurichloride on standing for several days crystallizes in hexagonal prisms and tetrahedra. The precipitate with Kraut's reagent can be made to crystallize in presence of excess of acid on a microscope slide by warming and scratching with a glass rod, the crystals being rhomboidal plates.

---

[1] This is easily prepared by warming phenol in hydrochloric acid and gradually adding excess of potassium chlorate. Yellow crystals separate. These are filtered off and washed with much water and afterwards with a little alcohol.

CHAPTER XI

MISCELLANEOUS POISONS

TOXALBUMINS

THESE exist in certain seeds. Some of these which also contain purgative oils have already been partially dealt with.

The symptoms produced by toxalbumins show some general resemblance to those of bacterial toxins: there may be a rise of temperature followed by a fall, albuminuria, and sometimes convulsions.

The following observations have been made at post-mortem examinations: agglutination of the erythrocytes accompanied by some haemolysis and cell-destruction; punctiform haemorrhages on serous surfaces; general enlargement of lymphatic glands; prominent Peyer's patches; dark and enlarged spleen.[1]

The chief sources of toxalbumins are the seeds of *Croton tiglium*, *Ricinus communis* (castor oil plant), *Abrus precatorius* (jequirity seeds), *Jatropha curcas* (physic nut).

The toxalbumins are called, respectively, crotin, ricin, abrin and curcin.

Abrus seeds are very characteristic in appearance. They are oval in shape, the major axis being about 6 or 7 mm. and the minor axis about 4 mm. The surface is very bright red except for a black cap at one end of the seed.

The seeds contain a powerfully irritant juice which is the active principle of a cattle-poison used in India.[2] The powdered seeds, either alone or mixed with datuar, opium or even onions, are made into a paste with alcohol and fashioned into spikes called " suis " which are then hardened by drying in the sun. The spikes, weighing 10–12 c.gm., are fitted into handles and forced through the skin of animals. The spikes are less toxic than freshly powdered seeds. A spike weighing 12 c.gm., rubbed with water and injected into a chicken causes death in about thirty-six hours, whereas 3 c.gm. of freshly powdered seeds kills a similar chicken in about eighteen hours.[3]

By powdering the seeds and rubbing with cold water a suspension is obtained which causes vomiting and diarrhoea; it can be made

[1] Byam and Archibald's " Tropical Diseases ". Article by Colles. Vol. 1, p. 815. Article by Scott, *ibid.*, p. 764.
[2] COLLES. *Loc. cit.* MODI. " Text-book of Medical Jurisprudence and Toxicology ", p. 638.
[3] MODI. *Op. cit.*

non-toxic by boiling. If the liquid obtained by rubbing the decorticated seeds with water is instilled into the eye it causes purulent ophthalmia which may lead to fatal results. Colles[1] recommends a preliminary test for abrin in which the substance, in 1 per cent. saline solution, is dropped into the eye of a frog; it causes conjunctivitis which is easily seen.

The seeds of croton, castor, jequirity and jatropha have been studied in Madras.[2]

The seeds are cleared by warming with hot 5 per cent. potassium chlorate solution, mixed with dilute nitric acid, on the boiling water-bath until the colour is bleached and the tissues are softened. The following details are given of the microscopic features of the seeds.

(i) Cross-section at the top.

All the seeds have polygonal cells of which the diameters are, in castor, croton and jatropha seeds 17μ; in jequirity seeds 9μ.

Lumen: castor, almost circular; jatropha, slit-like; croton and jequirity, slit-like with radiating creases.

(ii) Side view.

(a) Length of cells
$\left\{\begin{array}{l}\text{jequirity seeds, about } 160\mu \\ \text{castor seeds,} \quad\text{''} \quad 250\mu \\ \text{croton seeds,} \quad\text{''} \quad 300\mu \\ \text{jatropha seeds,} \quad\text{''} \quad 400\mu\end{array}\right.$

(b) Width of cells
$\left\{\begin{array}{l}\text{castor and croton, tapering from } 17\mu \text{ to } 8\mu \\ \text{jatropha, tapering from } 17\mu \text{ to } 12\mu \\ \text{jequirity (not tapering), about } 9\mu\end{array}\right.$

(c) Lumen
$\left\{\begin{array}{l}\text{castor, } 3\mu \text{ in diameter}. \\ \text{croton, } 1\mu \text{ in diameter} \\ \text{jatropha, } 1\mu \text{ to } 6\mu \text{ in diameter} \\ \text{jequirity, } 1\mu \text{ to } 3\mu \text{ in diameter}\end{array}\right.$

(d) Cell-walls
a ribbed appearance due to transverse striae is seen in the cell-walls of castor and jatropha seeds, not in the others.

As the toxalbumins are not dialyzable they are best isolated by dialysis. The material (seeds or stomach-contents) is extracted with dilute sodium chloride solution; the extract is saturated with magnesium sulphate and transferred to the inner compartment of a dialyzer. The outer water is renewed from time to time during the day and the process is allowed to continue overnight. The contents of the inner compartment are then tested, using the agglutination test, and a portion is injected into a frog.

[1] COLLES. (Byam and Archibald.) *Loc. cit.*
[2] Report for the year 1937. Abstract in *Analyst*, 1939, **64**, 120.

The Agglutination Test. A sample of freshly drawn blood is diluted to about 100 times its volume with normal saline (0·9 per cent. NaCl). A drop of this diluted blood is placed on a microscope slide, a drop of the test solution (also in normal saline) is added, and the two are thoroughly mixed with a glass rod or by rocking the slide. After five minutes the cells are examined under the low power microscope. Normally they remain separate and more or less evenly distributed; agglutination has occurred if they form clumps or aggregates. The examination should be repeated, if there is no agglutination, after a further five minutes, and so on to a total of twenty minutes. A negative result can then be taken as indicating the absence of agglutinins. To prevent evaporation, the slide may be covered by a Petri dish and alongside it may be placed a small piece of wet cotton wool or filter paper.

Inoue,[1] working on ricin, concluded that agglutination only occurs when the hydrogen-ion concentration of the extract is either between pH 5·6 and 5·8 or between pH 8·9 and 9·1.

The Precipitin Test. By repeated injections, animals can be immunized to the individual toxalbumins. Specific antibodies are produced, so that the animal's serum gives a precipitin reaction with the particular toxalbumin used.

Rabbits are generally used for the preparation of antisera. Various methods are described with differences in detail. Active antisera are usually produced by daily intravenous injection, for three weeks, of 0·5 cc. of the protein solution which is being used as the antigen. Alternatively, 3 cc. of the protein solution may be given intravenously at intervals of three days to a total of four injections, and followed by three intraperitoneal injections, each of 10 cc., at intervals of five days. In either case, the serum is then tested and if not sufficiently active, the injections are continued for a longer period.

For preparation of the serum, the animal is bled after a 24-hours fast, the blood is allowed to clot in a refrigerator at about 4° C. and the serum is pipetted off into sterile 1 cc. ampoules which are at once sealed. All operations must be done aseptically. The serum, which must be clear when used, is best stored, frozen solid, in a refrigerator. An antiserum may be considered satisfactory if 0·1 cc.:

(*a*) gives no precipitate when added to 0·9 cc. of normal (physiological) saline,

(*b*) gives a turbidity within five minutes and a definite precipitate within an hour when added to 0·9 cc. of 0·1 per cent. neutral solution of the antigen.

(*c*) gives no precipitate with other protein solutions of similar concentration.

[1] *J. Soc. Chem. Ind. Japan*, 1937, **40**, 122–3 B. *Analyst*, 1937, **62**, 565–6.

For the actual test, measure 0·9 cc. of the suspected protein solution (which must be neutral to litmus) into a small test-tube of quarter-inch diameter and a similar quantity of the diluted protein solution (e.g. 1 : 10, 1 : 100) into other similar tubes. As " controls " have one tube containing 0·9 cc. saline and others containing 0·9 cc. of various protein solutions (neutral). To each tube add 0·1 cc. of the antiserum, mix, and observe against a dark background. It is ideal to have the tubes illuminated evenly from below. A positive result is obtained when precipitation occurs only in the tubes which may contain the antigen to the serum used (or only in the more concentrated of these); opalescence in all the tubes invalidates the test.

POISONOUS PLANTS

The following is a list of plants reputed to be poisonous, the majority of which have been very incompletely studied, or not studied at all from the point of view of chemical toxicology. It is compiled mainly from Bernhard Smith's " Poisonous Plants of all Countries ".

(1) The Spurge family, *Euphorbiaceae*; these are all supposed to contain euphorbium resin (see p. 204).

BOTANICAL NAME	COMMON NAMES
E. resinifera	Dark mons.
E. peplus	Purple spurge. Hyssop spurge. Petty spurge.
E. pilosa	Downy spurge. Hairy spurge.
E. helioscopia	Sun spurge. Churn spurge. Little goody. Wart grass. Wart wort.
E. Hiberna	Irish spurge. Makinboy.
E. Portlandia	Portland spurge.
E. paralias	Sea spurge.
E. lathyris	Caper spurge. Caper bush. Mole plant. Myrtle spurge.
E. Amygdaloides	Wood spurge.

The following, also euphorbiaceae, contain oil of euphorbia and other active principles:

Boxus sempervirens	Common box; contains buxine.
Mercurialis perennis	Dog's mercury. Herb mercury. Wild spinach. Kentish balsam; contains mercurialine and choline.

(2) The members of the daphne family, *Thymelaceae*, contain as active principles mezerein and mezerinic acid, chiefly in the fruits. They are intensely poisonous, the symptoms being colic and constipation followed by dysentery. Post-mortem examinations

have revealed inflammation of the stomach and intestines. Death has been known to follow the swallowing of twelve berries of the spurge laurel, but it has been stated that the supposed active principles, after extraction from the plants, are much less toxic than the fruits themselves.

BOTANICAL NAME	COMMON NAMES
Daphne laureola	Spurge laurel. Copse laurel. Wood laurel. Dwarf bay.
D. mezereum	Common mezereon. Spurge flax. Spurge olive.
D. Gnidum	Spurge flax. Flax-leaved daphne.

(3) The narcissus family, or *Amaryllidaceae*, contain the toxic alkaloid narcissine. The following are some of the varieties:

BOTANICAL NAME	COMMON NAMES
Narcissus Moschatus	Musk-scented daffodil.
N. Poeticus	Poet's daffodil. Whitsun lily.
N. Johnstonii	Queen of Spain.
N. pseudo narcissus	Common double daffodil.
Galanthus nivalis	Common snowdrop.

(4) The buttercup family, *Ranunculaceae*. Among the toxic substances found in varieties of this family are (*a*) the acrid juice of *Ranunculaceae* which contains a volatile oil and a saponin-like substance, ficaric acid, (*b*) oil of anemone which is volatile in steam and soluble in chloroform (it has vesicant properties; the chloroform extract from the steam distillate yields a blood-red colour when treated with sodium nitro-prusside and caustic soda), (*c*) clematin, a purgative, irritant and vesicant substance resembling anemonin.

Some of the commoner varieties are the following:

BOTANICAL NAME	COMMON NAMES
Clematis vitalba	Traveller's joy. Bindwith. Biting clematis. Hedge vine. Lady's bower. Old man's beard. Smokewood.
C. rubro violaceae	Purple clematis.
C. hybrides	Large-flowered clematis. Jackman's clematis.
Anemone nemorosa	Wood anemone. Windflower.
A. appennina	Blue anemone. Apennine wind-flower.
A. coronaria	Poppy anemone. Poppy wind-flower. Common garden anemone.
Ranunculus flammula	Small spear-wort.
R. auricormus	Wood crowfoot. Goldilocks.
R. ficaria	Lesser celandine. Crowfoot. Marsh pile-wort.

BOTANICAL NAME	COMMON NAMES
R. sceleratus	Celery-leaved crowfoot.
R. acris	Buttercup. Blister-plant. Crowflower. Yellow gowan.
R. bulbosus	Bulbous crowfoot. St. Anthony's turnip.
R. asiaticus	Garden ranunculus. Turban ranunculus.
Peonia officinalis	Garden peony.
Aquilegia vulgaris	Columbine.

(5) The lily family, *Liliaceae*. Many of the plants in this family contain a toxic acid juice, e.g. *Hyacinthus non-scriptus* or *Scilla nutans*, the common English bluebell.

Others contain glycosides, e.g. *Fritillaria Meleagris*, snake's head, chequered lily or chequered daffodil. The glycoside of this plant has been called imperialine.

(6) The sumach family, *Anacardiaceae*, contains the plants, common in America, of which the toxic principle is toxicodendrol, viz. *Rhus toxicodendron*, poison ivy or trailing poison oak; and *R. venata*, poison elder, poison ash, poison sumach. Toxicodendrol is probably a mixture of polyhydric alcohols. It is insoluble in water, but soluble in ether and chloroform. It is a powerful irritant and vesicant.

(7) The iris family, *Irideae*. Most of the iris or flag family contain the toxic, purgative glycoside, iridin, which is supposed to be especially dangerous to pigs. The following are some of the varieties:

BOTANICAL NAME	COMMON NAMES
Iris pseudacorus	Yellow iris. Yellow flag. Fleur de Luce. Jacob's sword. Water flag.
I. foetidissima	Stinking iris. Stinking Gladwin. Roast beef plant.
I. florentina	Florentine iris. Orris root plant.
I. variegata	Variegated iris.
I. amaena	Delicately tinted iris.
I. neglecta	German flag iris. Broad-leaved iris.
I. reticulata	Early bulbous iris.

(8) Poppy family, *Papaveraceae*. One of the commonest of the poppy family in England (apart from the common poppy) is *Chelidonium majus*, the greater celandine, which contains a poisonous juice; it is nauseous and irritant, but it also contains the toxic principle chelidonine, which resembles morphine in its pharmacological properties.

Another is *Glaucinum luteum*, the yellow horned poppy, or sea poppy, which contains the toxic principles glaucine and chelerythrine.

(9) The following are some miscellaneous poisonous plants belonging to different natural orders:

Natural Order	Botanical Name	Common Names	Toxic Principle
Compositae.	Anacyclus pyrethrum.	Pellitory, Alexander's foot. Bertram Lungwort.	Inulin.[1]
Compositae.	Arnica montana.	Medicinal leopard's bane. Mountain tobacco. Mountain alkanet.	Arnicin.
Boraginaceae.	Cyanoglossum officinale.	Hound's tongue. Common dog's tongue. Gipsy flower.	Oil of hound's tongue. Consolidine. Cyanoglossine.
Dioscoreaceae.	Tamus communis.	Black bryony. Isle of Wight vine. Ladies' seal. Oxberry.	Acrid juice.
Cucurbitaceae.	Bryonia dioica.	Red-berried bryony. Common white bryony. White wild vine. Wild hop.	Bryonin (a glycoside; a drastic purge).
Celastrineae.	Euonymus euopoeus.	Common spindle-tree. Skewer-wood. Dog wood. Cat wood. Louse-berry tree.	Euonymin (a purgative glycoside).
Oleaceae.	Ligustrum vulgare.	Common privet.	Ligustrin, Syringin (said to have caused the death of horses).
Umbelliferae.	Oenanthe crocata.	Water Dropwort.	Oenanthotoxin[2] $C_{18}H_{22}O_4$

POISONOUS FUNGI

Of the many hundreds of varieties of mushrooms that are known, the majority are harmless if not valuable foods, but there are at least eighty varieties known to be poisonous. Only a few of these have been adequately investigated chemically, and the identification should, in general, be left to the expert mycologist. Reference can only be made here to one or two of the commonest.

Fly Agaric, *Amanita muscaria*, has already been mentioned as the source of the alkaloid muscarine, and its abuse will be discussed in the chapter on Drugs of Addiction. It consists of a cap or pileus with a brilliantly coloured upper surface (yellow, orange or red) and light-coloured gills, and a stem. The upper surface is spotted with wart-like excrescences which can be scraped off. The stem is hollow, and bloated at the base; it is surrounded by a fragile annulus. This fungus has been responsible for a large proportion of the cases of mushroom poisoning, but the rate of mortality is low. The symptoms of poisoning are: increased secretions, vomiting, diarrhoea, slow pulse, rapid breathing, mucus

[1] Pure inulin, a polysaccharide of fructose, is non-toxic.
[2] *J. Pharm. Pharmacol.*, 1949, 1, 368.

in the bronchi, giddiness, hallucinations and contracted pupils. Patients usually sleep for several hours and recover. Since there have been very few fatalities, little is known of post-mortem lesions; ulcers in the mucous membrane of the stomach have been described.[1]

A fungus which has caused many more deaths than fly agaric is known under many names: *Amanita phalloides, A. Bubosa, A. Viridis, A. Mappa, A. Virosa* and *A. Venenosa*.[2] The common name is death cup. It grows on a stalk 4–6 in. high and $\frac{1}{2}$–$\frac{3}{4}$ in. thick. The pileus is 3-4 in. in diameter. White spores are found on the gills. The stalk, like that of fly agaric, is surrounded by a filmy annulus.

The symptoms of phalloides poisoning are those of a violent irritant: vomiting, diarrhoea and severe abdominal pain; blood in both vomit and stools; rapid loss of strength; jaundice and cyanosis. After the fungus has been eaten the onset of symptoms may be delayed for as long as fifteen hours and death may occur at any time between two and eight days afterwards. The rate of mortality is very high.

The post-mortem lesions are similar to those of phosphorus poisoning, fatty degeneration of the liver being common. Death appears to be due to cell-destruction in the internal organs.

The identity of the active principle is in doubt. An aqueous or saline extract of the fungus has a powerful haemolytic action, but this is destroyed by boiling. On the other hand the toxicity of the whole fungus is not perceptibly reduced by cooking, therefore the soluble haemolytic agent cannot be the chief toxic constituent.

Abel and Ford[3] described a method for the isolation of the haemolytic principle, which has been called *A. haemolysin*, by adding methyl alcohol to the aqueous extract; the haemolytic constituent is precipitated while the heat-resistant poison (amanita-toxin) remains in solution. The precipitate was found to contain a glycoside which could be hydrolyzed to yield a pentose and a nitrogenous, sugar-free fraction.

Amanitatoxin is not glycosidal, nor (in spite of the fact that it can be precipitated by phosphotungstic acid) is it alkaloidal. Schlesinger and Ford[4] came to the conclusion that it was either an indol derivative or a substance which could be readily converted into either an indol or a pyrrol derivative. A solution of amanita-toxin, injected into animals, produces the characteristic lesions of *A. phalloides* poisoning.

No chemical methods of identifying these toxic principles are known. The contents of the alimentary organs must be searched for fragments of the fungus.

[1] PETERSON, HAINES and WEBSTER. "Legal Medicine and Toxicology". Vol. 2.
[2] PETERSON, HAINES and WEBSTER. *Loc. cit.*
[3] *J. Biol. Chem.*, 1907, **2**, 273. Schmiedeberg Festschr., 1908.
[4] *J. Biol. Chem.*, 1907, **3**, 279.

THE SULPHONAMIDE DRUGS

Although, in the beginning, sulphonamide therapy was used only for the destruction of streptococci and staphylococci, its applications have been greatly extended, and as new compounds are being synthesized the field is growing still larger.

The true sulphonamide (or more properly sulphanilamide) drugs are derivatives of p-sulphanilic acid amide, $H_2N.C_6H_4.SO_2NH_2$ (prontosil album). There are two main series—one in which the primary amino group is substituted yielding a compound which may or may not be an amine according to the substituting radicle, and one in which a substituting group replaces one of the hydrogens of the sulphonamide group to yield a compound which is still a primary amine.

In addition to these derivatives of sulphanilic acid, derivatives of $4 \cdot 4$-diamino-diphenyl-sulphone, $H_2N.C_6H_4.SO_2.C_6H_4.NH_2$ are employed in medicine as bacteriostatic or bactericidal agents, as are various related substances such as p-aminomethyl-phenyl-sulphonamide (Marfanil), $H_2N.CH_2.C_6H_4.SO_2NH_2$.

The following table gives the structure and names of the commoner sulphonamide drugs:

Sulphonamides

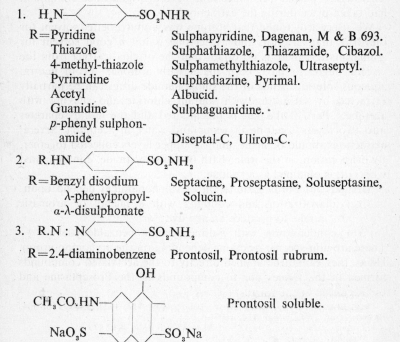

1. $H_2N-\langle\quad\rangle-SO_2NHR$

R = Pyridine	Sulphapyridine, Dagenan, M & B 693.
Thiazole	Sulphathiazole, Thiazamide, Cibazol.
4-methyl-thiazole	Sulphamethylthiazole, Ultraseptyl.
Pyrimidine	Sulphadiazine, Pyrimal.
Acetyl	Albucid.
Guanidine	Sulphaguanidine.
p-phenyl sulphon-amide	Diseptal-C, Uliron-C.

2. $R.HN-\langle\quad\rangle-SO_2NH_2$

R = Benzyl disodium
    λ-phenylpropyl-
    α-λ-disulphonate

Septacine, Proseptasine, Soluseptasine, Solucin.

3. $R.N : N\langle\quad\rangle-SO_2NH_2$

R = 2.4-diaminobenzene   Prontosil, Prontosil rubrum.

OH

$CH_3CO.HN-$

NaO_3S- $-SO_3Na$

Prontosil soluble.

Mild toxic symptoms are not uncommon after administration of sulphonamides—dizziness, headache, nausea, diarrhoea, pyrexia, cyanosis, skin rash, etc. More dangerous effects are seen in an appreciable number of cases; deaths attributable to the drugs have been reported. The more serious toxic actions of the sulphonamides are on the skin and, more importantly, the bone marrow and blood. Acute haemolytic anaemia ending fatally has been described.[1] Severe neutropenia, sometimes resulting in a fatal agranulocytosis, has been reported more often.[2]

In the notorious affair in Oklahoma in which seventy-three people died after treatment with " elixir of sulphanilamide ", death was attributed to the solvent used, diethylene glycol.[3] The dosage was 3 teaspoonfuls every four hours for one or two days.

Sulphonamide compounds are partially excreted in the urine, and of this excreted portion part may be in the form of acetyl derivatives.[4]

In the one case we investigated in which the death of a child followed the administration of Prontosil rubrum, the intestines and kidneys were stained red by the drug; nevertheless, we were only able to isolate traces of the unchanged colouring matter by the Stas-Otto process. An arylamino compound was isolated and recognized by diazotization and coupling with β-naphthol.

Evidently partial decomposition of the original azo-compound had taken place during the extraction process.

We afterwards found that acetone was a much better solvent for the drug than alcohol, and as acetone is not a good solvent for animal matter, there is no doubt that the original extract from the viscera ought to have been made with acetone. From neutral aqueous solutions some of the sulphonamide drugs can be partially extracted by saturating with sodium chloride and shaking with acetone. Part of the salt is precipitated and the liquid separates into two layers, acetone in water and water in acetone. Several extractions should be made, and the upper layers collected together. By evaporation on the water-bath the sulphonamide, contaminated with salt, is obtained as a residue.

Methods for the determination of sulphonamides depend upon:
    (a)   diazotization and coupling with a phenol or aromatic amine to produce an azo dye; or
    (b)   condensation with p-dimethylaminobenzaldehyde.

These are non-specific reactions depending on the arylamino group. Hence they cannot be applied directly to the acetylated compounds formed in the tissues nor to compounds of the Proseptasine and

[1] e.g. WOOD. *South. Med. J.*, 1938, **31**, 646.
[2] e.g. LONG *et al.* *J. Amer. Med. Assoc.*, 1939, **112**, 115; 1940, **115**, 364. BROWN *et al.* *Ibid.*, 1940, **114**, 1605.
[3] *J. Amer. Med. Ass.*, 6.11.37 and 20.11.37. *B.M.J.*, 4.12.37.
[4] WERNER. *Lancet*, 1939, *i*, 18–20.

Soluseptasine type. The acetyl derivatives and Soluseptasine are readily hydrolyzed by boiling with dilute hydrochloric acid for thirty minutes. Proseptasine, however, is very stable to chemical hydrolysis but is partially decomposed to sulphanilamide in the body, and this substance may be detected in the urine.

Identification of the sulphonamides must depend on their isolation —often a difficult process—and examination of physical properties. Hucknall and Turfitt[1] have evolved a systematic procedure on this basis. The crude material is purified by treatment with activated charcoal in acetone, and the presence of sulphonamide is demonstrated by production of ammonia, aniline, sulphite (and in some cases sulphide) on heating with soda-lime. The presence of a primary amino group is detected by the red colour given with furfuraldehyde in acetic acid, and final identification is made by means of crystalline form and mixed melting point. Mixtures are separated by taking advantage of differing solubilities.

Generally, however, the history of the case, combined with the results of the non-specific diazotization and condensation reactions suffice to establish (or, more usually, to confirm) the nature of the poison. Urine and blood form the most useful material for analysis.

Werner's Method. Add 1 ml. of blood to 4 ml. of 5 per cent. trichloracetic acid solution, mix, allow to stand for 10 minutes and filter. Measure 2 ml. of the filtrate, add $1 \cdot 5$ ml. of $0 \cdot 25$ N.NaOH to neutralize the acid, and $0 \cdot 5$ ml. of a solution of 3 g. dimethylaminobenzaldehyde in 100 ml. of 7 per cent. (w/v) sulphuric acid. Compare the yellow colour, which develops immediately, with that produced in standard solutions of the sulphonamide similarly treated.

For urine, dilute until the amount of sulphonamide present is from $0 \cdot 5$ to $1 \cdot 5$ mg. per 100 ml. Add 1 ml. of the dimethylaminobenzaldehyde reagent to 9 ml. of this diluted urine. Compare with standards.

These methods give "free" sulphonamide. To include the acetylated derivative, treat the measured 2 ml. of blood filtrate in a boiling water bath for 30 minutes, cool, and proceed; heat 1 ml. of urine with 2 ml. of N.HCl similarly, add 2ml. of N. NaOH, dilute and proceed as before.

An appreciable colour is given by $0 \cdot 2$ mg. sulphanilamide in 100 ml. solution. High concentrations give an orange precipitate.

Marshall's Method (modified) depends on the production of an azo dye by diazotizing and coupling with a suitable amine. It can be used for whole blood, plasma, cerebrospinal fluid, urine, etc. Blood should be well oxalated and free from clots, which adsorb the sulphonamides.

[1] *J. Pharm. Pharmacol.* 1949, **1**, 368.

REAGENTS: *p*-toluene sulphonic acid, 16·7 per cent. (w/v).

sodium nitrite, 0·1 per cent. (w/v) made fresh every fortnight.

urea, 0·5 g. urea and 6·9 g. sodium dihydrogen phosphate in 100 ml. distilled water.

dimethyl-α-naphthylamine, 0·4 g. in 100 ml. of 97 per cent. alcohol.

standard solution: prepared by dilution from a stock solution containing 20 mg. of the appropriate sulphonamide per 100 ml. dissolved with the aid of sodium hydroxide.

(It is possible to use a single standard of, say, sulphapyridine, using the appropriate factor for the determination of other members of the group. With a sulphapyridine standard the factors are: sulphanilamide 0·68, sulphathiazole 1·04, sulphamethylthiazole 1·11, sulphadiazine 1·0.)

Lake 2 ml. of blood with an equal volume of water in a 25 ml. graduated flask, add 4 ml. of the toluene-sulphonic acid solution, mix, make up to the mark with water, stand five minutes and filter. Similar quantities of plasma or C.S.F. are treated similarly except that there is, of course, no laking. Urine is best diluted to give a solution containing about 5 mg. sulphonamide per 100 ml. and then treated as plasma. (The colour with urine is, however, less satisfactory than with blood.)

To determine " total " sulphonamide, heat 10 ml. of the filtrate on the boiling water-bath for an hour, cool, and make up to the original volume before proceeding further. For " free " sulphonamide, to 10 ml. of filtrate (unboiled), add 1 ml. of the nitrite solution, mix and stand three minutes. Add 1 ml. of the buffered urea solution to destroy excess nitrite and, after standing three minutes, add 5 ml. of the dimethyl-α-naphthylamine. Compare the colour with that of a standard similarly treated.

OTHER SYNTHETIC DRUGS

It is impossible, in a book of this character, to describe the identification in biological material of the host of synthetic therapeutic agents which, because of accidental or purposeful over dosage, may produce more or less toxic effects. The large and growing group of antihistaminics, and the morphine substitutes do, however, merit brief mention.

Antihistaminic Drugs

The antihistaminic drugs are synthetic substances which block most of the physiological actions of histamine (possibly by competing for the same receptor sites in sensitized cells) and are widely employed as palliatives in aiding the allergic patient. Many hundreds have been synthesized, but insufficient activity or excessive toxicity have eliminated most of these and only about a dozen are in common use. Most of them have one or other of the general formulae :

(1) $R-O-CH_2 \cdot CH_2 \cdot N\langle^{R''}_{R'''}$ (e.g. Decapryn, Benadryl)

(2) $^{R}_{R'}\rangle N-CH_2 \cdot CH_2 \cdot N\langle^{R''}_{R'''}$ (e.g. Antergan, Neoantergan, Diatrin, Pyribenzamine, Histadyl)

(3) $^{R}_{R'}\rangle CH-CH_2 \cdot CH_2 \cdot N\langle^{R''}_{R'''}$ (e.g. Trimeton).

in which R'' and R''' are usually methyl groups, whilst R and R' may be phenyl, benzyl, pyridyl, thenyl, etc., or substituted derivatives of these cyclic radicles. In some members of group (2), R and R' form a single heterocyclic ring system as in Phenergan ; in others the dimethylaminoethyl side chain is replaced by a cyclic derivative (e.g. Antistin, Histantin).

The compounds are nitrogenous and some, at least, form well-defined salts. They can be extracted from alkaline solution by various organic solvents such as ether and benzene. Perlman[1] working with Pyribenzamine found that although the drug, given orally, appeared to be completely absorbed from the alimentary tract, only about 10 per cent. appeared in the urine. This was excreted in 8-10 hours, the most rapid excretion being $1\frac{1}{2}$-$4\frac{1}{2}$ hours after ingestion. It was wholly or nearly wholly in combination with some unknown substance from which it was liberated by hydrolysis with alkali. The very small recoveries reported by other authors suggest that this may be true of other antihistaminic drugs and that Perlman's method of isolation may be useful generally. Little is known of the metabolism of these drugs, or of their persistence in the tissues. However, urine is likely to be the usual source in which their detection is required.

Perlman found that those drugs containing a pyridine nuclear nitrogen (e.g. Thenylene, Pyribenzamine, Neoantergan) developed a blue fluorescence when treated with cyanogen bromide in aqueous solution. Others containing pyridine without the additional nitrogen atom give a colour but no fluorescence (Decapryn succinate, pink ; Trimeton maleate, yellow ; Phenergan, pink). His method of isolation and of estimating these substances on the basis of the cyanogen bromide test, was as follows. 5 cc. of the subject's urine was placed in a glass stoppered 15 cc. centrifuge tube and made alkaline with $0 \cdot 5$ cc. of a 10 per cent. solution of NaOH. The tube containing the alkaline urine was placed in a boiling water bath

[1] *J. Pharmacol. Exp. Ther.*, 1949, **95**, 465.

for twenty minutes, after which it was quickly cooled. Five cc. of benzene was then added and the tube stoppered and shaken vigorously twenty-five times. Four cc. of the upper benzene layer was then transferred to another tube of the same type. This benzene solution was then shaken with 1 cc. of N/2 HCl. The lower aqueous layer was removed as completely as possible with a glass capillary and was transferred to a 15 cc. graduated test tube. The benzene solution was extracted a second time with 1 cc. of N/20 HCl and this was transferred in the same manner to the graduated test tube. The contents of the latter were then neutralized with N/1 NaOH and the volume made up to 5 cc. by the addition of sufficient M/15 phosphate buffer of pH 6·6. To this was added 2 cc. of a freshly prepared saturated solution of CNBr. After half an hour the contents were transferred to the specially selected fluorophotometer tubes and the fluorescence measured.

Dubost[1] has determined Antergan in urine and in blood deproteinized by trichloracetic acid) by means of a green colour given by its nitroso derivative with resorcinol. The substance is extracted with ether from weakly alkaline fluid, shaken out from the extract into 0·1N hydrochloric acid and treated with a little 1 per cent. resorcinol followed by aqueous sodium nitrite. In the case of urine an interfering yellow colour is eliminated by use of a red filter. Standard solutions for comparison are made in normal urine of the same colour as the test sample. The method has been developed further, for use with a Step-photometer, by Ehrlen.[2]

Crystallographic data have been reported for salts of various antihistaminic drugs with aurochloride,[2] chloroplatinic acid, etc.[3] Ehlén (*loc. cit.*) and Haley (*loc. cit.*) also describe colour reactions with various alkaloidal reagents. It is not yet possible, however, to give a systematic scheme of identification covering all of even the commoner drugs of this class.

Ultra-violet absorption spectrophotometry offers useful possibilities. This has been used by Perlman (*loc. cit.*) and in the Editor's laboratory Histantin, isolated from urine and stomach contents by alkalinization and ether extraction, has been identified and roughly determined in this way.

Synthetic Morphine Substitutes

The first successful synthetic substitute for morphine seems to have been ethyl-1-methyl-4-phenyl-piperidine-4-carboxylate hydrochloride, which was reported by Eisleb and Schaumann[4] in 1939 to

---

[1] *Ann. Pharm. Franc.*, 1943, **1**, 145.
[2] Ehlen. *Coll. Pharm. Suec.*, 1946, **1**, No. 7.
[3] Haley, *J. Amer. Pharm. Assoc.*, 1948, **37**, 2, 94. Haley and Keenan, *ibid.*, 1949, **38**, 85, 381. Keenan, *ibid.*, 1947, **36**, 281.
[4] *Deut. med. Woch.*, 1939, **65**, 967.

have effects similar to those of morphine and atropine. This substance, also known as *Demerol*, *Dolantin*, *Isonipecaine*, or *Meperidine*, appears in the British Pharmaceopoeia as *Pethidine*. Of the many compounds since prepared, *Amidone* (known also as *Dolophine*, *Methadone* or *Physeptone*) is outstanding ; it is 4·4-diphenyl-6-dimethylamino-heptanone hydrochloride.

Pethidine itself is soluble in water, sparingly soluble in ether, and more soluble in chloroform ; hence it may be at least partially extracted with non-basic poisons in the Stas-Otto process. The free base, however, is more readily soluble. The hydrochloride melts sharply at 187-189° C., and the picrate, precipitated from a solution of the hydrochloride on addition of picric acid, forms yellow needles which melt at 189-190° C. Potassium mercuric iodide, added to an aqueous solution of pethidine, gives a creamy yellow precipitate ; sodium hydroxide precipitates the nearly insoluble free base as an oil which slowly solidifies on scratching with a glass rod.

Way, Swanson and Gimble[1] describe a method of determining pethidine in blood or tissues and state that liver, in particular, destroys the substance. This doubtless accounts, at least in part, for the finding of Lehmann and Aitken[2] that of an ingested dose of pethidine, only 5 to 20 per cent. could be recovered in urine collected over a period of twenty-four hours.

Method of Determination. The tissue (1 g.), finely minced in a Waring blendor with 10-20 cc. of 0·1 M sodium phosphate solution of pH 7·5,[3] and 1·0 cc. of N.NaOH, is thoroughly shaken in a mechanical shaker with ten times its volume of ethylene dichloride. The layers are separated by centrifuging, the upper aqueous layer is removed and the ethylene dichloride layer (containing the pethidine) is washed with half its volume of M/1 phosphate buffer solution of pH 7·0. The ethylene dichloride layer, or a suitable aliquot, e.g. 10 cc., is then used for the determination, based upon the most useful observation (applied, e.g. by Brodie, Udenfriend and Dill[4] to determination of cinchonine) that many organic bases form, with certain acids, including various indicator dyes, stable compounds which can be separated by extracting with benzene, ethylene dichloride, chloroform, etc. Since such compounds are often coloured or show strong absorption in the ultra violet, they may be determined by absorptiometry or colorimetry. In the case of pethidine, Lehmann and Aitken (*loc. cit.*) used bromthymol blue, but Way *et al.* considered methyl orange preferable. In their procedure the

[1] *J. Pharm. Exp. Ther.*, 1947, **91**, 178.
[2] *J. Lab. Clin. Med.*, 1942-43, **28**, 787.
[3] The phosphate was used for the authors' experimental purposes and is presumably replaceable in purely analytical work by 10-20 cc. of N/10 NaOH.
[4] *J. Biol. Chem.*, 1947, **168**, 335.

ethylene dichloride solution of pethidine is added to 0·5 cc. of methyl orange solution (alkaline) and thoroughly shaken for three minutes. After centrifuging, the excess methyl orange is aspirated off, the residual solution is recentrifuged, and 5 cc. are pipetted into a colorimeter tube containing 1·0 cc. of alcoholic sulphuric acid. The colour developed is measured at 540 mμ. " Blank " values for normal tissue should be measured, but are very small. The instrument is calibrated in the usual way against standard pethidine solutions (2·0 to 20 mg. per litre).

Amidone is a white crystalline compound, melting point 236-236·5° C., soluble in water and alcohol, insoluble in ether. The free base is soluble in benzene. According to Scott and Chen,[1] 20-35 per cent. of an oral dose of 5-7·5 mg. was excreted over a period of twenty-four hours, but Cronheim and Ware,[2] using a more sensitive method, recovered only 5-13 per cent. of 20-40 mg. given subcutaneously in 10 mg. doses, and at the end of the observation period, 28-35 hours after the last dose of amidone, small amounts were still being excreted. The drug appeared to be excreted entirely free. Elliott *et al.*[3] on the basis of measurements with a specimen of amidone having C^{14} at the second Carbon atom, considered the intestine to be the main excretory route.

Cronheim and Ware describe a method of determination in urine based upon the formation of a coloured compound with bromcresol purple, which they found superior to methyl orange. Interference by other basic substances in urine necessitated a preliminary purification, for which an adsorption procedure was satisfactory. The total colour-forming substances were determined, the amidone was removed by adsorption on " Superfiltrol "[4] (certain other, unspecified, adsorbents could also be used) and the " blank " was determined in the filtrate.

Procedure. In a separating funnel mix 5 cc. of phosphate buffer, pH 5·3 (19·0 g. $NaH_2PO_4 \cdot H_2O$ and 1·0 g. of Na_2HPO_4 in 500 cc.), 5 cc. of dye solution (0·200 g. bromcresol purple and 3·2 cc of 0·1 N NaOH in 250 cc.) and 10 cc. of the urine (diluted or concentrated if necessary to bring the amidone content in the range 0·01 to 0·1 mg.). Add 50 cc. of benzene, shake for two minutes, remove the benzene, and re-extract the aqueous layer with a second 50 cc. of benzene. Extract the combined benzene solutions (or an aliquot based on an assumed volume of 100 cc.) with two portions, each 10 cc., of $\frac{N}{20}$ NaOH. Make up the combined NaOH extracts to

[1] *J. Pharm. Exp. Ther.*, 1946, **87**, 63.
[2] *Ibid.*, 1948, **92**, 103.
[3] *Ibid.*, 1949, **95**, 494.
[4] Superfiltrol (Thiamine grade), an aluminium silicate supplied by the Filtrol Corporation, Los Angeles, California.

25 cc. with $\frac{N}{20}$ NaOH and measure the colour density at 580 mμ.
For the blank determination use 10 ml. of urine after shaking 20 cc.
of the sample with 0·4 g. of superfiltrol for an hour and filtering.
Calibrate against standard solutions, using 10 ml. as for urine, over
the range 0·001 to 0·01 mg. per cc. An amount of 0·005 mg.
in 10 cc. can be measured with an accuracy of ± 3 per cent.

FUR AND HAIR DYES

The organic substances used as fur and hair dyes are of the same
class as photographic developers; i.e. they are readily oxidized,
forming dark-coloured products. In contact with the skin they
are liable to cause dermatitis, and some people are much more
sensitive to their action than others. Among workmen engaged
in the manufacture of such substances the disease is very common.
Wearers of dyed furs have frequently brought actions against
vendors sueing for damages because of dermatitis, and chemists
are sometimes asked to examine the furs and state whether or not
they have been properly dyed. Again, chemists are sometimes
asked to state whether an accused person, supposed to have adopted a
disguise, has dyed his hair or not.   The subject has been exhaustively
studied by Cox, whose work has been published in numerous papers
in the *Analyst* and *The Medico-Legal and Criminological Review*.

This worker has described methods of extracting the colouring-
matter from furs and hair and has devised tests for their identification.[1]

The commonest of the substances used are: the phenylene- and
toluylenediamines, the methylated phenylenediamines, the toluidines, the amino- and diamino-phenols, *p*-amino-diphenylamine,
metol (*p*-methylaminophenol), hydroquinone and pyrogallol.

Furs and hair are treated with solutions of these substances and
the colour is developed by subsequent air-oxidation in the presence
of a slight excess of alkali.   The oxidation products are derivatives
of Bandrowski's base, which is itself produced by the oxidation of
p-phenylene diamine to quinone di-imide, of which three molecules
combine to form Bandrowski's base.

p-phenylenediamine   quinone   Bandrowski's base
                       di-imide

[1] *Analyst*, 1929, **54**, 694-703.

According to Cox, this oxidation is often incomplete, and from an incompletely oxidized fur the original amino- or phenolic compound can be extracted with water or acetic acid, whereas well-dyed furs yield no extracts to these solvents.

The method of extraction is to remove fatty or oily matter with light petroleum and afterwards to soak the material in (*a*) cooled, boiled water, and (*b*) 1 per cent. acetic acid, for twenty-four hours each. The petroleum used for de-fatting is also shaken with acidified water to remove bases.

The following reagents are used for the identification of the substances extracted:

REACTIONS O[

Reagent	*m*-phenylene-diamine	*p*-phenylene-diamine	1 : 2 : 4 *m*-toluylenediamine	1 : 3 : 4 *m*-toluylenediamine	*p*-amino-phenol
1	Intense bright yellow	Faint transient brown	Orange-yellow	Brownish pink	Faint yellow
2	Red-brown	Brownish	Intense red	Dirty yellow or brown	Fluorescent green, turning red
3	Slight white precipitate	—	—	Slight precipitate	—
4	Pink	Violet or blue	Pink	Violet	Blue
5	Bright yellow	Red	Yellow	Yellow	Yellow
6	—	Violet	—	Violet	—
7	—	Intense violet[1] (Lauth's violet)	—	Claret colour	Violet
8	—	—	—	—	—
9	—	—	—	—	—

[1] Blue colour (methylene blue) indi[

(1) Dilute sodium nitrite solution, used in the cold, in presence of dilute mineral acid.

(2) Dilute alkaline solution of β-naphthol, used for coupling with product of (1).

(3) Bromine water.

(4) Phenol (5 per cent. solution with a few drops of hypochlorite solution).

(5) Acidified alcoholic solution of p-dimethylaminobenzaldehyde.

(6) Dilute ferric chloride solution.

(7) Hydrogen sulphide solution added after ferric chloride.

(8) Mercuric acetate solution.

(9) Potassium cyanide solution.

FUR DYES

p-amino-diphenylamine	o, m and p-toluidine	Amidol	Metol	Quinone	Hydro-quinone	Pyrogallol
Red	—	Bright red	Faint yellow	—	Faint yellow	—
Yellow or brown	Bright red colour or precipitate	Brown colour	Faint brown	Faint red	Red	—
Brownish precipitate	White precipitate	White precipitate	—	—	—	—
Yellow	Brown at first o- and m- turning blue	Red	Blue slowly turning violet	—	—	Brownish
Faint yellow	Greenish yellow	Orange. On warming redder	—	Faint yellow	Faint yellow	Faint yellow
Red-violet	—	Red	—	—	—	Reddish, turning greenish black
Brick-red	—	—	Green	—	—	—
—	—	Purple	Very faint pink on standing	Pale yellow with mercuric sulphate	—	Yellowish
—	—	Greenish blue	Slowly yellow	Brownish	Yellow	Pink

ates dimethyl-p-phenylenediamine.

CHAPTER XIII

DRUGS OF ADDICTION

SINCE civilization began, human weakness has shown itself in the habitual use of drugs in one form or another, and at the present time it is almost certainly true to say that no nation is entirely free from drug addiction, using the term in its widest sense.

The essential characteristics of the drug habit are the more or less insatiable craving of the victim for the drug, the mental, physical and moral degradation produced by the continued use of it and the mental and physical suffering which result from the withholding of it. In the early stages, although not always in the absolute beginning of the habit, there are sensuous pleasures which may or may not persist. As time goes on, these sensations can only be reproduced by increasing the dose of the drug, and here we encounter the complicated and astonishing phenomenon of tolerance. The fact that addicts can, with apparent safety, take daily doses of poisonous substances in quantities which are much more than enough to kill ordinary people is well known, but has never been satisfactorily explained. The question is discussed at great length by Lewin,[1] who emphatically denies that there is any parallel between tolerance for drugs and immunity to infection which is explained by the production of anti-toxins in the blood. He also casts doubt on the hypothesis that the habituated organism acquires an increased power of destroying the drug in the tissues of the body. In this he is in opposition to the general opinion of toxicologists who have frequently found difficulty in detecting drugs in the viscera of known addicts. His own suggestion is that tolerance is due to a weakening of the vitality of the body-cells, probably caused by chemical action. It might be possible to accept this hypothesis without denying that organic drugs break down chemically in the tissues of addicts.

The effects of the many drugs in question vary not only in kind, but in seriousness, from the mild stimulation produced by tea and coffee, which may be regarded as wholly benign, or at the most harmful only when carried to most unusual excess, to the highly toxic effects of cocaine and morphine. Between these two extremes, lie, approximately in the order of increasing harmfulness: tobacco, betel-nut, alcohol, hashish and opium.

[1] " Drugs, Their Use and Abuse ". Kegan Paul, 1938.

It has been suggested that the drug which is indigenous to a country and which has been long in use is relatively less harmful than drugs newly introduced into that country, that, for example, the chewing of coco leaves by South American natives and the smoking of opium by Chinese coolies are comparatively innocuous. There is probably some truth in this assertion, but it is obviously possible to over-emphasize it.

There is no necessity here to discuss at length the effects of tea, coffee, cocoa (which, by the way, was once regarded as a baneful foreign drug which might wean the working man from honest beer), tobacco or alcohol. Betel chewing may also be briefly dismissed. According to Lewin[1] the chewing of the nuts and the leaves of the areca palm of which they are the fruit, is one of the most widespread habits in the world. He estimates the number of addicts to be about 200,000,000. The custom is to chew the nut or leaf with a morsel of slaked lime, and the effect, as a rule, is to produce mild stimulation comparable to that of drinking tea; the habitué merely feels good-humoured and happy. Lewin regards betel as being rather beneficial than otherwise, especially to people living on a diet of meagre protein content. Nevertheless, the pure alkaloid arecoline is by no means harmless, and as the nuts vary considerably in alkaloidal content, such unpleasant symptoms as vertigo are not unknown.

Opium and its Alkaloids

Addiction to opium and its constituent alkaloids may be considered under three headings: smoking, eating, and the use of morphine and heroin either by sniffing or by injection. Smoking is the least harmful of these, and it has been stated on good authority that moderate opium smokers are as capable of doing their work as non-smokers. Moreover, the smoking habit is relatively easy to give up. Opium eating is more deleterious, and the victim of this habit approximates to the condition of the morphinist. Death from an overdose is a common occurrence in the East.

The craving for opium is not unknown even in young children, and this is especially true in India, where some of the ayahs have the reputation of administering poppy-juice to infants to stop their crying. It is also said that some of them put opium under the finger-nails of the babies so that they will swallow it when sucking their fingers. Foster-mothers with the opium habit have also been blamed for passing on the morphine to their infant charges in their milk. Such children do not develop either physically or mentally, and many of them die in infancy.

---

[1] *Op. cit.*, p. 232.

Beyond doubt, the constituent of opium which is almost entirely responsible for the craving for the drug is morphine. Addiction to morphine as such is, in Western countries at least, a vice of the wealthier and more educated classes, and no individual class in the community contains so large a proportion of morphinists as the medical profession and other people closely associated with this profession; naturally, the accessibility of the drug is an important factor. In addition to symptoms common to most drug-habits, morphine diminishes digestive powers and causes emaciation; it frequently causes fever, headache, pains in the gastro-intestinal tract and the urinary system, and disturbances of vision. It leads to impotence in men and to menstrual derangements in women. Curative treatment is painful and distressing in the extreme, and is seldom successful. After apparent cures in hospital the great majority of patients quickly revert to the habit.

Narcotine, which, next to morphine, is the most abundant alkaloid in opium, has only slight physiological activity in itself, and has never been regarded as a very dangerous drug. Nevertheless, there is much evidence to indicate that the admixture of narcotine with morphine intensifies the narcotic effect and toxicity of the latter, so that the ingestion of a given amount of opium may produce more severe symptoms than could be ascribed to the morphine in it. In Egypt, a new and disquieting practice which is growing is the hypodermic injection of unfiltered decoctions of opium; in the consideration of this habit the presence of narcotine may be of great significance.

Codeine, which is relatively abundant only in Persian opium, but which can readily be made artificially from morphine, is, like its homologue dionine, specifically excluded from the schedule of dangerous drugs. The reason for this is the almost universal belief that the use of codeine does not lead to addiction. It is said that there is no evidence of tolerance for codeine, but that, on the contrary, a patient receiving a course of treatment with this drug requires smaller doses as the treatment proceeds. Lewin stands almost alone in his opinion that this belief in the peculiarity of codeine is based on the misinterpretation of experiments on animals, and he describes a case which came under his notice in which the patient did become addicted to codeine.

Papaverine is also regarded as one of the harmless constituents of opium; nevertheless, we know of one instance in which a European doctor in Egypt supplied clients with this alkaloid without any legitimate reason. He ultimately fled from the country in order to escape arrest, which would seem to indicate that papaverine is not quite free from the qualities desired by drug addicts.

In Egypt, white drugs began to become a serious menace about the year 1924, and at that time morphine and cocaine were the most abundant of them. By 1929 the white drug trade in this country reached its climax. In that year nearly 17,000 samples of drugs were examined in the chemical laboratory of the Medico-Legal Department; of these, 10,000 were reported to be heroin, 134 morphine, and 112 cocaine. The remainder, apart from 2,000 samples containing no drug at all, were mainly hashish and opium.

It is generally agreed that heroin is more toxic than morphine, although in certain respects its advocates claim that the symptoms produced are less painful. This may be in part responsible for the replacement of morphine by this derivative in the illicit trade, but there is another possible explanation. About the year 1928 certain manufacturers in Europe discovered that there was a loophole in the international law restricting the manufacture and sale of narcotic drugs. Morphine was controlled and so was diacetyl morphine (heroin), but there was no mention in the law of other acid-esters of morphine. It was only necessary to substitute another acid radical for the acetyl group to obtain a drug which would completely satisfy the addict and yield profits to the manufacturers and traffickers on the usual colossal scale without infringing the law. Thanks to the vigilance and extraordinary acumen of Russell Pasha (now Sir Thomas Russell, K.B.E.), the Central Narcotics Intelligence Bureau in Cairo obtained large samples of a drug which was described by the manufacturer in Europe as dipropionyl morphine, but which was being sold illicitly in Egypt as heroin. We were able to hydrolyze a sample with sulphuric acid in the presence of alcohol, and to distil off the ethyl ester or esters so produced. After washing the distillate with water to remove excess of alcohol, we fractionated the remainder by distillation and found that it contained approximately equal quantities of ethyl acetate and ethyl propionate. Obviously the original drug was either a mixture of heroin and dipropionyl morphine, or it was a homogeneous substance, acetyl-propionyl morphine. Attempts were made by fractional crystallation to isolate heroin from it; if even a small proportion of it could have been proved to be heroin legal proceedings could have been taken against the manufacturer. However, all the fractions we obtained had the same melting point, and we had to conclude that the substance was homogeneous and was in fact acetyl-propionyl morphine.

This conclusion was afterwards confirmed by the manufacturer under cross-examination.

This affair had far-reaching consequences, of which the most important was the modification of the international law so as to include all esters of morphine in the schedule of dangerous drugs.

This unrestricted manufacture may have been in part responsible for the great increase in " heroin " addiction during the year 1929. The 10,000 samples examined in our laboratory responded to all the routine tests for heroin, and were described as heroin in our reports ; but, since a very large proportion of them were examined before we knew of the existence of the propionyl compound, it is more than likely that many of the samples consisted of the latter substance.

Since 1929 there has been a great reduction in the amount of heroin consumed in Egypt, which is mainly due to the untiring efforts of Sir Thomas Russell and his staff ; but, as he has been the first to point out, other factors have contributed to this improvement. One of these is the avarice of the traders. Both wholesale merchants and retail peddlers have sought to add to their already clossal profits by adulteration to such an extent that the substance finally sold is often so mild in its effect that it is not worth buying.

In order to estimate the scale of profit made in the trade, the Narcotics Bureau in Cairo has for some years made periodic purchases of white drugs from dealers in many of the Egyptian towns. The drug is nearly always heroin, and the quantity sold in one packet varies from about 5 to 15 c.gm. ; the price is from about one shilling to half a crown. The quantity of heroin in the powders is estimated colorimetrically using the reaction of Denigés, [1] [2] and it is found to vary from about 5 per cent. to 70 per cent., and is usually below 20 per cent. The aldulterant is always some cheap material such as chalk or sodium bicarbonate, the price of which need not be considered ; occasionally we have found salicin as an adulterant, but even this substance is cheap enough for the price to be inconsiderable in this connection. An example, by no means an extreme one, will illustrate the almost incredible amount of profit made in the trade. A sample weighing 5 c.gm. and containing 20 per cent. of heroin is sold for one shilling ; the price of a kilo-gramme of this powder is therefore £1,000, and the price of the pure heroin in it, £5,000 per kilogramme. The price of a kilogramme of heroin (about 80 per cent. pure) at the factory has varied from £40 to a little more than £100 during the last ten years. With profits on this scale, even when they are divided among a number of middle-men and when considerable percentages have to be deducted for losses due to seizures and money paid in bribes, sufficient remains in the hands of the traffickers to induce them to risk long terms of imprisonment. The converse is also true, that punishments less severe than those inflicted in Egypt, where the maximum sentence is five years penal servitude, are not likely to the
act as a deterrent to merchants working on a large scale.   cotics.

[1] *Comptes. rend.*, **151**, 1,062.
[2] BAMFORD. *Analyst*, 1931, **56**, 586.

plants and afterwards scraped their outer garments to collect the resin adhering to them. At the present time[1] much more efficient methods are adopted.

Hashish as usually seen in Egypt is a dark brown or greenish brown mass pressed into cakes weighing from $1\frac{1}{2}$ to 3 lb. and wrapped in thin cloth.

The odour of hashish is characteristic and is more especially so when the substance is burnt. It is used by habitués either for smoking or eating. For smoking the water-pipe called in English a nargileh and in Arabic a goza is used. In the commonest type of goza the water reservoir is a coconut shell. The bowl of the pipe is filled with tobacco, which is ignited, and the hashish is put on the top of the glowing tobacco. Hashish for eating is generally mixed with chocolate, honey, or sweetened oils; these mixtures are known as " manzouls ".

As far as we know there is no record of fatal poisoning of human beings by hashish (at least in Egypt), but the symptoms of chronic poisoning are sufficiently serious and it has been shown that the active principles are toxic to animals in quite small doses. The inveterate addict lives in a state of stupor, interrupted by outbreaks of silly gaiety. He may also suffer from melancholia and from terrifying hallucinations. Crimes of violence have been frequently attributed to hashish intoxication, but there is probably little truth in this; the ordinary hashish addict is a coward and a weakling, but not, as a rule, dangerous to other people.

The effects of the drug on people unaccustomed to its use have frequently been described. They are:

(1) A feeling of well-being and stimulation with sometimes alternating sensations of warmth and cold.

(2) A period of mental confusion with hallucinations which are often of an erotic nature.

(3) A period of depression, followed by sleep. Before falling asleep the subject sometimes has the illusion of double personality.

After mild intoxication the patient wakes feeling more or less normal, but after deeper indulgence there is acute mental and physical debility. Under restraint, hashish addicts can be deprived of the drug with the mildest of withdrawal symptoms, but relapse into addiction is almost universal.

Until recently little work had been done on the physiological effects of cannabis on animals. The reactions of dogs have been described and biological methods of assay based on these reactions have been suggested, but they are unsatisfactory. Dogs vary in

---

[1] F. D. BAKER BEY. *Annual Report of the Central Narcotics Intelligence Bureau, Cairo*, 1937. Statement presented to the Advisory Committee on Dangerous Drugs: League of Nations.

their susceptibility to hashish intoxication, and even the same dog may show different symptoms when tested at intervals of a week. According to Balozet[1] of the Pasteur Institute of Tunis, mydriasis is the most constant symptom. He also states that moderate doses sometimes produce gaiety and friendliness in dogs normally surly. Sometimes there is excitement shown by jumping alternately on the fore and hind legs. In severe intoxication the dog becomes somnolent, the eyes tend to close, but may be opened by an effort of will. This author also states that the degree of intoxication appears to bear no relationship to the amount of the drug administered or to the size or the breed of the dogs. In experiments in Egypt on small mongrel dogs we have not observed gaiety or excitement, but only general lethargy and some slight indication of ataxia in the back legs. The most marked symptom we noticed was an absolute refusal by dogs which had once been intoxicated with hashish to taste food containing it a second time. It has been shown by Negm[2] that small fish such as minnows immersed in water containing a small amount of an alcoholic solution of hashish-resin show signs of intoxication after the lapse of a short time depending on the concentration of the extract and the size of the fish. Similar fish in water containing the same proportion of pure alcohol were not intoxicated. He also found that earth-worms immersed in an oily solution of cannabis behaved in a characteristic manner, becoming at first very active and afterwards limp.

An important physiological reaction which was first described by Gayer[3] is the production of corneal anaesthesia when an extract of cannabis is injected hypodermically into such animals as cats, mice and rabbits. This reaction has been investigated more thoroughly by Work, Bergel and Todd working at the Lister Institute in London; their investigation will be referred to later.

For the identification of hashish in the forms in which it is used by addicts, microscopic examination should be made and chemical tests applied. Neither of these methods should be considered sufficient in itself, although the microscopic forms of the botanical features of the flowering tops of the hemp plant are very characteristic and some of the chemical tests are as nearly specific as such tests can be. The microscopic examination is carried out in the following way. With hashish free from foreign matter the material is rubbed as gently as possible with a little water in a mortar and transferred to a test-tube; a little chloral hydrate solution is added and the liquid is boiled. A drop of the liquid containing the

---

[1] *League of Nations Publication*, O.C. 1542 (t), Addendum, 14.9.37.

[2] *Contribution à l'etude toxicologique du hachisch et de sa prohibition en Egypte*. (Thése), Strasbourg, 1938.

[3] *Arch. exp. path. Pharm.*, **49**, 266.

vegetable matter which floats on the top is put on to a slide and covered with a cover-slip. It is then examined with the medium-powered objective. For the microscopic examination of "manzouls", the fat, sugar and other added matter must first be removed by successive washings with light petroleum, alcohol and hot water. The botanical features of diagnostic importance are:

(1) The resin-secreting glands, of which some are sessile and others are supported by multicellular stalks, although the glands are so easily detached from the stalks that, as usually seen, they are separate.

(2) Short, alembic-shaped cystolithic hairs.

(3) Long, thin, tapering hairs.

Of the chemical tests for hashish resin the best known are the two which are due to Beam. The most characteristic of these is the

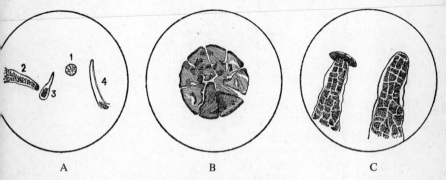

FIG. 23. *Cannabis sativa (C. indica).*

   A. 1. Resin-secreting gland.
          2. Stalk deprived of gland.
          3. Cystolithic hair.
          4. Simple hair.

   B. Gland showing details.

   C. Stalk, with and without gland.

alkali test. An extract is made by grinding hashish in the cold with a suitable solvent such as light petroleum, alcohol, ethyl acetate or amyl alcohol and this, after filtration, is evaporated to dryness. The solution is usually very pale brown in colour, but it may be green owing to the presence of chlorophyll, or there may be other foreign colouring matter present. In such cases the solution should be treated in the cold with the smallest possible quantity of animal charcoal and re-filtered before evaporating to dryness. One or two drops of alcoholic potash (5–10 per cent.) are added to the dry residue and the presence of hashish-resin is indicated by the *gradual* formation of a violet colour. If one or two drops of resinous solution are evaporated on a piece of filter paper and the alcoholic potash is spotted on to the residue, the colour test is more sensitive than it is when made in the ordinary way in a porcelain basin. It can be easily demonstrated that the colour is due to the formation of an oxidation product, for if the dried spot of solution on filter-paper is put at the bottom of a filter-flask attached to a vacuum pump, and after the evacuation of the flask the alcoholic potash is added from a tap-funnel passing through the stopper, no colour appears until air is admitted.

Much of the criticism to which this test has been subjected is based on insufficient experience of it, and careless observation of the gradual colour change. In the course of very long experience of the application of this test to plant extracts of many kinds, we have not found any which behaves exactly like that of hashish; nevertheless, as in all forensic chemistry, one test alone cannot be admitted as a proof of identity.

Beam's second test consists in adding to the concentrated, but not completely evaporated, solution of the resin in light petroleum a freshly-prepared solution of dry hydrochloric acid gas in absolute alcohol; a wine-red colour is produced. This test is less specific than the first and the preparation of the reagent as required is troublesome. A modified acid test is described by Bouquet.[1] The extracted resin, treated with decolorizing charcoal if necessary, is dissolved in acetone, and to this is added a few drops of a freshly-prepared mixture of concentrated sulphuric acid (2 vols.) and absolute alcohol (3 vols.). The colour darkens and becomes cherry-red in about half an hour. A similar colour is formed with extracts of myrrh and benzoin (and probably many other substances), but the cherry-red solution from cannabis behaves differently from these on dilution with water: it becomes almost colourless but opalescent, whereas the coloured liquids from myrrh and benzoin yield white resinous precipitates and dirty violet-coloured liquids.

Bouquet has also modified the alkaline test. He grinds the suspected sample with caustic potash or soda, adds 95 per cent. alcohol, and re-grinds. This mixture is filtered through paper into a test-tube, the mouth of which is plugged with cotton. The filtrate is usually violet-coloured and so is the edge of the residue on the filter. About 1 ml. of the filtrate is diluted with 5–10 ml. of water, or more if the colour of the solution is very dense. The diluted liquid is turbid and dirty violet in colour: this colour is discharged on the addition of an acid, even an organic acid. The coloured liquid is shaken with about 1 ml. of amyl alcohol and allowed to stand. The alcoholic layer which separates is coloured pink to reddish violet according to the amount of resin present, and this

---

[1] *Loc. cit.*

colour persists for several days.   Bouquet claims that if the reaction is carried out in this way it is very much more sensitive than the original Beam's test; and experiments made in our laboratory confirm this claim.

Another very sensitive reaction of hashish is the bright violet colour produced by evaporating a trace of the resin with a reagent made by dissolving 1 gm. of *p*-dimethylaminobenzaldehyde in 100 ml. of alcohol and adding 20 drops of concentrated sulphuric acid; the violet-coloured residue becomes bluer on moistening with 1 drop of water.   A somewhat similar reaction is that of Negm.[1]   His reagent is a mixture of vanillin (0·4 gm.), acetaldehyde (4 drops) and 95 per cent. alcohol (20 ml.).   The residue left on evaporating a petroleum ether extract of hashish is mixed with 2 ml. of this reagent and 2 ml. of concentrated hydrochloric acid.   The liquid becomes pale green, quickly changing to slate-grey and in about ten minutes to indigo-blue.   In half an hour the colour changes again to violet and after one hour this violet colour is intense. It is well known that certain galenical preparations of cannabis fail to respond to the ordinary Beam's test, and this is particularly true of old samples.   We have found that many such samples give definite colours in Negm's test.

Blackie[2] has developed and extended these tests, claiming that his technique gives the results stated only with cannabis resin.   A petroleum ether extract containing about 2 mg. of the resin is allowed to evaporate to dryness in the depression of a spotting plate. 3 mg. of a suitable aldehyde dissolved in 0·5 ml. of isobutyl (or benzyl) alcohol is added, the mixture is stirred, and concentrated hydrochloric acid is added drop by drop until the maximum colour is obtained.   Benzaldehyde gives an intense violet which fades rapidly (this is the most sensitive, and detects 0·03 mg. of the resin); vanillin a more persistent greenish-blue, sometimes with a violet tinge ; *p*-dimethylaminobenzaldehyde a violet-red fading slowly but still visible after twenty minutes; salicylaldehyde an emerald green fading similarly slowly; and *o*-nitrobenzaldehyde a light yellow to brownish yellow (with more of the resin than is required for detection by the other reagents).

In our routine examinations for hashish we accept the unsupported evidence of Beam's alkaline test only in the examination of the pipes called gozas, as we have found that when these have been used for tobacco alone the petroleum washings give absolutely negative results in the alkaline Beam's test.

Bouquet and others have attempted to base a colorimetric assay of cannabis on the reaction above described, but there is no evidence

---

[1] *Loc. cit.*
[2] *Ind. Eng. Chem., Anal. Ed.*, 1941, **13**, 96.

to show that the amount of the colour-producing constituent bears any relationship to the physiologically active principles of the drug. Further research is necessary to elucidate this point before any useful work on these lines can be done.

Until recently (1939) we had no certain knowledge of the physiologically active constituents of hashish. Various workers had obtained from the resinous extract an oil boiling at about 264° C. under reduced pressure (22 mm.) which was called cannabinol and was assumed to be the active principle.

From this oil Cahn[1] succeeded in obtaining an acetyl derivative by treating it with acetyl chloride in pyridine solution. The yield was about 28 per cent. of a white crystalline substance melting at 75° C. This, on hydrolysis, yields an oil boiling at 263–264° C. under a pressure of 20 mm.; reacetylation of this oil gives a quantitative yield of the acetyl compound. Cahn reserved the name cannabinol for the product of hydrolysis and called the distillate from the resin " crude oil of hashish ". He reported that this oil was physiologically inactive when given by the mouth to dogs.

Work, Bergel and Todd[2] have obtained Cahn's pure cannabinol by another method. They treated the crude oil of hashish with p-nitrobenzoyl chloride, also in pyridine solution, and from the crystalline derivative so obtained they prepared pure cannabinol by hydrolysis. They studied its pharmacological properties by injecting it in acetone solution into rabbits and found it to be a very powerful poison: doses of 5 mg. per kg. of body weight causing convulsions and death in less than one minute. With smaller doses, no sign of the Gayer effect (anaesthesia of the cornea) could be detected.

These workers also studied the non-crystalline portion of the p-nitrobenzoylated product. They failed to obtain any chemically pure substance from it by ordinary methods of fractionation, but after repeated selective adsorption on activated alumina, they found that the portion least readily adsorbed contained the drug which anaesthetized the cornea. Hydrolysis of this compound yielded a product of which 0·25 mg. produced a definite Gayer effect in a rabbit weighing 1 k.gm. The fractions entirely free from cannabinol were found to cause deep sleep, and in large doses death, but no convulsions.

Adams, Hunt and Clark[3] have isolated a substance cannabidiol, $C_{21}H_{30}O_2$, which responds to Beam's alkaline test but not to Gayer's test, and Jacob and Todd[4] have found this substance in Egyptian hemp in about the same amounts as cannabinol.

[1] R. S. CAHN. J.C.S., 1930, p. 986. Ibid., 1931, p. 630.
[2] Biochem. J., 1939, 33, 123–7.
[3] J. Amer. Chem. Soc., 1940, 62, 196.
[4] J. Chem. Soc., 1940, 649.

It has therefore been shown that cannabis contains at least two constituents which have totally different pharmacological properties; but the investigation is not yet complete.

Nutmeg

Within the last few years, partly owing to the difficulty in obtaining hashish, it has become the practice in Egypt to substitute powdered nutmeg. In sufficiently large doses this produces symptoms similar to those of hashish intoxication and the effects may even be much more severe. Death has been ascribed to eating two powdered nutmegs. Unpleasant symptoms have also been experienced as a result of putting powdered nutmeg in cocktails. The active principle of nutmeg is said to be myristicin, which also occurs in oil of mace. It is a yellowish liquid which boils at 149° C. under a pressure of 15 mm. By prolonged heating with alcoholic potash it is converted into iso-myristicin, a crystalline solid melting at 49° C. Either of these substances can be converted by cautious oxidation into myristic aldehyde and finally into myristic acid, methyl-methylene gallic acid. Myristicin and iso-myristicin are represented by the following formula:—

$$R-\!\!\!\bigwedge\!\!\!\begin{array}{c} O \\ \diagdown CH_3 \\ O \end{array}$$
$$OCH_3$$

in which R is $CH_2=CH-CH_2$ (myristicin) or $CH_3-CH=CH$ (iso-myristicin). The pharmacology of nutmeg would repay further study.

The Atropine Group

Such plants as datura and hyoscyamus grow wild in arid areas in the East and some of these have been used habitually by the Sudanese and some Bedouin tribes. The leaves of the plants are made into cigarettes for smoking and the small seeds of the hyoscyamus are commonly put into manzouls. One effect of atropine and drugs of the same group is to produce hallucinations which are reputed to be most unpleasant. In spite of the very high toxicity of the atropaceous alkaloids the sale of sweetmeats containing them is not an offence against the narcotic laws but merely a contravention of the law controlling pharmacies.

Gelsemine

One case of addiction to the derivatives of *Gelsemium sempervirens*, the yellow jasmine, has been recorded by Lewin. The patient gradually increased his daily dose to 30 gm. of the tincture. He began to suffer from a wasting disease and died in a mental state bordering on idiocy.

Chloroform, Ether and Petrol

People who have ready access to these liquids are apt to become habitual inhalers of the vapours. In acute cases both chloroform and ether act as irritant poisons. Chronic poisoning produces the usual symptoms of mental and moral deterioration; in addition, chloroform sometimes causes jaundice, and ether may cause glycosuria.

Petrol inhalation among, for example, dry-cleaners sometimes causes hallucinations and terrifying nightmares.

Chloral

The therapeutic use of chloral has greatly decreased, but formerly it was definitely to be feared as a drug of addiction. The chloral addict was in more danger of sudden death than the morphinist owing to the action of the drug on the heart. Chloral causes gastro-intestinal disturbances; the skin becomes blotchy and in severe cases ulcerated, while among other symptoms are yellowness of the eyeballs, facial paralysis and ataxia of the limbs.

The Barbiturates

Derivatives of barbituric acid such as veronal and its many modern analogues vary greatly in their pharmacological effects, but they are all now recognized as drugs likely to produce habits. They are listed in the first schedule under the Poisons Act and special restrictions now control the sale of them. The habitual use of such quantities as 1–2 gm. daily may cause chronic poisoning and death within a few months.

The simpler ureides such as adalin are considered to be much less dangerous.

Fly Agaric

Lewin has given a description of the habitual use of fly agaric, the poisonous mushroom containing the alkaloid muscarine, by the inhabitants of North-eastern Asia. The craving of these people for the fungus is sometimes so great that it is said that a reindeer has been bartered for a single mushroom. The addict has a wild expression in the eyes, a bloated face and trembling hands. He becomes madly excited, jumping about and banging drums until, overcome by fatigue, he falls asleep. Even on waking he still staggers like a man intoxicated with alcohol. Symptoms of muscarine intoxication are excessive salivation, vomiting and diarrhoea.

The Anhalonium Drugs

Certain species of cactus which grow in the dry regions of Central America, and which are known to the natives as peyotl and to Europeans as mescal buttons, have been used for hundreds of years if not longer by the Mexican Indians for making intoxicating drinks. The botanical name of the species is *Anhalonium* and several varieties are known, of which the commonest are *A. Lewinii* and *A. Williamsii*. The drink is a decoction made by infusing the plants in hot water, and indulgence in the drug is a social function. The tribes gather together on feast days and drink at intervals for twenty-four hours or more, and for the period they are sublimely happy.

Europeans who have experimented with the drink have described sensory effects of almost incredible intensity and variety. They have seen visions full of colour and vividness and have heard imaginary music of fantastic beauty. They have had sensations of complete remoteness from the everyday world and illusions of unlimited power. So potent is the drug that the Indians used to worship it as a deity, and even after their conversion to Christianity the ceremonial indulgence has often been associated with religious rites. The after effects of intoxication with anhalonium are, naturally, the reverse of the symptoms of the intoxication itself: depression and mental and physical heaviness.

The most abundant active principle of anhalonium is the alkaloid mescaline, but other alkaloids are also present in the plants and it is believed that the varied sensory experiences may be due to more than one of these constituents.

This is not the whole story of drug addiction. Much has been written on the history of such habits and, in modern times, on the ways of drug-smugglers. The works of Lewin and the annual reports of the Central Narcotics Intelligence Bureau of the Egyptian Government may be recommended for further reading.

INDEX

HEADLEY BROTHERS, 109 KINGSWAY, LONDON, W.C.2; AND ASHFORD, KENT